# Essential GCSE
# Maths 4–5

## Michael White

Elmwood Education

First published 2015 by
Elmwood Education
Unit 5
Mallow Park
Watchmead
Welwyn Garden City
Herts. AL7 1GX
Tel. 01707 333232

ISBN 9781 906 622 459

Typeset and illustrated by Tech-Set Ltd., Gateshead, Tyne and Wear.

# Preface

This book covers the material mainly required for grades 4 to 5 of the Maths GCSE.

Nowadays there is a wealth of enriching resources available to teachers, particularly on the internet. This book can be used alongside these to enable students to work at topics in a systematic way which helps to build up their confidence.

The 'M' exercises cover the main part of the syllabus. Exercises are labelled as 'E' when the author believes the content is particularly difficult relative to the other material in this book.

Constant revisiting of topics is essential for mathematical fluency and success. Throughout this book, the author provides 'Can you still?' sections to encourage this continual reviewing process. This material is designed for short (e.g. 5 to 15 minutes) sessions within lessons to keep ideas 'fresh' in students' minds.

Questions are provided at the end of each unit for students to test themselves against each learning objective stated at the start of the unit. These are then backed up with a selection of GCSE examination questions.

The author has chosen to retain a functional 'Use your maths' section in each unit. These sections are designed to encourage discussion and to highlight the maths required in a variety of situations. There is also an additional unit devoted to raising students' awareness of money matters.

Each unit in this book is designed to match up with the corresponding unit in the 'Foundation Core GCSE Maths 1–3' book. This provides many extension possibilities.

The author hopes that the contents of this book will contribute towards each student developing a greater mastery of this subject.

Thanks are due to AQA, CEA, EDEXCEL, OCR and WJEC for kindly allowing the use of questions from their past examination papers. The answers are solely the work of the author and are not ratified by the examining groups.

The author is indebted to the contributions from Hilary White and Peter Gibson.

Michael White

# Contents

## Unit 9

### Geometry 2

## Unit 10

### Statistics 2

## Unit 11

### Geometry 3

**In this unit you will learn how to:**

- consolidate previous number work
- use negative powers
- calculate with roots
- use power notation for prime factors
- find HCF/LCM using prime factors
- use standard form
- ( USE YOUR MATHS! ) – makeover

## Non calculator arithmetic

**M1.1**

*Do not use a calculator.*

**1** Callum's puppy eats 0·1 of a packet of dog food each day. How often must Callum buy a packet of this dog food?

**2** The product of three numbers is 336. Two of the numbers are 4 and 12. Find the third number.

**3** Find the value of $3 \times 3 \times 3 \times 3$.

**4** Louise pays £41·40 for 30 litres of petrol. Work out the cost per litre of petrol.

**5** Work out

(a) $37 \times 46$        (b) $246 \times 42$        (c) $57 \times 318$

(d) $782 \div 17$        (e) $1764 \div 28$        (f) $1224 \div 34$

**6** How many 27p stamps can I buy with a £20 note?

**7** Tom has to put 1000 containers into boxes.
One box will take 24 containers.
How many containers will Tom need?

**8** Denise says that 'an even number multiplied by an odd number is always an odd number'. Is she correct?
Justify your answer.

**9** Write down the answer to each of the following:

(a) $9 - 3{\cdot}07$      (b) $0{\cdot}03 \times 0{\cdot}5$      (c) $0{\cdot}9 \times 0{\cdot}003$

(d) $0{\cdot}1^2$      (e) $0{\cdot}04 \times 30$      (f) $16 - 0{\cdot}713$

(g) $0{\cdot}21 \times 0{\cdot}6$      (h) $0{\cdot}3 \times 500$      (i) $0{\cdot}28^2$

(j) $31{\cdot}6 \times 0{\cdot}27$      (k) $0{\cdot}2^3$      (l) $0{\cdot}48 \times 3{\cdot}77$

**10**
> One box can hold 48 packets of crisps

> One crate can hold 30 boxes

> One van can hold 12 crates

How many vans are needed to transport 60 480 packets of crisps?
Show all your working out.

**11**

 1 litre £2.40     1.5 litres £3.20     2 litres £4.10

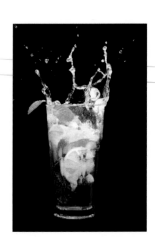

The prices of different bottles of a drink are shown above.

Ariana needs to buy 5 litres of this drink.

Which bottles should she buy so that she spends the least amount of money?

2

Estimate the cost of 58 radios at £62 each.

Cost $\approx 60 \times 60$    (round off to one significant figure often)

Cost $\approx$ £3600    (actual cost = £3596)

---

**M1.2**

**1**   Copy the grid below.

Use a calculator to fill in the grid using the clues (*ignore any decimal points*).

| | **Clues across** | | **Clues down** |
|---|---|---|---|
| 1. | $3{\cdot}8 + 1{\cdot}7 + 1{\cdot}42$ | 1. | $\dfrac{5{\cdot}1 - 1{\cdot}7}{0{\cdot}5}$ |
| 3. | $7 \times (3{\cdot}6 - 1{\cdot}9)$ | 2. | $3{\cdot}9 \times 4{\cdot}8 \times 13{\cdot}4$ |
| 5. | $\dfrac{17{\cdot}6}{0{\cdot}4} - 3{\cdot}88$ | 3. | $(3{\cdot}1 + 1{\cdot}8) \times (6{\cdot}1 - 3{\cdot}8)$ |
| 7. | $4{\cdot}9 \times 150$ | 4. | $121 - (31{\cdot}2 - 4{\cdot}85)$ |
| 9. | $(0{\cdot}62 + 0{\cdot}08) \times 70$ | 6. | $\dfrac{13{\cdot}8 + 9{\cdot}12}{0{\cdot}25}$ |
| 10. | $-24{\cdot}1 - 2{\cdot}3 + 61{\cdot}2$ | 8. | $(15{\cdot}1 - 7{\cdot}6) \times 3{\cdot}5 + 5{\cdot}2$ |
| 11. | $-900 \times (-0{\cdot}09)$ | 10. | $\dfrac{18{\cdot}1 - 1{\cdot}1}{0{\cdot}38 + 0{\cdot}12}$ |
| 12. | $4{\cdot}9 \times \left(\dfrac{40}{0{\cdot}8}\right)$ | | |

**2**   (a) A cab driver fills up his car with petrol costing 64·9p per litre. If he was charged £29·33 then how many litres did he get (give your answer to 1 decimal place)?

    (b) Without using a calculator, use suitable approximations to check your answer to part (a). Show your working.

**3**   A minibus hire company charges £45 for the day plus 28p per kilometre travelled.

    (a) How much would it cost to hire a minibus for a day-trip for a journey of 350 km?

    (b) How many kilometres did a woman travel if she paid the company £96·80 for the day?

**4** Calculate the following, giving each answer to 2 decimal places.

(a) $3 \cdot 1^3 \times (5 \cdot 9 - 1 \cdot 312)$

(b) $\dfrac{5 \cdot 12}{(7 \cdot 8 + 0 \cdot 314)}$

(c) $\dfrac{17 \cdot 2 + 11 \cdot 25}{3 \cdot 89 + 1 \cdot 63}$

(d) $\dfrac{16 \cdot 18 - 3 \cdot 892}{12 \cdot 62 + 19 \cdot 31}$

(e) $\dfrac{5 \cdot 1^2 + 6 \cdot 34}{17 \cdot 162 - 2 \cdot 8^2}$

(f) $\dfrac{3 \cdot 81^2 + 2 \cdot 6^3}{1 \cdot 41^2 - 1 \cdot 317}$

*Can you still?*

**Negative numbers**

**Do not use a calculator**

**1** Work out

(a) $2 \times (-3) \times (-5)$    (b) $(-7) \times 6 \times (-2)$

(c) $5 \times 4 \times (-2)$    (d) $\dfrac{(-3) \times (-8)}{12}$

(e) $\dfrac{(-4) \times 5}{2}$    (f) $\dfrac{(-8) \times (-9)}{2 \times (-12)}$

(g) $4 \cdot 5 \times (-2)$    (h) $5 \cdot 5 \times (-4)$

**2** Write down the missing number for each question below:

(a) $\square + (-3) = -2$    (b) $\square - (-7) = -3$

(c) $-3 \times \square = 36$    (d) $\square \div (-4) = -5$

(e) $-28 \div \square = 14$    (f) $-8 - \square = -13$

---

**5** (a) There are 42 matches in a matchbox.
Estimate how many matches there are in 89 matchboxes.

(b) Use a calculator to work out the exact answer.

---

**6** Morgan needs to choose one of the phone plans below.

| CARE PLAN | ALL PLAN |
|---|---|
| £25 fixed monthly payment | £32 fixed monthly payment |
| includes: 1000 texts 400 minutes phone calls | includes: unlimited texts 600 minutes phone calls |
| Each extra minute phone call: 8·6p Each extra text: 4·5p | Each extra minute phone call: 23p |

In May, Morgan made 722 minutes of phone calls and 1089 texts.
Which plan is cheaper and by how much?

**7** (a) Jess burns off 590 kcals each time she goes for a jog. Estimate how many kcals she burns off if she jogs on 21 different occasions.

(b) Use a calculator to work out the exact answer.

**8** Estimate, correct to 1 significant figure:

(a) $41{\cdot}56 \div 7{\cdot}88$

(b) $\dfrac{5{\cdot}13 \times 18{\cdot}777}{0{\cdot}952}$

(c) $\dfrac{1}{5}$ of £14 892

(d) $\dfrac{0{\cdot}0974 \times \sqrt{104}}{1{\cdot}03}$

(e) 52% of $0{\cdot}394\,\text{kg}$

(f) $\dfrac{6{\cdot}84^2 + 0{\cdot}983}{5{\cdot}07^2}$

(g) $\dfrac{2848{\cdot}7 + 1024{\cdot}8}{51{\cdot}2 - 9{\cdot}98}$

(h) $\dfrac{2}{3}$ of £3124

(i) $18{\cdot}13 \times (3{\cdot}96^2 + 2{\cdot}07^2)$

**9** Copy and use a calculator to complete the table below.

| + | $\dfrac{3}{8}$ | | $2\frac{1}{2}$ | $1\frac{2}{3}$ |
|---|---|---|---|---|
| $\dfrac{1}{4}$ | | | | |
| $\dfrac{3}{5}$ | | $\dfrac{19}{20}$ | | |
| | | | $4\frac{5}{6}$ | |
| | | $2\frac{13}{20}$ | | |

**10** Katrina uses a calculator to work out the value of

$$\frac{\sqrt{63{\cdot}89} + 3{\cdot}04^2}{\sqrt{80{\cdot}7} - 6{\cdot}99}$$

and says that the answer is $0{\cdot}864$ to 3 significant figures.

Carl does not have a calculator but says that Katrina is incorrect.
Explain fully why Carl believes this to be the case.

## Negative powers

Reminder:

$$a^m \times a^n = a^{m+n}$$
$$a^m \div a^n = a^{m-n}$$
$$(a^m)^n = a^{mn}$$
$$a^0 = 1$$

## M1.3

**1** Copy and complete the following, giving each answer in index form.

(a) $6^5 \times 6^3 = 6^\square$     (b) $3^4 \times 3^6 = 3^\square$     (c) $9^8 \div 9^5 = 9^\square$

(d) $5^8 \div 5^4 = 5^\square$     (e) $(4^3)^2 = 4^\square$     (f) $(6^4)^3 = 6^\square$

**2** Work out and write each answer as a number in index form.

(a) $8^6 \times 8^2$     (b) $7^6 \div 7^3$     (c) $(3^2)^4$

(d) $(9^3)^5$     (e) $6^0$     (f) $(3^2)^3 \times 3^5$

(g) $\dfrac{8^9}{8^4}$     (h) $\dfrac{(6^2)^3}{(6^2)^2}$     (i) $\dfrac{5 \times (5^3)^4}{5^6}$

(j) $\dfrac{7^4 \times (7^3)^6}{7^{10}}$     (k) $\dfrac{3^6 \times 3^5}{(3^3)^3}$     (l) $\dfrac{(9^4)^3 \times (9^2)^4}{9^5 \times 9^4}$

**3** Which is larger?

A   $\dfrac{(5^2)^4 \times 5^3}{5^2 \times (5^3)^3}$   or   B   $\dfrac{(5^4)^3 \times 5^4}{5^{10} \times 5^3}$

**4** Copy and complete

(a) $7^3 \times 7^4 = \boxed{\phantom{x}}$     (b) $\boxed{\phantom{x}} \times 5^3 = 5^7$     (c) $\boxed{\phantom{x}} \times 8^4 = 8^9$

(d) $3^5 \times \boxed{\phantom{x}} = 3^9$     (e) $6^4 \times \boxed{\phantom{x}} = 6^5$     (f) $2^6 \div 2^2 = \boxed{\phantom{x}}$

(g) $5^7 \div \boxed{\phantom{x}} = 5^4$     (h) $9^{11} \div \boxed{\phantom{x}} = 9^7$     (i) $\boxed{\phantom{x}} \div 6^5 = 6^9$

**5** Write down the area of this square in index form.

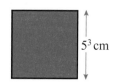

$5^3$ cm

**6** The area of a square is $3^8$ cm$^2$. Write down the length of the square in index form.

# Key Facts

$$a^0 \div a^n = \frac{a^0}{a^n} = \frac{1}{a^n}$$

$$a^0 \div a^n = a^{0-n} = a^{-n}$$

$$\longrightarrow \quad a^{-n} = \frac{1}{a^n}$$

**Note**   $\frac{1}{a}$ is known as the *reciprocal* of a

so $a^{-n}$ is the *reciprocal* of $a^n$   $\left(\frac{1}{a^n}\right)$

(a) $5^{-2} = \frac{1}{5^2} = \frac{1}{25}$

(b) $8^{-1} = \frac{1}{8^1} = \frac{1}{8}$

(c) $7^{-3} = \frac{1}{7^3} = \frac{1}{343}$

(d) $\left(\frac{1}{4}\right)^{-2} = \frac{1}{\left(\frac{1}{4}\right)^2} = \frac{1}{\frac{1}{16}} = 16$

---

**E1.1**

*Do not use a calculator.*

**1**  Copy and complete the following:

(a) $6^{-2}$

$$= \frac{1}{6^\square}$$

$$= \frac{1}{\boxed{\phantom{xx}}}$$

(b) $3^{-1}$

$$= \frac{1}{3^\square}$$

$$= \frac{1}{\boxed{\phantom{xx}}}$$

(c) $6^{-3}$

$$= \frac{1}{6^\square}$$

$$= \frac{1}{\boxed{\phantom{xx}}}$$

**2**  Write the following as ordinary numbers.

(a) $3^{-2}$  (b) $10^{-3}$  (c) $2^{-1}$  (d) $10^{-1}$

(e) $8^{-2}$  (f) $2^{-2}$  (g) $3^{-3}$  (h) $2^{-4}$

(i) $7^{-2}$  (j) $4^{-4}$  (k) $20^{-1}$  (l) $5^{-4}$

**3**  Which of the statements below are true?

(a) $\frac{1}{4} = 4^{-1}$  (b) $\frac{3}{4} = 4^{-3}$  (c) $\frac{2}{5} = 5^{-2}$  (d) $\frac{1}{3^4} = 3^{-4}$

**4**  Write the following in negative index form.

(a) $\frac{1}{5^3}$  (b) $\frac{1}{6^4}$  (c) $\frac{1}{3^7}$  (d) $\frac{1}{9^5}$

**5**  Which is greater – the reciprocal of 4 or the reciprocal of 5?

Write down the difference between the two reciprocals.

**6** Express the following in negative index form using the stated numbers.

(a) $\dfrac{1}{36}$ as a power of 6

(b) $\dfrac{1}{16}$ as a power of 2

(c) $\dfrac{1}{125}$ as a power of 5

(d) $\dfrac{1}{1024}$ as a power of 2

**7** $\left(\dfrac{3}{5}\right)^{-2} = \dfrac{1}{\left(\dfrac{3}{5}\right)^2} = 1 \div \left(\dfrac{3}{5}\right)^2$

$= 1 \div \dfrac{9}{25} = 1 \times \dfrac{25}{9} = \dfrac{25}{9}$

Write $\left(\dfrac{7}{3}\right)^{-2}$ as an ordinary number.

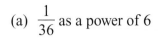

**Can you still?**

**Negative numbers**

**Do not use a calculator**

**1** Work out

(a) $(-8)^2$      (b) $0{\cdot}04 \times (-0{\cdot}08)$

(c) $(-0{\cdot}7) \times 0{\cdot}6$      (d) $(-6)^2$

(e) $(-0{\cdot}4) \times (-0{\cdot}01)$    (f) $(-3)^3$

(g) $5 \times (-6) - 2 \times 4$   (h) $-4 + (-5) \times 3$

(i) $\dfrac{(-3) \times (-10) + 4}{15 - (-2)}$   (j) $\dfrac{(-5)^2 \times (-2)^2}{40 - (-10)}$

(k) $\dfrac{(-6) \times 5 + 2}{7}$   (l) $\dfrac{(-9) \times (-8) - 12}{15 \times (-2)}$

---

**8** Write the following as ordinary numbers.

(a) $\left(\dfrac{1}{2}\right)^{-1}$     (b) $\left(\dfrac{2}{7}\right)^{-1}$     (c) $\left(\dfrac{2}{3}\right)^{-2}$     (d) $\left(\dfrac{1}{4}\right)^{-3}$

(e) $\left(\dfrac{2}{9}\right)^{-2}$     (f) $\left(\dfrac{3}{10}\right)^{-1}$     (g) $\left(\dfrac{1}{4}\right)^{-4}$     (h) $\left(\dfrac{5}{9}\right)^{-2}$

**9** Express the following in the form $8^n$

(a) $\dfrac{1}{8}$      (b) 8      (c) 1

(d) 64      (e) $\dfrac{1}{64}$      (f) $\dfrac{1}{512}$

**10** Which of the statements below are true?

(a) $5^3 \times 5^{-1} = 5^2$    (b) $7^{-2} \times 7^{-2} = 7^4$    (c) $\left(\dfrac{1}{4}\right)^{-1} = -3$

(d) $6^2 \div 6^5 = 6^{-3}$    (e) $8^{-1} = -8$    (f) $3^{-1} > 4^{-1}$

(g) $\left(\dfrac{1}{2}\right)^0 = -1$    (h) $\left(\dfrac{2}{5}\right)^{-2} = \dfrac{25}{4}$    (i) $6^{-1} \times 6^{-1} = 6^{-2}$

**M1.4**

> **Note**  $\sqrt{3} \times \sqrt{3} = \sqrt{9} = 3$
> $\sqrt{5} \times \sqrt{5} = \sqrt{25} = 5$

**1** Work out without a calculator:

(a) $\sqrt{7} \times \sqrt{7}$  (b) $\sqrt{8} \times \sqrt{8}$  (c) $2 \times \sqrt{5} \times \sqrt{5}$

(d) $4 \times \sqrt{6} \times \sqrt{6}$  (e) $10 \times \sqrt{11} \times \sqrt{11}$  (f) $7 \times \sqrt{2} \times \sqrt{2}$

**2** Work out

(a) $\dfrac{6\sqrt{4}}{\sqrt{9}}$  (b) $\dfrac{2\sqrt{9} + \sqrt{16}}{\sqrt{4} + \sqrt{9}}$  (c) $\dfrac{2\sqrt{100} + \sqrt{16}}{\sqrt{4} + 1}$

(d) $(\sqrt{225} - \sqrt{196})^2$  (e) $(\sqrt{49} + \sqrt{16})(\sqrt{49} - \sqrt{16})$  (f) $(\sqrt{169} - \sqrt{64})^2$

**3** 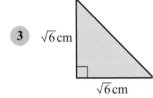 Work out the area of this triangle.

**4** 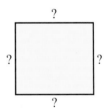 The area of the square opposite is equal to the area of the rectangle. Work out the perimeter of the square.

**5** Evaluate

(a) $\sqrt[3]{125}$  (b) $\sqrt[3]{27}$  (c) $\sqrt[3]{(20 - 12)}$  (d) $\sqrt[3]{(40 + 2 \times 12)}$

**6** Work out

(a) $\dfrac{\sqrt[3]{(5 \times 25)}}{\sqrt{4}}$  (b) $\dfrac{\sqrt[3]{(2 \times 3 \times 36)}}{\sqrt{(13 - 4)}}$  (c) $\dfrac{\sqrt{36} \times \sqrt[3]{125}}{\sqrt[3]{8} + \sqrt{(5^2 - 4^2)}}$

**7** 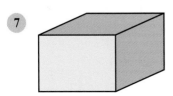 The volume of this cube is 80 cm³.
Find the area of the front face, giving the answer correct to 1 decimal place.

**8** Use a calculator to work out each of the following, leaving answers to 1 decimal place.

(a) $\sqrt[4]{4096}$

(b) $\sqrt[5]{243}$

(c) $\sqrt[7]{(64 \times 2)}$

(d) $\dfrac{\sqrt[4]{256} \times \sqrt[4]{256}}{\sqrt[4]{65\,536}}$

(e) $\dfrac{\sqrt[7]{2187} + \sqrt[3]{8}}{\sqrt[4]{(7700 + 2300)}}$

(f) $\sqrt[3]{\left( \dfrac{4^4 - 120 - \sqrt{121}}{3^4 - 4^2 \times 5} \right)}$

**9**

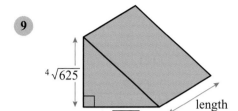

$\sqrt[4]{625}$

$\sqrt[5]{1024}$   length

The volume of a prism is its cross-sectional area multiplied by its length. The volume of this prism is 50 cm³. Work out its length. All lengths are given in cm.

## Products of prime factors, HCF and LCM

**Factor tree**

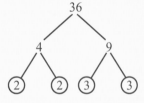

split into 4 and 9
because 4 × 9 = 36
split 4 into 2 × 2
split 9 into 3 × 3

stop splitting when all numbers are prime numbers.
We can say 36 = 2 × 2 × 3 × 3

prime factors

2 × 2 × 3 × 3 is the *product of its prime factors*
(sometimes written as 2² × 3² known as index form)

**Dividing by prime numbers**

Divide by any prime number

$\downarrow$

2 ) 36
2 ) 18 ← 36 ÷ 2 = 18
3 ) 9 ← 18 ÷ 2 = 9
3 ) 3 ← 9 ÷ 3 = 3
      1 ← 3 ÷ 3 = 1

stop when you get to 1

These are the prime factors.
We can say 36 = 2 × 2 × 3 × 3

---

**M1.5**

**1** Work out these products

(a) 2 × 3 × 3 × 5

(b) 3 × 5 × 7 × 7

(c) 2³ × 3 × 7

(d) 2² × 3² × 5

(e) 3³ × 5 × 11²

(f) 2⁴ × 5² × 13

② Using any method, write the following numbers as *products of prime factors*.

    (a) 44          (b) 48          (c) 100          (d) 52          (e) 140

    (f) 160        (g) 98          (h) 490        (i) 660        (j) 936

③ Write all your answers to question ② in index form if you have not already done so.

④ Find each number described below

    (a) a multiple of 70 between 500 and 600

    (b) the square of the smallest prime number

    (c) an odd number which is greater than one and a factor of both 28 and 42

    (d) a square number whose digits add up to 10

    (e) a prime number whose digits add up to a cube number

---

**Highest Common Factor (HCF) and Lowest Common Multiple (LCM) using a Venn diagram**

Example 120 and 195                Find the prime factors:

$$120 = 2 \times 2 \times 2 \times 3 \times 5$$
$$195 = 3 \times 5 \times 13$$

Write the prime factors in a Venn diagram with the common prime factors in the intersection part (ie. the pink part where the rings for each number overlap).

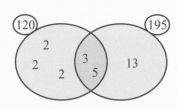

- multiply all prime numbers inside the Venn diagram to give the LCM.
  LCM $= 2 \times 2 \times 2 \times 3 \times 5 \times 13 = 1560$

- multiply all prime numbers in the intersection (pink) part of the Venn diagram to give the HCF.
  HCF $= 3 \times 5 = 15$

**1**  (154)                    (1365)

$\begin{array}{c} 2 \\ 11 \end{array}$   7   $\begin{array}{c} 3 \\ 13 \end{array}$ 5

Use this Venn diagram to find

(a)  the HCF of 154 and 1365

(b)  the LCM of 154 and 1365

**2**  (975)                    (550)

$\begin{array}{c} 3 \\ 13 \end{array}$   $\begin{array}{c} 5 \\ 5 \end{array}$   $\begin{array}{c} 2 \\ 11 \end{array}$

Use this Venn diagram to find

(a)  the HCF of 975 and 550

(b)  the LCM of 975 and 550

**3**  Draw factor trees and Venn diagrams to find the HCF and LCM of:

(a)  28 and 120          (b)  200 and 420          (c)  196 and 420

**4**  $336 = 2^4 \times 3 \times 7$ and $308 = 2^2 \times 7 \times 11$

Find the HCF and LCM of 336 and 308.

**5**  $5544 = 2^3 \times 3^2 \times 7 \times 11$ and $45738 = 2 \times 3^3 \times 7 \times 11^2$

Find the HCF and LCM of 5544 and 45738.

**6**  Two cars complete laps of a circuit.

One takes 315 seconds per lap, the other takes 525 seconds per lap.

They start their circuits of the laps at the same time.

(a)  Express 315 and 525 as the product of their primes.

(b)  Use this to find how many laps the faster car will do before the cars first get to the starting point at the same time.

**7**  (a)  Find the highest common factor and lowest common multiple of 210 and 550.

(b)  Multiply the two numbers that you found in part (a) together.

(c)  Multiply 210 and 550 together.

(d)  What do you notice about the answers to parts (b) and (c)? Can you explain why?

## Key Facts

A number written in standard form will have the form

A is a number between
1 and 10, actually $1 \leq A < 10$ → $A \times 10^n$ ← n is an integer (a whole number)

$16700 = 1.67 \times 10000 = 1.67 \times 10^4$          $0.096 = 9.6 \times 10^{-2}$

### M1.7

1  Copy each statement below and fill in the empty boxes
(a)  $400000 = 4 \times 10^{\square}$   (b)  $82000 = \boxed{\phantom{0}} \times 10^{\square}$   (c)  $6400 = \boxed{\phantom{0}} \times 10^3$
(d)  $0.08 = 8 \times 10^{\square}$   (e)  $0.000067 = 6.7 \times 10^{\square}$   (f)  $0.052 = 5.2 \times 10^{\square}$
(g)  $0.4 = \boxed{\phantom{0}} \times 10^{-1}$   (h)  $42000 = 4.2 \times 10^{\square}$   (i)  $0.00082 = \boxed{\phantom{0}} \times 10^{-4}$

2  Write the numbers below in standard form.
(a)  60000        (b)  900        (c)  5800        (d)  690000
(e)  850          (f)  74000000   (g)  47 000      (h)  4 million
(i)  0.008        (j)  0.003      (k)  0.00000007  (l)  0.95

3  500 million litres of rain can fall from a single thunderstorm. Write this in standard form.

4  The annual budget for the Holland High School is £4126000. Write this in standard form.

5  A hydrogen atom has a mass of 0.000 000 000 000 000 000 000 0017 grams. Write this in standard form.

6  In 1902, the cost of a pint of beer was 0.8 pence! Write this in standard form.

7  Write each number below as an *ordinary number*.
(a)  $5 \times 10^2$        (b)  $6.8 \times 10^3$     (c)  $8.1 \times 10^5$     (d)  $7 \times 10^{-2}$
(e)  $9.8 \times 10^{-4}$   (f)  $6.12 \times 10^4$    (g)  $3.7 \times 10^{-3}$  (h)  $8.41 \times 10^{-2}$

**8** Write each number below in standard form.

(a) 0·02           (b) 0·0006     (c) 209                   (d) 31600

(e) 5800000        (f) 316·8      (g) 32·71              (h) 0·0065

(i) three thousand million    (j) 0·073     (k) five thousandths    (l) 590000

## Using standard form numbers without a calculator

# Key Facts

*To multiply standard form numbers:* multiply the numbers, add the powers.

*To divide standard form numbers:* divide the numbers, subtract the powers.

*To add or subtract:* make sure the powers of 10 are the same before adding or subtracting.

(a) $\dfrac{9 \times 10^{14}}{2 \times 10^{3}} = 4{\cdot}5 \times 10^{11}$

(b) $(7 \times 10^{4}) \times (3 \times 10^{3}) = 21 \times 10^{7}$
$$= (2{\cdot}1 \times 10^{1}) \times 10^{7}$$
$$= 2{\cdot}1 \times 10^{8}$$

(c) $(3{\cdot}6 \times 10^{8}) - (7{\cdot}1 \times 10^{7})$

Convert $7{\cdot}1 \times 10^{7}$ into $0{\cdot}71 \times 10^{8}$

so $(3{\cdot}6 \times 10^{8}) - (7{\cdot}1 \times 10^{7}) = (3{\cdot}6 \times 10^{8}) - (0{\cdot}71 \times 10^{8})$
$$= 2{\cdot}89 \times 10^{8}$$

### M1.8

*Do not use a calculator.*

**1** Write each number below in *standard form*.

(a) $36 \times 10^{5}$      (b) $21 \times 10^{9}$      (c) $47 \times 10^{-4}$      (d) $0{\cdot}38 \times 10^{7}$

(e) $0{\cdot}8 \times 10^{12}$      (f) $0{\cdot}71 \times 10^{-6}$      (g) $586 \times 10^{10}$      (h) $413 \times 10^{-9}$

**2** Work out the following, leaving each answer in *standard form*.

(a) $(4 \times 10^{3}) \times (2 \times 10^{5})$          (b) $(3 \times 10^{8}) \times (3 \times 10^{4})$

(c) $(2 \times 10^{7}) \times (3 \times 10^{5})$          (d) $(5 \times 10^{9}) \times (1{\cdot}5 \times 10^{6})$

(e) $(2 \times 10^{6}) \times (8 \times 10^{2})$          (f) $(4 \times 10^{7}) \times (3 \times 10^{6})$

(g) $(2{\cdot}5 \times 10^{-4}) \times (3 \times 10^{9})$      (h) $(9 \times 10^{16}) \times (4 \times 10^{-8})$

(i) $(3 \times 10^{-4}) \times (5 \times 10^{14})$

**3** Evaluate the following, leaving your answers in *standard form*.

(a) $(8 \times 10^{14}) \div (2 \times 10^{6})$    (b) $(9 \times 10^{17}) \div (3 \times 10^{4})$    (c) $\dfrac{6 \times 10^{21}}{2 \times 10^{8}}$

(d) $(3 \times 10^{26}) \div (2 \times 10^{13})$    (e) $\dfrac{8\cdot1 \times 10^{42}}{3 \times 10^{17}}$    (f) $(8 \times 10^{7}) \div (4 \times 10^{17})$

(g) $(4\cdot5 \times 10^{12}) \div (3 \times 10^{-6})$    (h) $\dfrac{2 \times 10^{27}}{4 \times 10^{9}}$    (i) $(6\cdot6 \times 10^{-8}) \div (2\cdot2 \times 10^{-19})$

**4** The average speed of a plane is $2\cdot3 \times 10^{7}$ metres per hour. How long will it take to travel a distance of $4\cdot6 \times 10^{8}$ metres? (time = distance ÷ speed)

**5** UK households produce 29 million tonnes of general waste per year – half of which could be recycled. How many tonnes could be recycled? Give your answer in standard form.

**6** 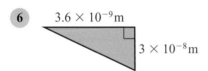    Work out the area of this triangle. Give the answer in standard form.

$3.6 \times 10^{-9}\,\text{m}$

$3 \times 10^{-8}\,\text{m}$

**7** Copy and complete:

(a) $(4 \times 10^{7}) + (3 \times 10^{6})$

  $= (4 \times 10^{7}) + (3 \times 10^{7} \times 10^{\square})$

  $= (4 \times 10^{7}) + (\boxed{\phantom{0}} \times 10^{7})$

  $= \boxed{\phantom{0}} \times 10^{7}$

(b) $(8\cdot6 \times 10^{-8}) - (3 \times 10^{-9})$

  $= (8\cdot6 \times 10^{-8}) - (3 \times 10^{-8} \times 10^{-1})$

  $= (8\cdot6 \times 10^{-8}) - (\boxed{\phantom{0}} \times 10^{-8})$

  $= \boxed{\phantom{0}} \times 10^{-8}$

**8** Work out the following, leaving each answer in *standard form*.

(a) $(6 \times 10^{3}) + (3 \times 10^{4})$    (b) $(8 \times 10^{9}) + (5 \times 10^{8})$

(c) $(3\cdot1 \times 10^{11}) + (5\cdot6 \times 10^{12})$    (d) $(5 \times 10^{3}) - (4 \times 10^{2})$

(e) $(2 \times 10^{5}) - (6 \times 10^{4})$    (f) $(3\cdot5 \times 10^{3}) - (2\cdot1 \times 10^{2})$

(g) $(4 \times 10^{-7}) - (8 \times 10^{-8})$    (h) $(6\cdot1 \times 10^{-12}) - (2 \times 10^{-13})$

**9** Two electronic components have widths of $(8 \times 10^{-7})$ m and $(3\cdot4 \times 10^{-6})$ m respectively. What is their combined width if they are placed side by side? Give the answer in standard form.

**10** At a time when Jupiter, Pluto and the Sun are in a line, the distances of Jupiter and Pluto from the Sun are respectively $7{\cdot}9 \times 10^8$ km and $6 \times 10^9$ km.

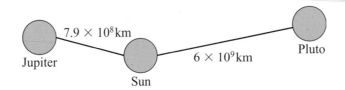

7.9 × 10⁸ km
Jupiter
Sun
6 × 10⁹ km
Pluto

What is the distance (in standard form) between Pluto and Jupiter when the two planets and the Sun are in line with:

(a) the planets on opposite sides of the Sun?

(b) the planets on the same side of the Sun?

**11** Every day, $2 \times 10^7$ text messages are sent in the UK.
How many text messages are sent in the UK in one year?
(Assume 1 year = 365 days).

**12**

| Town | Population |
|------|-----------|
| Hatton | $3{\cdot}6 \times 10^4$ |
| Rentwich | $8{\cdot}9 \times 10^3$ |
| Corbridge | $9{\cdot}2 \times 10^4$ |
| Sidwell | $6{\cdot}7 \times 10^2$ |

The populations of 4 places are shown in the table above.
Write the names down in order of size, starting with the smallest.

**13** What standard form number must be subtracted from 83000 to give the answer $7{\cdot}2 \times 10^4$?

**14** If $m = 5{\cdot}6 \times 10^8$ and $n = 3{\cdot}7 \times 10^9$, find the value in standard form of $2m + 3n$.

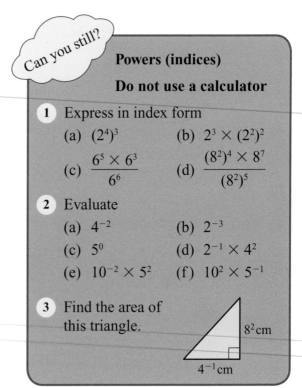

Can you still?

**Powers (indices)**

**Do not use a calculator**

**1** Express in index form

(a) $(2^4)^3$

(b) $2^3 \times (2^2)^2$

(c) $\dfrac{6^5 \times 6^3}{6^6}$

(d) $\dfrac{(8^2)^4 \times 8^7}{(8^2)^5}$

**2** Evaluate

(a) $4^{-2}$

(b) $2^{-3}$

(c) $5^0$

(d) $2^{-1} \times 4^2$

(e) $10^{-2} \times 5^2$

(f) $10^2 \times 5^{-1}$

**3** Find the area of this triangle.

$8^2$ cm

$4^{-1}$ cm

**15** Use Einstein's formula $E = mc^2$ to work out E when $m = 2 \times 10^6$ and $c = 3 \times 10^8$. Give the answer in standard form.

16

## Using standard form numbers with a calculator

Remember: use the $\boxed{\times\,10^x}$ button

$6{\cdot}4 \times 10^{17}$ is typed in as $\boxed{6}\ \boxed{\cdot}\ \boxed{4}\ \boxed{\times\,10^x}\ \boxed{1}\ \boxed{7}$

### M1.9

**1** Use a calculator to work out the following and write each answer in standard form.

(a) $(6{\cdot}5 \times 10^{17}) \div (1{\cdot}3 \times 10^{-6})$

(b) $(8{\cdot}4 \times 10^{13}) \times (2 \times 10^{19})$

(c) $\dfrac{(2 \times 10^{10})^2}{5 \times 10^{-7}}$

(d) $(3{\cdot}6 \times 10^{23}) - (4 \times 10^{22})$

**2** The distance of the Earth from the Sun is about $1{\cdot}496 \times 10^{11}$ m. The distance of Pluto from the Sun is about $5{\cdot}91 \times 10^{12}$ m. How many times further from the Sun is Pluto compared to the Earth (Give your answer to the nearest whole number)?

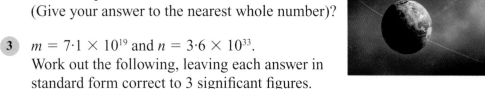

**3** $m = 7{\cdot}1 \times 10^{19}$ and $n = 3{\cdot}6 \times 10^{33}$.
Work out the following, leaving each answer in standard form correct to 3 significant figures.

(a) $m \times n$      (b) $m \div n$      (c) $m^2$      (d) $m^2 \div n^2$

**4** The radius of a circle is $4{\cdot}7 \times 10^{-8}$ m. Calculate the area of the circle (Give your answer to 3 significant figures).

**5** The mass of an electron is $9{\cdot}1 \times 10^{-28}$ grams. What is the total mass of $5 \times 10^{12}$ electrons?

**6** Work out the following, leaving each answer in standard form, correct to 3 significant figures.

(a) $\dfrac{(2{\cdot}1 \times 10^9) \times (4{\cdot}6 \times 10^{16})}{4 \times 10^7}$

(b) $\dfrac{(2{\cdot}7 \times 10^{31}) \times (8{\cdot}6 \times 10^{-14})}{5{\cdot}6 \times 10^{-12}}$

(c) $\dfrac{(4{\cdot}3 \times 10^9) \times (2{\cdot}6 \times 10^{24})}{(6{\cdot}6 \times 10^5)^2}$

(d) $\dfrac{(3{\cdot}7 \times 10^{-9}) \times (2{\cdot}6 \times 10^{-18})}{(5{\cdot}3 \times 10^{17}) \times (1{\cdot}8 \times 10^{-4})}$

(e) $\dfrac{\sqrt{(7{\cdot}8 \times 10^{16})}}{(3{\cdot}2 \times 10^{-4}) \times (1{\cdot}9 \times 10^{-17})}$

(f) $\sqrt{\dfrac{(3{\cdot}7 \times 10^{10})}{(1{\cdot}8 \times 10^{-9})^3}}$

**7**

| A | $2.84 \times 10^9$ |
|---|---|

| B | $1.8 \times 10^{10}$ |
|---|---|

| C | $9 \times 10^8$ |
|---|---|

| D | $4.5 \times 10^9$ |
|---|---|

| E | $3.55 \times 10^8$ |
|---|---|

| F | $6.2 \times 10^7$ |
|---|---|

(a) Calculate the value of A − F

(b) Which number is four times the value of D?

(c) Which number is eight times smaller than the value of A?

(d) Write the numbers in order of size, starting with the smallest number.

**8** A thunderstorm is taking place 6 km away. Light travels $3 \times 10^5$ km in one second. Sound travels $1.226 \times 10^3$ km in one hour.

(a) How long does it take for the light from the lightning to travel 6 km? (Give your answer in standard form).

(b) Show that sound travels approximately 340 m in one second.

(c) How long (to the nearest second) does it take for the sound of the thunder to travel 6 km?

**9** The centre of the Milky Way is $2.6 \times 10^4$ light years from Earth, and the nearest galaxy is $1.6 \times 10^5$ light years from the Earth.

(a) (i) Which of these distances is greater?

(ii) By how many light years?

(b) If one light year is $9.46 \times 10^{12}$ km then find the distance of the nearest galaxy from the Earth in km. Leave your answer in standard form correct to 3 significant figures.

**10** Write down the reciprocal of 450, leaving your answer in standard form correct to 3 significant figures.

**11**

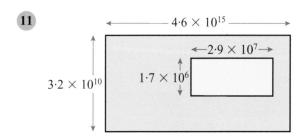

Work out the blue area, leaving your answer in standard form. All lengths are in cm.

Jenny has been given some money to do a bedroom makeover. A plan of her bedroom is shown below.

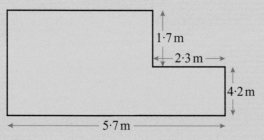

**Task A**

Jenny starts by painting her ceiling with acrylic matt paint. The paint will cover 11 to 13 square metres per litre. If Jenny gets the worst coverage of paint on her ceiling, how many litres of paint will she need for one coat?

**Task B**

Jenny wants to paint all her walls yellow. Each wall is shown below. Again, the paint will cover 11 to 13 square metres per litre but Jenny only gets the worst coverage.

1   How many litres of paint will Jenny need for one coat?

2   A 5 litre tin of paint costs £35·95. A 2·5 litre tin of paint costs £21·95.
    How much will Jenny need to spend on her yellow paint?

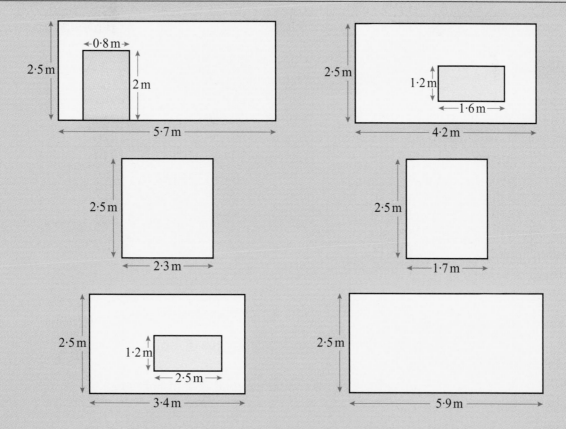

## Task C

Jenny chooses a new carpet. She can only buy carpet which has a 4 m width.

Each piece of carpet must be laid in the same direction.

1  What length of carpet must Jenny buy to cover her entire bedroom as cheaply as possible?

2  Multiply this length by the 4 m width to find the area of carpet that Jenny must buy.

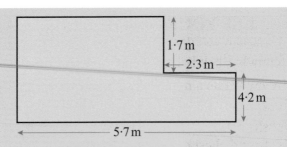

| Single size beds | |
|---|---|
| Name | Price |
| Winchester | £178 |
| Tamworth | £231 |
| RDU | £155 |
| Leonardo | £284 |
| Paulton | £202 |
| Relaxe | £301 |
| Porter | £199 |
| Memory foam | £324 |

| Sofas | |
|---|---|
| Name | Price |
| Colston 2 Seater | £364 |
| Mowbray 2 Seater | £473 |
| Edwins 3 Seater | £719 |
| Parkhead 2 Seater | £506 |
| Canston Leather 3 Seater | £1120 |
| Bintons Luxury 2 Seater | £790 |
| Harrows Deluxe 2 Seater | £685 |
| Tindwells Deluxe 3 Seater | £1065 |

| Carpet | |
|---|---|
| Name | Price per m² |
| Howton Twist | £25·40 |
| Palton Weave | £22·65 |
| Cotswold Twist | £19·85 |
| Mendip Supreme | £31·35 |
| Classic Weave | £24·90 |
| Winchester Pile | £28·30 |
| Dalbury Tuff Weave | £14·70 |
| Cheasley Deluxe Twist | £37·40 |
| Canton High Pile | £16·15 |
| Paris Classic Twist | £38·25 |

| Chest of Drawers | |
|---|---|
| Name | Price |
| Holton 3 Drawer | £173 |
| Holton 5 Drawer | £256 |
| Busby 3 Drawer | £206 |
| Coventry 3 Drawer | £249 |
| Chiltern Pine 4 Drawer | £186 |
| Chiltern Pine 5 Drawer | £227 |
| Parlton 4 Drawer | £284 |

## Task D

Jenny has £1900 to do her bedroom makeover. A 5 litre pot of Brilliant White ceiling paint costs £27·95

1  Use your answers from parts A and B to find the total cost of her paint.

**2**  Choose a carpet from the table opposite and use your answer from part C to find out the total cost of her carpet.

**3**  Jenny wants a new bed, sofa and chest of drawers. Choose one of each from the tables opposite.

   If she chooses all three, she gets a 20% discount. Find the total cost of the bed, sofa and chest of drawers.

**4**  Jenny must not spend more than £1900 on everything. Change your choices if you need to and show clearly how the total bill is less than £1900.

# TEST YOURSELF ON UNIT 1

**1.** Consolidating previous number work

**Do not use a calculator**

Work out

(a) $\dfrac{9 + 2 \times 3}{5}$    (b) $73 \times 216$    (c) $\dfrac{8 + (4 \times 3)}{\sqrt{16}}$

(d)  A market gardener has planted 37 rows of cabbages.
   Each row contains 26 cabbages.
   All the cabbages are picked and placed in boxes.
   Each box contains 65 cabbages.
   How many boxes are needed in total?

(e)  Find the missing values A, B, C and D below:

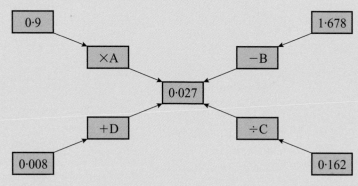

(f)  *Use a calculator* to work out the following, giving each answer to 3 significant figures.

(i) $\dfrac{2 \cdot 16 + 3 \cdot 8^2}{5 \cdot 97^2}$    (ii) $\dfrac{(\sqrt{8} + \sqrt{3})^2}{\sqrt{15}}$    (iii) $\dfrac{\sqrt{15 \cdot 21} \div 0 \cdot 083}{0 \cdot 018^2}$

21

**2.** Using negative powers

Evaluate (work out the value of)

(a) $2^{-3}$        (b) $4^{-2}$        (c) $9^{-1}$        (d) $10^{-3}$

(e) $5^{-2} \times 10^2$     (f) $4^3 \times 8^{-1}$

(g) Copy and complete the box: $2^\square = \dfrac{1}{16}$

**3.** Calculating with roots

Evaluate

(a) $\sqrt[3]{(6^2 - 3^2)}$        (b) $(\sqrt{256} - \sqrt{36})^2$        (c) $\dfrac{3\sqrt{25} + \sqrt{100}}{1 + \sqrt{16}}$

(d) Work out the volume of the cuboid opposite.

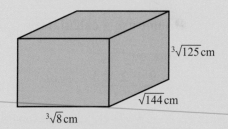

$\sqrt[3]{125}$ cm

$\sqrt{144}$ cm

$\sqrt[3]{8}$ cm

**4.** Using power notation for prime factors

(a) $936 = 2^x \times 3^y \times z$. Find the values of $x$, $y$ and $z$.

(b) Express 2646 as a product of its prime factors in index form.

**5.** Finding HCF/LCM using prime factors

(a) $440 = 2^3 \times 5 \times 11$ and $3300 = 2^2 \times 3 \times 5^2 \times 11$

Find the HCF and LCM of 440 and 3300.

(b) Write 105 and 330 as products of their prime factors.

Use a Venn diagram to find the HCF and LCM of 105 and 330.

(c) Find the HCF and LCM of 84 and 490.

## 6. Using standard form

Write the numbers below in standard form.

(a) 273000    (b) 380    (c) 0·8    (d) 0·0018

Write each number below as an ordinary number.

(e) $7·2 \times 10^2$    (f) $5·21 \times 10^{-2}$    (g) $5·9 \times 10^{-4}$    (h) $6·14 \times 10^6$

Evaluate the following *without a calculator*, leaving your answers in standard form.

(i) $(2 \times 10^9) \times (1·5 \times 10^3)$    (j) $(3 \times 10^7) \times (5 \times 10^6)$

(k) $(6·9 \times 10^{16}) \div (2·3 \times 10^5)$    (l) $(6·6 \times 10^4) \div (1·1 \times 10^{-7})$

(m) $(5 \times 10^7) + (3 \times 10^6)$    (n) $(7·2 \times 10^{-6}) - (9 \times 10^{-7})$

*Use a calculator* to work out the following, leaving each answer in standard form.

(o) $(8·3 \times 10^{12}) \times (4·2 \times 10^{10})$    (p) $\dfrac{(3 \times 10^8)^2}{2 \times 10^{-7}}$

(q) $\dfrac{8 \times 10^{-8}}{\sqrt{4 \times 10^{18}}}$    (r) $\dfrac{(5·8 \times 10^{14}) - (3·4 \times 10^{13})}{(2 \times 10^{15})^2}$

(s) The speed of light is approximately 300000 km/s. Calculate how far in km light travels in one year (365 days). Give the answer in standard form.

## Mixed examination questions

**1** Calculate

$$\sqrt{\frac{16·4 - 5·87}{5·42 + 1·09}}$$

Write your answer correct to 2 decimal places.    (OCR)

**2** Sherri says

"If you multiply an odd number by 7 and take away 2 you always get a prime number".

Show that Sherri is wrong.    (EDEXCEL)

**3** (a) Express 84 as a product of its prime factors **in index form**.

(b) Find the Lowest Common Multiple (LCM) of 63 and 84       (CEA)

**4** In an examination, candidates sit 2 written papers called Paper A and Paper B.

In a forthcoming examination there are 1200 candidates, each sitting Paper A and Paper B.

In 1 day, markers can either mark 60 Paper As or mark only half as many Paper Bs.

The marking must be completed in 10 days.

How many markers are needed to complete the marking in this time?    (WJEC)

**5** Michael writes down 4 different factors of 60.

He added the 4 factors together.

He gets a number greater than 20 but less than 35

What 4 factors could Michael have written down?       (EDEXCEL)

**6** One sheet of paper is $9 \times 10^{-3}$ cm thick.

Mark wants to put 500 sheets of paper into the paper tray of his printer.

The paper tray is 4cm deep.

Is the paper tray deep enough for 500 sheets of paper?

You must explain your answer.       (EDEXCEL)

**7** Evaluate

(a) $6^{-2}$            (b) $4^{-1}$            (c) $2^{-2} \times 6^2$

**8** (a) Estimate the value of $\sqrt{17} + \sqrt{83}$

You must show how you arrived at your answer.

(b) Calculate the value of

(i) $5 \times 4 + 6 \times 2$

(ii) $30 \div 6 + 4$       (CEA)

**9** Express 2250 as a product of its prime factors **in index form**.

**10** (a) Use your calculator to work out $\dfrac{\sqrt{7056}}{0{\cdot}35 \times 12{\cdot}8}$

Write down all the figures on your calculator display.
You must give your answer as a decimal.

(b) Write your answer to part (a) correct to 1 significant figure. (EDEXCEL)

**11** Hailey says that $3^{-3} = -9$.

Is she correct? Explain your answer.

**12** (a) Write 16 000 in standard form.

(b) Here are some facts about four planets.

|  | Mercury | Venus | Earth | Mars |
|---|---|---|---|---|
| Mass (kg) | $3{\cdot}30 \times 10^{23}$ | $4{\cdot}87 \times 10^{24}$ | $5{\cdot}97 \times 10^{24}$ | $6{\cdot}42 \times 10^{23}$ |
| Volume (m³) | $6{\cdot}08 \times 10^{19}$ | $9{\cdot}28 \times 10^{20}$ | $1{\cdot}08 \times 10^{21}$ | $1{\cdot}63 \times 10^{20}$ |

(i) Complete this sentence giving your answer correct to 3 significant figures.
The volume of Venus is _____ times the volume of Mercury.

(ii) Show that the Earth has the greatest density.
Make all you working clear
(density = mass ÷ volume) (OCR)

**13** Work out the volume of the prism.

All lengths are in cm.

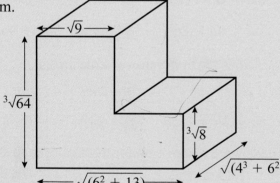

**14** $630 = 2 \times 3^2 \times 5 \times 7$ and $6600 = 2^3 \times 3 \times 5^2 \times 11$

Find the HCF abd LCM of 630 and 6600.

# ALGEBRA 1

**2**

### In this unit you will learn how to:

- consolidate previous algebra work
- find simple formulas
- substitute numbers into formulas
- expand two brackets
- solve equations with brackets and with unknown on both sides
- set up equations
- factorise quadratics of form $x^2 + bx + c$
- $\boxed{\text{USE YOUR MATHS!}}$ – electricity, gas and water

## Previous algebra work

**M2.1**

Collect like terms.

**1** $6m + 5n - 2m$    **2** $5a + 2b + 3a - b$    **3** $8x - 4x + 3y + 2y$

**4** $3a^2 + 4a + 2a^2$    **5** $4mn + 3m^2 - mn + m^2$    **6** $8n^2 - 4n^2 + 3n - n^2$

In questions **7** to **12** answer 'true' or 'false'.

**7** $a + a^2 = a^3$    **8** $20m \div 4 = 5m$    **9** $\dfrac{n}{m} = m \div n$

**10** $5a \times 3b = 15ab$    **11** $4m \times 2n = 6mn$    **12** $a \times 5 \times a = 5a^2$

Write down an expression for the area of each shape below:

**13**

**14**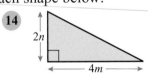

**15**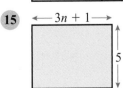

**16**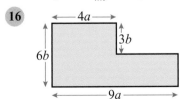

Expand (multiply out)

**17** $2(a + b)$  **18** $3(2a - b)$  **19** $5(3m + 2n)$  **20** $a(a + 2b)$

**21** $m(m - 4n)$  **22** $2n(3n + 4)$  **23** $6m(2m - 1)$  **24** $5a(a - 7b)$

**25** The length of the screen opposite is $(3x + 7)$ cm. The width of the screen is $(2x - 3)$ cm. Write down an expression for the perimeter of the screen.

---

**M2.2**

Expand and simplify.

**1** $4(2x + 3) + 3(4x + 5)$

**2** $5(3x + 2) + 6(7x + 4)$

**3** $3(5x + 6) + 2x + 4(x + 2)$

**4** $7(3x + 6) + 2(5x + 1) + 4x$

Write down the perimeter of each shape below:

**5**
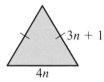

**6**
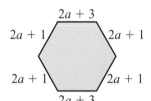

**7**
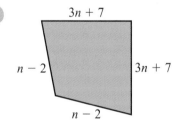

Solve these equations.

**8** $\dfrac{n}{4} = 3$  **9** $5n - 6 = 24$  **10** $3n + 1 = 28$

**11** $16 = 3n - 2$  **12** $5 = \dfrac{n}{7}$  **13** $4n - 2 = 34$

**14** In one week Tyler eats $n$ hamburgers. Stella eats twice as many hamburgers as Tyler. Anna eats 3 hamburgers less than Stella. If Anna eats 9 hamburgers, write down an equation and solve it to find $n$.

**15** $20a - 12b = 4(5a - 3b)$
4 is the common factor
above.
Factorise $15m + 10n$

**16** Factorise $a^2 - 3ab$

**17** Factorise $m^2 + 4mn$

**18** Factorise $6n^2 - 4ny$

Simplify the following:

**19** $5a \times a$

**20** $16m \div 8$

**21** $45n \div 15$

**22** $8x \times 3x$

**23** $2m \times 4n \times 5p$

**24** $20n^2 \div n$

Write each answer below in index form.

**25** $7^{10} \div 7^6$

**26** $5^4 \times 5^3$

**27** $2^3 \times 2^4 \times 2$

**28** $\dfrac{3^5 \times 3^2}{3^4}$

**29** $\dfrac{6 \times 6 \times 6}{6^2}$

**30** $\dfrac{2^8 \times 2^4}{2^2 \times 2^3}$

> **Can you still?**
>
> **Factors and multiples**
>
> **1** Express 504 as a product of prime factors in index form.
>
> **2** $60 = 2^2 \times 3 \times 5$
> $3080 = 2^3 \times 5 \times 7 \times 11$
> Write down the HCF and LCM of 60 and 3080.
>
> **3** Write down the HCF and LCM of 780 and 819.
>
> **4** Find the number between 10 and 25 which has a sum of all its factors equal to a square number.

(a) $-4m \times -2n = 8mn$

(b) $-7(2 - 3n) = -14 + 21n$

(c) $5n = -20$ so $n = -4$

(d) $4 - 3n = 22$

Subtract 4 from each
side of equation
$-3n = 18$
$n = -6$

**E2.1**

Simplify

**1** $3a \times -7b$

**2** $-4n \times -3n$

**3** $-8m \div 4$

**4** $-6m \times -4n$

**5** $-20n \div -10$

**6** $30a \div -6$

**7** $5a \times -8a$

**8** $-40a^2 \div -8a$

Solve these equations.

**9**  $6n + 5 = 4$    **10**  $8n + 4 = 1$    **11**  $5n + 8 = 9$

**12**  $6n + 3 = -2$    **13**  $-4 = 4n - 3$    **14**  $16 = 24 + 4n$

**15**  $3 = 2n + 5$    **16**  $17 - 5n = 7$    **17**  $30 - 5n = 31$

Write down and simplify an expression for the perimeter of each shape below.

**18**
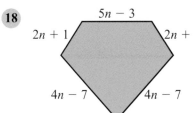
$5n - 3$
$2n + 1$      $2n + 1$
$4n - 7$      $4n - 7$

**19**
$6a - 4$      $6a + 1$
$5a + 3$

**20**
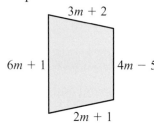
$3m + 2$
$6m + 1$      $4m - 5$
$2m + 1$

**21**  The area of the small square shown opposite is $16a^2$.
The perimeter of the larger square is 1.5 times longer than the perimeter of the small square.
Write down an expression for the area of the larger square.

**22**  Simplify the expression below.

(a)  $\dfrac{n^6 \times n^4}{n^8}$    (b)  $\dfrac{(m^3)^4 \times m^6}{(m^2)^3}$    (c)  $\dfrac{x^6 \times x^9}{(x^2)^2 \times x^6}$

(d)  $5m^4 \times 3m^2$    (e)  $\dfrac{20x^7}{4x^3}$    (f)  $\dfrac{3n^3 \times 6n^2}{2n^4}$

Factorise

**23**  $6n^2 - 18n$    **24**  $8mn + 12mp$

**25**  $15np - 10p^2$    **26**  $20m^2 + 15mn$

**27**  $28xy + 16x^2$    **28**  $10abc + 16a^2b - 6ab$

(a) Simplify $\underbrace{5(2a + 1) - 3(a - 2)}$

$= 10a + 5 - 3a + 6$

↑

Note

$= 7a + 11$

(b) Simplify $\underbrace{8(x + 3) - 2(2x + 4)}$

$= 8x + 24 - 4x - 8$

↑

Note

$= 4x + 16$

Expand and simplify

**1** $3(4a + 2) - 2(a - 2)$

**2** $5(3x + 1) - 3(3x - 2)$

**3** $6(2x + 3) - 4(2x + 2)$

**4** $5(3a + 2) - 3(2a + 1)$

**5** $3(4d + 1) - 2(6d - 5)$

**6** $9y - 5(y + 2) - 3$

**7** $11x + 2 - 3(2x - 5)$

**8** $6a + 2(3a + 1) - 7 + 2a$

**9** $9(x + 2) - 4 + 2(2 - 3x)$

**10** $6(c + 3) - 2(2c - 4)$

**11** $7(3a + 2) - 2(5a - 4)$

**12** $8(c + 9) - 3(2c + 6)$

**13** $5(2c + 6) - 4(c + 5)$

**14** $8x - 4(x - 9) - 10$

**15** $3a + 11 - 2(a + 3)$

**16** $9(3a + 4) + 2a - 4(2a - 3)$

**17** $15(n + m) - 6(2n - m)$

**18** $8(2a + b) - 3(3a + 2b)$

**19** $5(3x + 6) - 4(2x - 3)$

**20** $8x + 6(2 - x) + 2(3x + 5)$

**21** Find and simplify an expression for the total area of the three rectangles below.

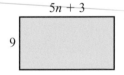
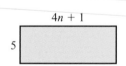

**22** $n$ people each pay £$(4m - 3)$ for concert tickets. The same people also each pay £$(7m + 5)$ for hotel rooms. Write down and simplify an expression for the total amount of money these people pay.

The length of a rectangle is 3 cm more than its width.
Let the width be $x$.
Write down a formula for the perimeter $P$ of the rectangle in terms of $x$.

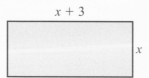

$x + 3$

$x$

$P = x + x + 3 + x + x + 3$
$P = 4x + 6$

### M2.3

**1** The length of a rectangle is 5 cm more than its width. Let the width be $x$. Write down the formula for the perimeter $P$ in terms of $x$.

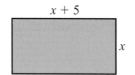

$x + 5$

$x$

**2** The base of a triangle is six times greater than its height $h$. Write down a formula for the area $A$ in terms of $h$.

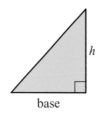

$h$

base

**3** Roger buys $n$ shirts at £18 for each shirt. He also buys $(n - 2)$ jumpers at £27 each. Write down the formula for the total cost $C$ of the shirts and jumpers, in terms of $n$.

**4** Grace hires a jigsaw for £8 plus £5 per day. Write down a formula, in terms of $n$, for the total cost $C$ of hiring the jigsaw for $n$ days.

**5** Paving slabs cost £6 each. Ivan charges £60 plus £2 for each slab he lays. Write a formula for the total cost $C$ of buying $n$ paving slabs and getting Ivan to lay them all.

31

**6**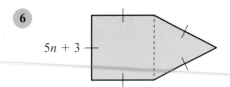

$5n + 3$

A square is attached to an equilateral triangle as shown. Write down a formula for the perimeter $P$ in terms of $n$.

**7** Andrea earns £9 per hour working at a chocolate factory. She also earns £7 per hour working as a barmaid.
Each week she works 10 more hours at the chocolate factory than as a barmaid.
Find a formula for her total pay $P$ when she works $n$ hours as a barmaid, giving your answer in terms of $n$.

*Can you still?*

**Standard Form**

**Do not use a calculator**

**1** Write the numbers below in standard form
(a) 0·049
(b) 26000
(c) 0·713

**2** Work out the following, leaving each answer in standard form.
(a) $(5 \times 10^{10}) \times (3 \times 10^4)$
(b) $(2 \times 10^{11}) \div (8 \times 10^{-6})$
(c) $(3·4 \times 10^8) + (2·5 \times 10^7)$

**8** A train engine has $x$ wheels on it. A train carriage has $(x - 4)$ wheels on it. Write down a formula for the number of wheels, $N$, on a train with 2 engines and 6 carriages. Give your answer in terms of $x$.

**3** Write the numbers below in order of size, starting with the smallest.
$(2·81 \times 10^{-7})$, $(3·12 \times 10^{-9})$,
$(5·16 \times 10^{-7})$, $(4·67 \times 10^{-9})$,
$(1·86 \times 10^{-8})$, $(2·13 \times 10^{-7})$

**9** A lorry can be hired for £90 per day plus £0·20 per mile.
Write down a formula for the total cost $C$ of hiring a lorry for $n$ days and driving it for $y$ miles.
Give your answer in terms of $n$ and $y$.

**10** Harry gives £$x$ to charity. Rosie gives £12 more to the charity than Harry. Spencer gives three times as much as Rosie. Isabel doubles the total amount given by Harry, Rosie and Spencer. Find a formula for the total amount $A$ given to the charity. Simplify the answer as much as possible.

**M2.4**

**1**

The surface area $A$ of a cone is roughly given by the formula

$$A = 3rl$$

Find the value of $A$ when

(a) $r = 2, l = 10$      (b) $r = 5, l = 3$      (c) $r = 8, l = 5$

**2** The position $P$ of the middle value of some numbers is found from the formula

$$P = \frac{1}{2}(n + 1)$$

where $n$ is how many numbers there are.

Find $P$ when      (a) $n = 7$      (b) $n = 99$

**3** The interest $I$ made by some money $P$ is given by the formula

$$I = \frac{PTR}{100}$$

where $T$ is the time and $R$ is the rate of interest. Find the value of $I$ when

(a) $P = 800, T = 2, R = 5$

(b) $P = 40, T = 5, R = 8$

**4** Using the formula $h = \sqrt{(a^2 - b^2)}$

find the value of $h$ when

(a) $a = 13, b = 12$      (b) $a = 25, b = 24$

**5** A ball is dropped. The distance $s$ it travels is given by the formula

$$s = 4 \cdot 9 \, t^2$$

where $t$ is the time taken.

Find the value of $s$ when

(a) $t = 10$      (b) $t = 2$

**6**

The volume $V$ of an orange is roughly given by the formula

$$V = 4r^3$$

where $r$ is the radius of the orange

Find the value of $V$ when     (a) $r = 5$     (b) $r = 10$

**7** The temperature in degrees Fahrenheit $F$ can be changed into degrees Centigrade $C$ by using the formula

$$C = \frac{5}{9}(F - 32)$$

Find the value of $C$ when

(a) $F = 50$     (b) $F = 68$

**8**

The surface area $A$ of a cylinder is roughly given by the formula

$$A = 6rh + 3r^2$$

Find the value of $A$ when

(a) $r = 2, h = 5$     (b) $r = 4, h = 20$

## E2.3

You may *use a calculator* for these questions.
Round off the numbers to the *nearest whole number*.

**1** Using the formula $x = \dfrac{y + z}{z - y}$ find the value of $x$ when

(a) $y = 6, z = 11$          (b) $y = 0 \cdot 3, z = -2 \cdot 8$

**2** Using the formula $A = \dfrac{2B + C}{B + 3C}$ find the value of $A$ when

(a) $B = -7, C = 4$          (b) $B = -24, C = -2$

**3** Here is a formula $M = \sqrt{(4N - 1)}$. Find the value of $M$ when

(a) $N = 6$     (b) $N = 20$     (c) $N = 5 \cdot 8$

**4**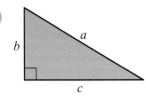

For any right-angled triangle

$$a = \sqrt{(b^2 + c^2)}$$

Find the value of $a$ when

(a) $b = 7, c = 2$     (b) $b = 12, c = 5$     (c) $b = 8, c = 15$

**5** Using the formula $f = \dfrac{uv}{u + v}$, find the value of $f$ when

(a) $u = 6, v = 4$     (b) $u = 8, v = 20$     (c) $u = 5, v = 32$

**6**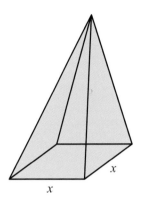

The volume $V$ of this pyramid is given by the formula

$$V = \frac{x^2 h}{3}$$

where $h$ is the height of the pyramid.

Find the value of $V$ when

(a) $x = 4, h = 10$     (b) $x = 5, h = 7$     (c) $x = 20, h = 15$

**7** The formula $v = \sqrt{u^2 + 2as}$ gives the final speed $v$ of a car whose initial speed is $u$, acceleration is $a$ and displacement is $s$. Find the value of $v$ (to 3 significant figures if necessary) when

(a) $u = 10, a = 3, s = 7$

(b) $u = -3{\cdot}6, a = 9{\cdot}8, s = 15{\cdot}3$

**8** The formula $A = \sqrt{s(s - a)(s - b)(s - c)}$ gives the area $A$ of a triangle with sides $a$, $b$ and $c$ where $s$ is half the perimeter. Find the area $A$ (to 2 significant figures if necessary) of the following triangles (by first finding and stating the value of $s$).

(a) $a = 3, b = 4, c = 5$

(b) $a = 7{\cdot}8, b = 18{\cdot}72, c = 20{\cdot}28$

# Key Facts

Each term in one bracket must be multiplied by each term in the other bracket.

Consider $(a + b)(c + d)$.

| | | | |
|---|---|---|---|
| F | $(\textcircled{a} + b)(\textcircled{c} + d)$ | multiply the <u>F</u>irst terms in each bracket ⮕ | $ac$ |
| O | $(\textcircled{a} + b)(c \textcircled{+ d})$ | multiply the <u>O</u>uter terms in each bracket ⮕ | $+\ ad$ |
| I | $(a \textcircled{+ b})(\textcircled{c} + d)$ | multiply the <u>I</u>nner terms in each bracket ⮕ | $+\ bc$ |
| L | $(a \textcircled{+ b})(c \textcircled{+ d})$ | multiply the <u>L</u>ast terms in each bracket ⮕ | $+\ bd$ |

First
Outer ⎫
Inner ⎬ Follow this order each time to make sure you do not miss any terms ⮕ $(a + b)(c + d) = ac + ad + bc + bd$
Last ⎭

---

(a) Multiply out $(x + 3)(x + 5)$

$(x + 3)(x + 5)$

$$\begin{array}{cccc} & F & O & I & L \\ = & (x^2 & +5x & +3x & +15) \end{array}$$

these middle 2 terms can be collected together

$= x^2 + 8x + 15$

(b) Expand $(x + 4)(x + 2)$

$(x + 4)(x + 2)$

$= x^2 + 2x + 4x + 8$

$= x^2 + 6x + 8$

---

**M2.5**

**1** Copy and complete the following.

(a) $(x + 3)(x + 4)$

$= x^2 + 4x + \square + 12$

$= x^2 + \square + 12$

(b) $(x + 1)(x + 6)$

$= \square + 6x + x + \square$

$= \square + 7x + \square$

(c) $(x + 9)(x + 4)$

$= x^2 + \square + \square + 36$

$= x^2 + \square + 36$

36

Expand the following:

**2** $(x + 2)(x + 6)$     **3** $(p + 1)(p + 5)$     **4** $(a + 3)(a + 7)$

**5** $(m + 2)(m + 8)$     **6** $(y + 3)(y + 6)$     **7** $(n + 1)(n + 1)$

Multiply out the following:

**8** $(x + 7)(x + 3)$     **9** $(y + 4)(y + 5)$     **10** $(p + 3)(p + 10)$

**11** $(a + 9)(a + 7)$     **12** $(f + 4)(f + 8)$     **13** $(y + 6)(y + 8)$

Find the area of each rectangle below:

**14** 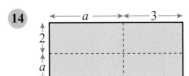     **15**

Expand     **16** $(x + 3)(x + 3)$     **17** $(x + 3)^2$     **18** $(x + 5)^2$

**19** $(x + 8)^2$     **20** $(x + 2)^2$     **21** $(x + 9)^2$

---

(a) Expand $(x - 4)(x + 2)$

$(x - 4)(x + 2)$

$= x^2 + 2x - 4x - 8 = x^2 - 2x - 8$

(b) Expand $(x - 5)^2$

$(x - 5)(x - 5)$

$= x^2 - 5x - 5x + 25 = x^2 - 10x + 25$

---

## E2.4

**1** Copy and complete the following.

(a) $(x + 2)(x - 6)$

$= x^2 - \square + 2x - 12$

$= x^2 - \square - 12$

(b) $(a - 5)(a + 3)$

$= \square + 3a - 5a - \square$

$= \square - 2a - \square$

(c) $(m - 7)^2 = (m - 7)(m - 7)$

$= m^2 - \square - \square + \square$

$= m^2 - \square + \square$

Expand

**2** $(m + 3)(m - 1)$     **3** $(n - 5)(n + 2)$

**4** $(b - 8)(b + 3)$     **5** $(x - 6)(x + 8)$

**6** $(c - 8)(c - 3)$     **7** $(q - 2)(q - 7)$

**8** $(f - 2)(f - 10)$     **9** $(a + 9)(a - 4)$

**10** $(y - 4)(y - 9)$     **11** $(x - 4)(x - 4)$

Expand

**12** $(x - 4)^2$

**13** $(x - 6)^2$

**14** $(m - 1)^2$

**15** $(y - 10)^2$

**16** $(a - 8)^2$

**17** $(2 + n)(n + 3)$

**18** $(x + 5)(6 + x)$

**19** $(y + 4)(3 - y)$

**20** $(x + 1)^2 + (x + 3)^2$

**21** Find an expression for the total area of the two rectangles shown below.

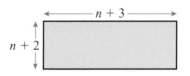

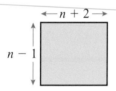

Can you still!?

**Number work**

**Do not use a calculator**

**1** Tony must buy 60 toilet rolls for his hotel. He can choose from 2 shops as shown.

| Shop A | Shop B |
|--------|--------|
| **£8·80** <br> for a <br> pack of 16 | **£5·15** <br> for a <br> pack of 9 |
| $\frac{1}{4}$ **off** <br> the shown price | *Buy 2 and get 1 free* |

What is the cheapest option? Show all your working out.

**2** Work out $\dfrac{23 \times 703}{19}$

**3** Estimate, to the nearest whole number, the value of

$\sqrt{125} \times \sqrt[3]{60}$

Multiply out the following.

**22** $(2x + 1)(3x + 4)$

**23** $(5y + 2)(y + 3)$

**24** $(4p + 2)(2p + 7)$

**25** $(3a - 4)(5a + 2)$

**26** $(6f - 1)(2f + 3)$

**27** $(9y - 4)(4y - 2)$

**28** $(3x - 4)(7x + 2)$

**29** $(3q - 4)(7q - 1)$

**30** $(4b - 3)(5b - 3)$

**31** $(4z - 6)(2z - 3)$

**32** $(x + 7)(4x - 9)$

**33** $(6a - 5)(5a + 4)$

Find the area of each red shape below:

**34**

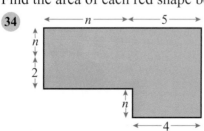

**35**

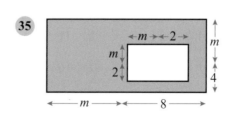

38

# Key Facts

$3m + 4n^2$ is an algebraic **expression** containing two terms $3m$ and $4n^2$.
An **expression** contains no '=' sign.

$2x + 5 = 11$ is an **equation**.
Only one value of $x$ works, i.e. $x = 3$

$x^2 = 9$ is an **equation**.
Only two values of $x$ work, i.e. $x = 3$ and $-3$

If a relationship works for all values of e.g. $x$, it is called an **identity**.
The symbol '$\equiv$' means 'is identical to'.

$(x + 2)(x + 3) \equiv x^2 + 3x + 2x + 6$
$(x + 2)(x + 3) \equiv x^2 + 5x + 6$

Try any value of $x$ and you will see both sides of this **identity** give the same value.

---

**M2.6**

**1**

| $x^2 + 2$ | $3x + 2 = 1$ | $4x^2 - 3x + 1$ |
|:---:|:---:|:---:|
| A | B | C |

| $5a^2 - 6ab$ | $x(x + 3) \equiv x^2 + 3x$ |
|:---:|:---:|
| D | E |

(a) Which of the above boxes contain expressions only?

(b) How many terms does box C contain?

(c) How many values of $x$ will work in box B?

(d) How many values of $x$ will work in box E?

**2** Show that

$$(x + 7)(x + 3) \equiv x^2 + 10x + 21$$

For how many different values of $x$ is this true?

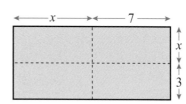

**3** $5n - 3 = 2n + 15$

Explain why this is an equation and not an identity.

**4** Expand $(x + 6)^2$

How many terms does the final simplified expression contain?

**5** Is $5(x - 2)$ equal to $(5x - 10)$ or identical to $(5x - 10)$?

Give a reason for your answer.

**6**

| $7x^2 + 3x$ |

| $2x(x - 4) \equiv 2x^2 - 8x$ |

| $7xy$ |

| $5x - 2 < 8$ |

| $5x - 2 = 8$ |

Copy all these boxes. Use arrows to link each box on the left hand side to its correct name

| term |

| equation |

| identity |

| expression |

| inequality |

**7** $3x^2(x - 2) \equiv 3x^3 - 6x^2$

For how many different values of $x$ is this true?

## Equations with brackets

(a) Solve $3(n + 2) = 12$

multiply out
brackets first        $3n + 6 = 12$

subtract 6 from each
side of equation        $3n = 6$

                        $n = 2$

(b) Solve $5(2n - 1) = 45$

multiply out
brackets first        $10n - 5 = 45$

add 5 onto each
side of equation        $10n = 50$

                        $n = 5$

In questions ① to ③, copy and fill the empty boxes.

① $3(n + 1) = 12$

$3n + \boxed{\phantom{0}} = 12$

$3n = \boxed{\phantom{0}}$

$n = \boxed{\phantom{0}}$

② $5(n - 2) = 30$

$\boxed{\phantom{0}} - 10 = 30$

$\boxed{\phantom{0}} = 40$

$n = \boxed{\phantom{0}}$

③ $4(2n + 3) = 28$

$8n + \boxed{\phantom{0}} = 28$

$8n = \boxed{\phantom{0}}$

$n = \boxed{\phantom{0}}$

Solve these questions

④ $4(n + 2) = 20$

⑤ $5(n + 1) = 50$

⑥ $8(n + 3) = 40$

⑦ $3(n - 4) = 6$

⑧ $3(2n + 1) = 27$

⑨ $2(4n - 4) = 12$

⑩ $5(2n + 3) = 75$

⑪ $9(2n + 1) = 27$

⑫ $3(5n - 6) = 42$

⑬ $20 = 2(2n - 4)$

⑭ $105 = 5(4n + 5)$

⑮ $3(3n - 4) = 33$

⑯ $52 = 4(2n + 5)$

⑰ $76 = 2(5n - 7)$

⑱ $6(n - 9) = 12$

⑲ $3(3n - 7) = 24$

⑳ $40 = 10(2n - 6)$

㉑ $8 = 8(2n - 3)$

In questions ㉒ to ㉕, I am thinking of a number. Write down an equation then solve it to find the number.

Add double the number onto 4 then multiply the answer by 3. This gives 24.

Let the number be $n$.

Equation is $\qquad (2n + 4) \times 3 = 24$

We write this as $\qquad 3(2n + 4) = 24$

Solve: $\qquad\qquad 6n + 12 = 24$

$\qquad\qquad\qquad\quad 6n = 12$

$\qquad\qquad\qquad\quad n = 2$

㉒ Add the number onto 5 then multiply the answer by 6. This gives 48.

㉓ Add treble the number onto 2 then multiply the answer by 2. This gives 46.

㉔ Take away 4 from double the number then multiply the answer by 5. This gives 30.

㉕ Subtract 7 from treble the number then multiply the answer by 4. This gives 8.

## Equations with brackets and 'trickier' numbers

(a) Solve $2(n + 3) = 5$

multiply out brackets first $\quad 2n + 6 = 5$

subtract 6 from each side of equation $\quad 2n = -1$

divide each side of equation by 2 $\quad \dfrac{2n}{2} = \dfrac{-1}{2}$

$$n = \dfrac{-1}{2}$$

(b) Solve $36 = 4(1 - 2n)$

multiply out brackets first $\quad 36 = 4 - 8n$

subtract 4 from each side of equation $\quad 32 = -8n$

divide each side of equation by $-8$ $\quad \dfrac{32}{-8} = \dfrac{-8n}{-8}$

$$-4 = n$$
$$\text{so } n = -4$$

### E2.5

In questions **1** to **6**, copy and fill the empty boxes.

**1** $\quad 5(x + 3) = 10$
$\quad\quad \boxed{\phantom{x}} + 15 = 10$
$\quad\quad\quad\quad \boxed{\phantom{x}} = -5$
$\quad\quad\quad\quad x = \boxed{\phantom{x}}$

**2** $\quad 2(x + 9) = 14$
$\quad\quad 2x + \boxed{\phantom{x}} = 14$
$\quad\quad\quad 2x = \boxed{\phantom{x}}$
$\quad\quad\quad\quad x = \boxed{\phantom{x}}$

**3** $\quad 3(2x + 5) = -3$
$\quad\quad 6x + \boxed{\phantom{x}} = -3$
$\quad\quad\quad 6x = \boxed{\phantom{x}}$
$\quad\quad\quad\quad x = \boxed{\phantom{x}}$

**4** $\quad 3(x + 2) = 4$
$\quad\quad 3x + \boxed{\phantom{x}} = 4$
$\quad\quad\quad 3x = \boxed{\phantom{x}}$
$\quad\quad\quad\quad x = \boxed{\phantom{x}}$

**5** $\quad 2(2x + 3) = 5$
$\quad\quad 4x + \boxed{\phantom{x}} = 5$
$\quad\quad\quad 4x = \boxed{\phantom{x}}$
$\quad\quad\quad\quad x = \boxed{\phantom{x}}$

**6** $\quad 33 = 3(2 - 3x)$
$\quad\quad 33 = 6 - \boxed{\phantom{x}}$
$\quad\quad 27 = -\boxed{\phantom{x}}$
$\quad\quad \boxed{\phantom{x}} = x$

Solve these questions

**7** $\quad 3(x + 2) = 6$

**8** $\quad 5(2x + 4) = 0$

**9** $\quad 4(x + 5) = 17$

**10** $\quad 5(x + 9) = 15$

**11** $\quad 2(4x + 10) = 4$

**12** $\quad 3(2x - 3) = -15$

**13** $\quad 4(2x - 3) = -20$

**14** $\quad 2 = 5(2x + 1)$

**15** $\quad 8 = 5(4x + 3)$

**16** $\quad 2(1 - 2x) = 14$

**17** $\quad 2(3 - 4x) = 30$

**18** $\quad 20 = 10(5 + x)$

**19** $\quad 85 = 5(5 - 2x)$

**20** $\quad 7 = 2(6 - 3x)$

*Can you still?*

### Indices

**Do not use a calculator**

Evaluate

**1** $7^{-2}$  **2** $5^{-3}$  **3** $9^{-1}$

**4** $\dfrac{2^{-2} \times 2^5}{2^2}$  **5** $\dfrac{(3^4)^3 \times 3^4}{3^7 \times 3^7}$

**6** Which of the statements below are true?

(a) $10^{-1} = 0{\cdot}1$  (b) $5^0 \div 5^3 = 5^{-3}$

(c) $2^{-1} < 3^{-1}$  (d) $\left(\dfrac{1}{3}\right)^{-1} = -3$

## Equations with the unknown on both sides

(a)  Solve  $6n - 2 = 2n + 18$

subtract $2n$ from each
side of equation          $4n - 2 = 18$

add 2 onto each
side of equation                $4n = 20$

$n = 5$

(b)  Solve  $8n + 6 = 3n + 41$

subtract $3n$ from each
side of equation          $5n + 6 = 41$

subtract 6 from each
side of equation                $5n = 35$

$n = 7$

**M2.8**

Find the value of $n$ in questions **1** to **6** :

**1**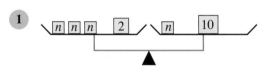

**2**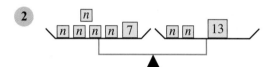

**3**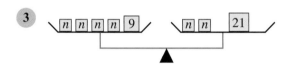

**4**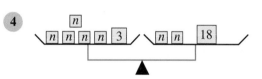

**5**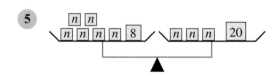

**6**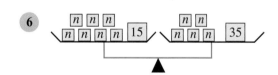

Solve these equations:

**7**  $8n + 6 = 3n + 26$      **8**  $9n - 4 = 5n + 20$

**9**  $6n - 1 = 4n + 11$      **10**  $7n + 3 = 3n + 27$

**11**  $7n + 5 = 5n + 25$      **12**  $10n + 2 = 7n + 14$

**13**  $5n + 4 = 2n + 22$      **14**  $6n + 8 = 2n + 36$

**15**  $7n - 3 = 4n + 12$      **16**  $5n - 2 = n + 10$

**17** $9n - 7 = 5n + 13$

**18** $11n - 9 = 5n + 27$

**19** $5n - 10 = 3n + 50$

**20** $8n - 3 = 2n + 39$

**21** $9n + 14 = 6n + 29$

**22** $10n + 17 = 3n + 52$

**23** $5n - 16 = n + 20$

**24** $8n - 22 = 2n + 8$

### 'Trickier' equations with the unknown on both sides

Solve $5(2x + 3) = 2(3x + 8)$

| | |
|---|---|
| multiply out brackets first | $10x + 15 = 6x + 16$ |
| subtract $6x$ from each side of equation, | $4x + 15 = 16$ |
| subtract $15$ from each side of equation, | $4x = 1$ |
| divide each side of equation by 4, | $\dfrac{4x}{4} = \dfrac{1}{4}$ |
| | $x = \dfrac{1}{4}$ |

### E2.6

Solve these equations.

**1** $6x - 4 = 3x - 16$

**2** $7x + 3 = 43 - x$

**3** $2(3x + 2) = 4(x + 3)$

**4** $5x + 2 = 3 - 2x$

**5** $6x + 4 = 3 - 3x$

**6** $5x - 2 = x - 10$

**7** $9x + 4 = 3x - 1$

**8** $2x - 8 = 12 - 3x$

**9** $2 + 9x = 3 - x$

**10** $7x - 2 = 1 - 3x$

**11** $6x + 5 = 41 - 3x$

**12** $5x + 8 = 1 - 4x$

In questions **13** to **16** below, Blake is thinking of a number. Write down an equation then solve it to find the number.

**13** If we multiply the number by 7 and add 4, the answer we get is the same as when we multiply the number by 3 and add 12.

**14** If we multiply the number by 8 and subtract 5, the answer we get is the same as when we multiply the number by 2 and add 19.

44

**15** If we treble the number and subtract from 9 we get the same answer as when we double the number and add 4.

**16** If we double the number, add 5 and then multiply the result by 3, the answer is 27.

Solve these equations.

**17** $3(2x + 3) = 2(x + 4)$

**18** $2(x + 2) = 5(x - 4)$

**19** $4(2x - 2) = 3(3x + 4)$

**20** $7(x - 1) = 2(2x + 4)$

**21** $8(x - 3) = 4(3 - x)$

**22** $6(x - 4) = 2(x - 1)$

**23** $3(x + 2) = 4(1 - x)$

**24** $3(2x + 1) = 4(7 - x)$

**25**

(2x + 1) cm | 4 cm rectangle

The area of each rectangle shown is equal. Work out the actual area of one rectangle.

(4x − 8) cm | 3 cm rectangle

**26**

Triangle with sides $(2 - 3x)$ cm, $(12 + 2x)$ cm, and base $(1 - x)$ cm

Work out the actual perimeter of the isosceles triangle above:

Solve these equations:

**27** $2(3x - 1) = 3(1 - 2x)$

**28** $5(2 - x) = 2(4 + 2x)$

**29** $3(x + 1) + 1 = 2(2x + 1) - 3$

**30** $2(x + 1) + 1 = 3(3x - 5) - 10$

**31** $\frac{1}{6}(x - 14) = 2(x - 3)$

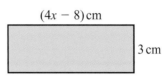

**Can you still!?**

**Standard Form**

**Use a calculator**

Work out the following, leaving each answer in standard form, correct to 3 significant figures.

**1** $(5 \cdot 6 \times 10^{-8}) \times (2 \cdot 3 \times 10^{-17})$

**2** $\dfrac{(4 \times 10^9)^2}{1 \cdot 96 \times 10^{-5}}$

**3** $\dfrac{(2 \cdot 7 \times 10^{-11}) \times (4 \cdot 4 \times 10^{-10})}{(5 \cdot 4 \times 10^4)^2}$

**4** $(8 \cdot 4 \times 10^{-4}) + \sqrt{(3 \cdot 9 \times 10^{-9})}$

**5** $\sqrt[3]{\dfrac{(4 \cdot 7 \times 10^{19}) - (9 \cdot 5 \times 10^{18})}{(1 \cdot 8 \times 10^{-8}) \times (7 \cdot 4 \times 10^{-4})}}$

The perimeter of this rectangle is 44 cm.

Find $x$ then write down the actual length and width of the rectangle.

*2x + 1*

*x* ▢ *x*

*2x + 1*

Perimeter $= x + 2x + 1 + x + 2x + 1 = 6x + 2$ (this is equal to 44 cm)

So $6x + 2 = 44$

$6x = 42$

$x = 7$

length $= 2x + 1 = 2 \times 7 + 1 = 15$ cm

width $= x = 7$ cm

---

**M2.9**

**1**

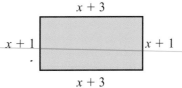

*x + 3*

*x + 1* ▢ *x + 1*

*x + 3*

The perimeter of this rectangle is 28 cm.

(a) Write down an equation using the perimeter.

(b) Find $x$.

(c) Write down the actual length and width of the rectangle.

**2**

*3x + 2*

*x + 3* ▢ *x + 3*

*3x + 2*

The perimeter of this rectangle is 58 cm.

(a) Write down an equation using the perimeter.

(b) Find $x$.

(c) Write down the actual length and width of the rectangle.

**3**

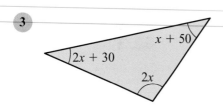

*x + 50*

*2x + 30*

*2x*

(a) Write down an equation using the angles.

(b) Find $x$.

(c) Write down the actual value of each angle in this triangle.

**4** A rectangle has its length 5 times its width. If the perimeter of the rectangle is 48 cm, find its length and width (remember: let width $= x$).

46

**5** £190 is divided by Jack and Evan so that Jack receives £72 more than Evan. How much does each person get?
(*hint:* let $x$ = Evan's money)

**6** Lily has three times more money than James. Ella has £20 more than Lily. The total money is £300. Form an equation then use it to find out how much money Lily has.

**7**

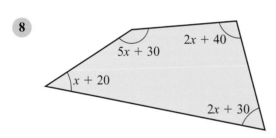

$(5x - 2)$ cm

$2(x + 5)$ cm

Work out the actual perimeter of the square.

**8**

$5x + 30$

$2x + 40$

$x + 20$

$2x + 30$

(a) Write down an equation using the angles.

(a) Find $x$.

(c) Write down the actual value of each angle in this quadrilateral.

**9** There are 3 children in a family. Each is 3 years older than the next and the sum of their ages is 21. How old is each child?

**10** A rectangle has its length twice its width. If its perimeter is 42 cm, find the width of the rectangle.

The sum of four consecutive numbers is 42. Let the first number be $x$ and write down the other three numbers in terms of $x$. Find the four numbers.

Other three numbers are $(x + 1)$, $(x + 2)$ and $(x + 3)$.

Sum is 42     so     $x + (x + 1) + (x + 2) + (x + 3) = 42$
$$4x + 6 = 42$$
$$4x = 36$$
$$x = 9$$

The four numbers are 9, 10, 11 and 12

## E2.7

**1**  The sum of four consecutive numbers is 78. Let the first number be $x$.
Set up an equation to find $x$ then find the four numbers.

**2**
2 cm

$(3x - 1)$ cm

The area of the rectangle opposite is 46 cm$^2$.
Find the perimeter of the rectangle.

**3**  The cost, C, of hiring a van is given by the formula

$$C = 60 + 25\,n$$

where $n$ is the number of days the van is hired for.
All values are given in £.
Find the value of $n$ if the cost was £210.

**4**  The sum of four consecutive odd numbers is 216.

(a) If $x$ is the smallest number, write down the other numbers in terms of $x$.
(b) Find the actual numbers.

**5**  Mr Harris is on holiday in his caravan.
Each day he sees more and more ducks.
The number of ducks, N, that he sees on
day $x$ is given by the formula

$$N = 3(2n + 1) - 8$$

(a) How many ducks does he see on day 5 of his holiday?
(b) On which day does the number of ducks equal the day number?

**6**

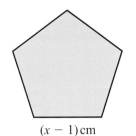

$(x - 1)$ cm

Each side of the regular pentagon is $(x - 1)$ cm.

Each side of the square is 4 cm more than one of the pentagon sides.

Find the actual perimeter of the square if the perimeter of the square is equal to the perimeter of the pentagon.

**7** It is given that

$$P = \frac{1}{3}(4x - 8)$$

A value of $x$ is used so that the value of P is equal to $x$. Find this value of $x$.

**8**

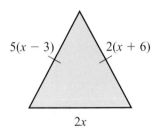

$5(x - 3)$    $2(x + 6)$

$2x$

Find the actual perimeter of the isosceles triangle above. All lengths are given in cm.

**9** You have three consecutive *even* numbers so that the sum of twice the smallest number plus three times the middle number is four times the largest number. Find the three numbers.

---

**Can you still?**    **Negative numbers**

**Do not use a calculator**

Work out

**1** $-3 + (-5)^2$

**2** $(-3)^3 \div 9$

**3** $\dfrac{-5 + 3}{-1 \times 2}$

**4** $\dfrac{(-8)^2}{-5 - 3}$

Copy and fill in the box:

**5** $\boxed{\phantom{x}} - 4^2 = -9$

**6** $(-1)^3 \times \boxed{\phantom{x}} = 7$

**7** $(-6)^2 \div \boxed{\phantom{x}} = -4$

**8** $\boxed{\phantom{x}} - -5 = -3$

**9** Find the value of $4n^2$ if $n = -2$

**10** Find the value of $n$ if $4n^3 = -108$

---

**10**

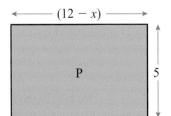

$2$    Q    $x$

The area of rectangle P is five times the area of rectangle Q. Find $x$.

$(12 - x)$    P    $5$

49

## Equations with fractions

Solve these equations.

**1** $\dfrac{x}{2} + 5 = 10$     **2** $\dfrac{x}{2} + 9 = 19$     **3** $\dfrac{1}{3}x + 4 = 9$

**4** $\dfrac{x}{3} - 2 = 2$     **5** $\dfrac{1}{4}x - 3 = 2$     **6** $8 = \dfrac{x}{5} + 6$

**7** $3 = \dfrac{1}{5}x - 2$     **8** $\dfrac{1}{6}x - 3 = 2$     **9** $\dfrac{x}{3} + 12 = 19$

Solve these equations.

**10** $\dfrac{x - 5}{3} = 4$     **11** $\dfrac{2x + 1}{4} = 5$

**12** $\dfrac{x + 6}{8} = -3$     **13** $\dfrac{3x - 2}{5} = 8$

**14** $\dfrac{20}{x} = 5$     **15** $9 = \dfrac{7x - 3}{2}$

**16** $8 = \dfrac{56}{x}$     **17** $\dfrac{9x - 5}{7} = 7$

**18** $7 = \dfrac{42}{x}$     **19** $\dfrac{5}{x} - 4 = 4$

**20** $9 = \dfrac{3}{x} + 7$     **21** $\dfrac{1}{9}x + 7 = 10$

## Factorising quadratics

We have seen that $(x + 2)(x + 5) = x^2 + 5x + 2x + 10 = x^2 + 7x + 10$.

$x^2 + 7x + 10$ is a *quadratic* expression ($x^2$ is the highest power).

Since $(x + 2)(x + 5) = x^2 + 7x + 10$, we can reverse the process to show that $x^2 + 7x + 10 = (x + 2)(x + 5)$.

$(x + 2)$ multiplied by $(x + 5)$ gives $x^2 + 7x + 10$ so $(x + 2)$ and $(x + 5)$ are both *factors* of $x^2 + 7x + 10$.

Expressing $x^2 + 7x + 10$ as $(x + 2)(x + 5)$ is known as *factorising the quadratic* $x^2 + 7x + 10$. The process is vital to solving many mathematical equations and for making algebraic expressions simpler.

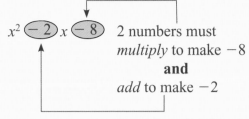

(a) Factorise $x^2 - 2x - 8$

$x^2 \; \fbox{$- 2$} \; x \; \fbox{$- 8$}$   2 numbers must
*multiply* to make $-8$
**and**
*add* to make $-2$

i.e. $+2$ **and** $-4$

$x^2 - 2x - 8 = (x + 2)(x - 4)$

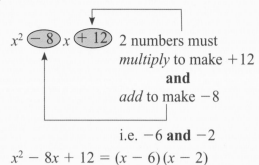

(b) Factorise $x^2 - 8x + 12$

$x^2 \; \fbox{$- 8$} \; x \; \fbox{$+ 12$}$   2 numbers must
*multiply* to make $+12$
**and**
*add* to make $-8$

i.e. $-6$ **and** $-2$

$x^2 - 8x + 12 = (x - 6)(x - 2)$

*Check each answer by multiplying back out*

**M2.10**

Copy and complete:

**1**   $x^2 + 10x + 21$
$= (x + 3)(x + \boxed{\phantom{0}})$

**2**   $x^2 - 7x + 12$
$= (x + \boxed{\phantom{0}})(x + \boxed{\phantom{0}})$

**3**   $x^2 + 7x + 10$
$= (x + \boxed{\phantom{0}})(x + 2)$

Factorise the following quadratics:

**4**   $a^2 + 11a + 30$

**5**   $y^2 + 8y + 15$

**6**   $b^2 + 12b + 20$

**7**   $p^2 + 5p + 6$

**8**   $x^2 + 4x + 4$

**9**   $f^2 + 10f + 25$

**10**   $c^2 + 5c + 4$

**11**   $y^2 + 3y + 2$

**12**   $x^2 + 12x + 35$

Copy and complete:

**13**   $m^2 - 6m + 5$
$= (m - 1)(m - \boxed{\phantom{0}})$

**14**   $x^2 - 3x - 28$
$= (x + \boxed{\phantom{0}})(x - \boxed{\phantom{0}})$

**15**   $m^2 - 2m - 35$
$= (m - 7)(m + \boxed{\phantom{0}})$

Factorise the following:

**16**   $x^2 - 17x + 30$

**17**   $n^2 - 9n + 8$

**18**   $y^2 - 4y - 12$

**19**   $a^2 - 8a + 16$

**20**   $q^2 - 14q + 13$

**21**   $w^2 + 5w - 24$

**22**   $n^2 + 5n - 14$

**23**   $p^2 + p - 6$

**24**   $x^2 - x - 20$

**25**   $y^2 - 7y + 10$

**26**   $a^2 + 3a - 40$

**27**   $q^2 - q - 42$

**28**   $x^2 + 2x - 24$

**29**   $n^2 - 5n + 6$

**30**   $y^2 - 4y - 60$

**31** Find the length of PQ in terms of $x$.

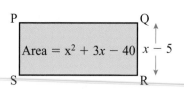

**32** Find the length of FG in terms of $a$.

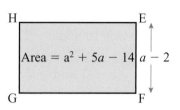

Factorise the following quadratics:

**33** $x^2 - 20x + 99$ **34** $y^2 - 10y + 25$ **35** $m^2 + 13m + 42$

**36** $p^2 - 14p + 24$ **37** $n^2 - 17n + 70$ **38** $z^2 - 18z - 40$

**39** $h^2 + 15h + 26$ **40** $m^2 - 3m - 130$ **41** $q^2 + 7q - 60$

## Factorising − the difference of 2 squares

$(a + b)(a - b) = a^2 - ab + ab - b^2 = a^2 - b^2$

So $a^2 - b^2$ can quickly be factorised into $(a + b)(a - b)$

Factorise the expressions below:

(a) $x^2 - y^2$
$= (x + y)(x - y)$

(b) $x^2 - 9y^2$
$= x^2 - (3y)^2$
$= (x + 3y)(x - 3y)$

(c) $m^2 - 25$
$= m^2 - 5^2$
$= (m + 5)(m - 5)$

Always check answers at the end by multiplying back out.

**M2.11**

Factorise the following expressions:

**1** $m^2 - n^2$ **2** $p^2 - q^2$ **3** $a^2 - 4^2$

**4** $n^2 - 7^2$ **5** $n^2 - 49$ **6** $x^2 - 4$

**7** $y^2 - 81$ **8** $m^2 - 1$ **9** $64 - a^2$

**10** $100 - y^2$ **11** $x^2 - \dfrac{1}{16}$ **12** $4b^2 - c^2$

(13) $p^2 - 16q^2$          (14) $25m^2 - 4$          (15) $9x^2 - 1$

(16) $36y^2 - 25$          (17) $16x^2 - 9$          (18) $49m^2 - 100$

(19) Use the difference of 2 squares to evaluate $1003^2 - 997^2$ without using a calculator.

(20) Find the value of $200002^2 - 199998^2$.

(21) Use the difference of 2 squares to evaluate $19.5^2 - 0.5^2$ without using a calculator.

(22)
The area of this rectangle is $(n^2 - 25)\,\text{cm}^2$
Write down an expression for the length CD.

Factorise the following expressions:

(23) $81b^2 - 4c^2$          (24) $49a^2 - 16b^2$          (25) $e^2 - 169$

(26) $\pi^2 - 9$          (27) $4\pi^2 - 25$          (28) $25m^2 - \dfrac{n^2}{4}$

Here are some 'trickier' factorising questions to finish with:
Factorise completely

(29) $a^2b + ab^2$          (30) $5m^2n^2 + 10mn^2$          (31) $m^3 - 25m$

(32) $6p^2 - 24$          (33) $n^3 - n$          (34) $5n^2 + 10n + 5$

(35) $(n + 4)$ people each pay for a concert ticket.
They pay a total of £$(n^2 - 3n - 28)$.
Write down an expression for how much each person pays.

Collect like terms then factorise:

(36) $2x^2 + 5x - x^2 + 12 + 2x$

(37) $3x^2 + 2(2x - 3) - 7x - 4 - 2x^2$

(38) $5x^2 + 4x - 2(2x^2 + 5x) + 8$

(39) $3x^2 - 20 - 2(x^2 - 1) - 3x$

Some people say 'you don't get 'owt for n'owt in this life'. Most things have to be paid for and that includes the electricity, gas and water you use in your home.

The amount of electricity, gas (and water in some homes) used is recorded on a *meter*. The meter is read every 3 months and a bill is sent. An electricity bill could look like the one below.

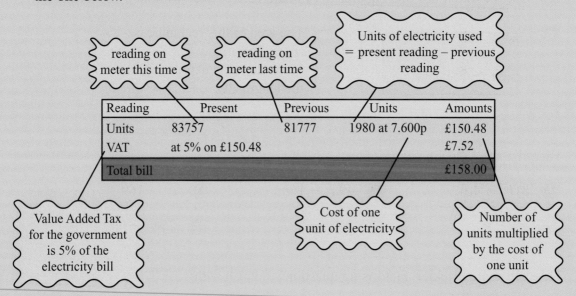

Units of electricity used = present reading − previous reading

reading on meter this time

reading on meter last time

| Reading | Present | Previous | Units | Amounts |
|---------|---------|----------|-------|---------|
| Units | 83757 | 81777 | 1980 at 7.600p | £150.48 |
| VAT | at 5% on £150.48 | | | £7.52 |
| Total bill | | | | £158.00 |

Value Added Tax for the government is 5% of the electricity bill

Cost of one unit of electricity

Number of units multiplied by the cost of one unit

## Payment

Some people simply pay their bill when it arrives, other people arrange to pay part of their bill each month. They are often given a small discount if they arrange to pay the bill each month.

Ally has received his electricity bill:

present reading = 61982      previous reading = 60732

cost of one unit of electricity = 7·6p

VAT is 5%

How much does Ally have to pay?

units used = present − previous = 61982 − 60732 = 1250

cost of units = 1250 × 7·6p = 9500p = £95·00

VAT = 5% of £95·00 = $\frac{5}{100}$ × 95·00 = £4·75

Total bill = £99·75

**1** Nerys has received her electricity bill:

present reading = 53164        prevous reading = 51083

cost of one unit of electricity = 9·3p

Copy and complete the bill below:

units used = present − previous = 53164 − ☐ = ☐

cost of units = ☐ × 9·3p = ☐ p = £☐

VAT = 5% of £☐ = $\frac{5}{100}$ × ☐ = £☐

Total bill = £ ‾‾‾‾‾

**2** Work out the cost of each electricity bill below. VAT is payable at 5% each time.

| Bill | present reading | previous reading | cost of one unit of electricity |
|------|-----------------|------------------|---------------------------------|
| a | 81659 | 80292 | 8·3p |
| b | 23748 | 22095 | 7·6p |
| c | 5186 | 4417 | 7·6p |
| d | 63746 | 62640 | 9·4p |
| e | 9187 | 8089 | 8·2p |
| f | 5613 | 4688 | 11·4p |
| g | 71248 | 69325 | 7·9p |

**3** During one year Marvin has bills of £138·17, £168·24, £171·38 and £138·21. He pays the bills in 12 *equal* monthly instalments. He is given a £40 discount *each* year for paying monthly. How much does Marvin have to pay *each month*?

**4** How much is paid for electricity, gas and water in your home? Find out. Get a 'feel' for how much these bills are before it is your turn to pay!

# TEST YOURSELF ON UNIT 2

**1. Consolidating previous algebra work**

Simplify these expressions.

(a) $7m \times 6n$

(b) $m^2 + m^2 + m^2$

(c) $8x + 4y - 3y - x$

(d) $-5x \times -7y$

(e) $\dfrac{10mn}{5n}$

(f) $6n - 10n$

Expand

(g) $4(3a + 2)$

(h) $7m(m - 4)$

(i) $4a(3b + a)$

Solve these equations.

(j) $4n - 6 = 18$

(k) $\dfrac{n}{6} = 7$

(l) $22 = 5n + 7$

Factorise

(m) $a^2 - ab$

(n) $8a - 20b$

(o) $18m^2 - 24mn$

Write each number below in index form.

(p) $(7^2)^4$

(q) $\dfrac{3^{12}}{3^7}$

(r) $\dfrac{2^7 \times 2^4}{(2^2)^3}$

**2. Finding simple formulas**

(a) Each time Eric goes fishing, he catches $x$ fish.
Eric goes fishing 6 times.
Write down a formula for the total number of fish, N, that Eric catches.

(b) Sofia is paid £65 plus £11 an hour for her work each week.
Write down a formula for her total pay, C, each week if she works for $n$ hours.

(c) Darryl loses $x$ golf balls each time he plays golf. Julian loses $y$ golf balls each time he plays golf. Write down a formula for the number of golf balls lost, N, if Darryl plays twice and Julian plays 6 times.

**3.** Substituting numbers into formulas

(a) A formula for power P is $P = \dfrac{E}{t}$

where E is energy used and $t$ is time taken.
Find the value of P when $E = 8000$ and $t = 25$.

(b) Force $= \dfrac{\text{change in momentum}}{\text{time}}$ so $F = \dfrac{mv - mu}{t}$

Find the value of F when $m = 4$, $t = 0{\cdot}1$, $v = 6{\cdot}8$ and $u = 2{\cdot}8$

**4.** Expanding 2 brackets

Expand

(a) $(n + 5)(n + 3)$　　　　　　　(b) $(m + 2)(m - 8)$

(c) $(x + 3)^2$　　　　　　　　　　(d) $(2y - 5)(3y + 7)$

(e) For how many different values of $x$ does
$(x + 1)(x - 6) \equiv x^2 - 5x - 6$?

**5.** Solving equations with brackets and with unknown on both sides

Solve these equations

(a) $6(n - 4) = 30$　　　　　　　(b) $3(n + 2) = 7$

(c) $8n - 4 = 5n + 14$　　　　　(d) $4(3n + 1) = 7n + 34$

(e) $4(n + 2) = 3(2n - 10)$　　　(f) $\dfrac{n}{7} - 3 = 4$

**6.** Setting up equations

(a)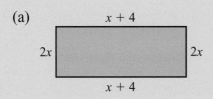

The perimeter of this rectangle is 50 cm.
(i) Write down an equation using the perimeter.
(ii) Find $x$.
(iii) Write down the actual length and width of the rectangle.

(b) One angle in a triangle is double the smallest angle and one angle is treble the smallest angle. Find the size of each angle.

(c) Three consecutive *odd* numbers add up to 105. Find the three numbers.

57

**7.** Factorising quadratics of form $x^2 + bx + c$

Factorise

(a) $x^2 + 3x + 2$

(b) $m^2 - 7m + 6$

(c) $b^2 + b - 6$

(d) $y^2 - z^2$

(e) $m^2 - 16$

(f) $n^2 + 2n - 8$

## Mixed examination questions

**1** $E = mv^2$

Work out the value of $E$ when $m = 3$ and $v = 10$ (AQA)

**2** Given $5W = 2P + 3R$, find the value of $P$ when $W = 4$ and $R = -4$. (WJEC)

**3** The length of this rectangular tile is 6 times the width.

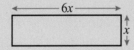

Two tiles are put together to make this shape.

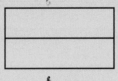

The perimeter of the new shape is 24 cm.

Work out the width of **one** tile. (AQA)

**4** (a) Factorise $24x + 3$.

(b) Factorise $x^2 - 6x$.

(c) Expand $2x(x^3 + 6)$. (WJEC)

**5** Expand and simplify $3(2w - 1) - 2(w - 4)$ (CEA)

**6** Work out the value of $4x + 3y$ when $x = -2$ and $y = 5$ (AQA)

**7** Expand and simplify $5(x - 3) - 2(x - 1)$ (AQA)

**8** (a) Factorise fully

   (i) $12p + 8$

   (ii) $x^3 + x$

   (b) Expand and simplify

   $6(y + 3) - 2(2y + 3)$                                           (CEA)

**9**

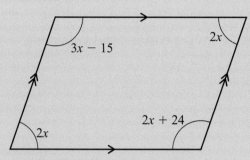

The diagram shows a parallelogram.
The sizes of the angles, in degrees, are

   $2x$

   $3x - 15$

   $2x$

   $2x + 24$

Work out the value of $x$.                                           (EDEXCEL)

**10** (a) Expand and simplify $3(x + 4) + 2(5x - 1)$

   (b) Expand and simplify $(2x + 1)(x - 4)$

   (c) Factorise completely $6y^2 - 9xy$                            (EDEXCEL)

**11** Expand and simplify $(3x + 2)(2x + 5)$                        (AQA)

**12** $x^2 - 16 \equiv (x + 4)(x - 4)$

   For how many values of $x$ is the above relationship true?

**13** The breadth of a cuboid is 1 cm less than the length y cm.
   The height is 6 cm.
   The volume of the cuboid is 72 cm³.

   (a) Show that $y^2 - y - 12 = 0$

   (b) Solve the equation $y^2 - y - 12 = 0$
       Explain why only one answer makes sense in the question.    (CEA)

**14** (a) Factorise  $5x^2 - 10x$

(b) Solve  $x^2 - 6x = 0$.                                                                  (WJEC)

**15** Cath has two favourite ways of exercising – dancing and swimming.
Each dancing class costs £6 and each swimming session costs £4.

During a month, Cath attends $x$ dancing classes and does $y$ swimming sessions.

(a) Write down a formula for the cost, $C$, of her dancing and swimming during one month.

(b) Write down a formula for the cost, $A$, of her dancing and swimming for one year.

**16** Factorise  $x^2 - 5x - 14$                                                     (WJEC)

**17** (a) Solve  $\dfrac{x}{3} + 15 = 25$

(b) Solve $5x - 7 = 3(x + 2)$                                              (WJEC)

**18** A farmer has just enough food to feed $x$ pigs for $y$ days.

(a) Write down an expression for the number of days the farmer could feed $z$ pigs with the same amount of food.

(b) Write down an assumption you have made in answering part (a).   (WJEC)

**19** The diagram shows a triangle ABC.
$AB = AC$

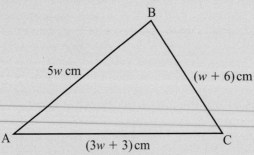

Show that the triangle is equilateral.                                        (AQA)

**20** (a) Solve  $3(x - 2) = x + 7$

(b) Solve  $\dfrac{2 - y}{5} = 1$                                              (EDEXCEL)

60

# NUMBER 2

**In this unit you will learn how to:**

– consolidate previous fraction work

– use division to convert fractions into decimals

– add and subtract fractions

– multiply and divide fractions

– USE YOUR MATHS! – save it in the home

## Previous fraction work

### M3.1

**1** A gym has 400 members.
160 of the members are women.
What fraction of the members
are men? Give the answer
in its simplest form.

**2** Callum says that $\frac{3}{4}$ is exactly half way between $\frac{1}{3}$ and $\frac{5}{6}$. Show clearly whether he is correct or not.

**3** What fraction of each of these shapes is red?

(a)

(b)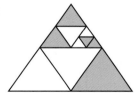

(c)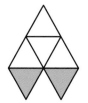

(d)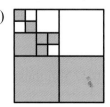

61

**4** Helen has £54 and Jake has £35.

Helen spends $\frac{1}{6}$ of her money and Jake

spends $\frac{2}{7}$ of his money.

How much more does Jake spend than Helen?

**5** There are 48 skydivers.

$\frac{3}{8}$ of them land in field A and

$\frac{5}{12}$ of them land in field B.

How many skydivers miss both field A
and field B?

**6**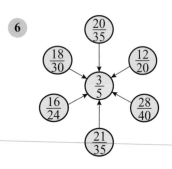

Write down which fractions

are equivalent to $\frac{3}{5}$.

**7** Tom says that $\frac{5}{12}$ is larger than $\frac{1}{3}$.

Explain clearly whether he is correct or not.

**8** Express $\frac{3}{5}$ as a decimal.

**9** Which motorcycle deal below is the cheaper?
By how much?

| Deal A | Deal B |
|---|---|
| £3600 | 24 equal |
| $\frac{1}{5}$ off | payments |
|  | of £125 |

**10** Is $\frac{7}{20}$ larger than 0·3? You must explain your answer fully.

**11** Write the following fractions in order of size, starting with the smallest.

$$\frac{3}{5} \qquad \frac{7}{20} \qquad \frac{7}{10} \qquad \frac{1}{4}$$

**12** $\frac{3}{5}$ of 120 people have dark hair.

$\frac{2}{3}$ of the remaining people have blue eyes.

How many of the remaining people do not have blue eyes?

---

**M3.2**

Write true or false for each of the following statements.

**1** $0\cdot4 = \frac{4}{5}$

**2** $0\cdot15 = \frac{3}{20}$

**3** $\frac{1}{4} > \frac{1}{3}$

**4** $\frac{1}{25} = 0\cdot04$

**5** $0\cdot3 > \frac{1}{5}$

**6** $\frac{9}{20} = 0\cdot35$

**7** $2\frac{3}{4} = \frac{11}{4}$

**8** $0\cdot036 > 0\cdot4$

**9** $\frac{17}{5} < 3\frac{3}{5}$

**10** $\frac{1}{3} = 0\cdot\dot{3}$

**11** Two boxers weigh in at 90·03 kg and 90·2 kg. Which is the heavier weight?

Can you still?

**Expanding brackets**

Expand and simplify

**1** $7(3x + 2) + 4(2x - 1)$

**2** $5(6y + 3) - 2(5y - 4)$

**3** $8n + 4(2n + 3) - 3(3n + 2)$

Expand

**4** $(x + 3)(x + 5)$

**5** $(a + 6)(a - 2)$

**6** $(n + 7)(n - 3)$

**7** $(m - 2)(m - 4)$

**12** 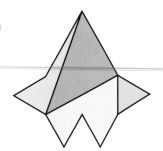 $\frac{1}{10}$ of this shape is green.

$\frac{1}{5}$ of the shape is blue.

The red area is equal to the yellow area. What fraction of the whole shape is the red area?

**13** Six sprinters finish a 100 m race with the following times. Write down the order in which they finished.

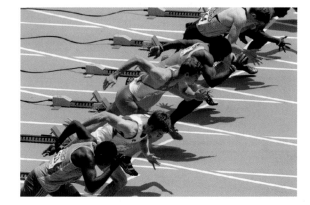

| A | B | C |
|---|---|---|
| 10·01 s | 9·94 s | 9·92 s |

| D | E | F |
|---|---|---|
| 10·05 s | 9·9 s | 10·1 s |

**14** What fraction is half way between $\frac{2}{3}$ and $\frac{5}{6}$?

**15** Write the following decimals in order of size, starting with the smallest.

0·382, 0·38, 0·039, 0·309, 0·32, 0·03

## Using division to convert fractions into decimals

$\frac{7}{20} = \frac{35}{100} = 0·35$ {change the denominator into a power of 10 if possible} $\frac{21}{200} = \frac{105}{1000} = 0·105$

$\frac{2}{9}$ ⟶ {cannot change the denominator easily into a power of 10 so divide to get a decimal answer} ⟶

$$9\overline{)2·^20^20^20}$$
$$0·\,2\ 2\ 2$$

so $\frac{2}{9} = 0·222... = 0·\dot{2}$

(0·2 recurring)

**Remember** 0·$\dot{6}\dot{3}$ means 0·63 63 63...     0·1$\dot{8}2\dot{7}$ means 0·1827 827...

1. Convert the decimals below into fractions in their lowest form:

    (a) 0·6      (b) 0·08      (c) 0·75      (d) 0·215

    (e) 0·836      (f) 0·517      (g) 0·7275      (h) 0·0625

2. Use division without a calculator to convert the fractions below into recurring decimals:

    (a) $\dfrac{2}{11}$      (b) $\dfrac{5}{9}$

    (c) $\dfrac{7}{11}$      (d) $\dfrac{7}{15}$

    (e) $\dfrac{4}{9}$      (f) $\dfrac{7}{12}$

**Can you still?**  **Solving equations**

Solve

1. $5(n - 2) = 10$

2. $12 = 3(2a - 1)$

3. $5x - 4 = 2x + 17$

4. $7(2x - 6) = 4(3x + 2)$

5. $\dfrac{1}{3}x + 6 = 10$

6. $9 = \dfrac{5n - 8}{3}$

7. $6(3m - 1) = 3(5m + 2)$

3. By using recurring decimals, write down which of the fractions below is the larger:

$$\frac{6}{7} \quad \text{or} \quad \frac{11}{13}$$

4. Pair off each fraction with an equivalent decimal:

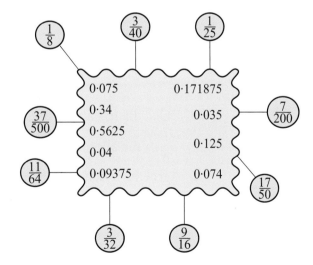

5. Jackson says that $\dfrac{5}{12}$ is smaller than 0·417. Kayla disagrees.

    Explain clearly who is correct.

## Adding and subtracting fractions

**Remember:** the denominators must be the same before adding.

$$\frac{3}{5} + \frac{1}{3} = \frac{9}{15} + \frac{5}{15} = \frac{14}{15}$$

$$2\frac{1}{7} - 1\frac{1}{2} = \frac{15}{7} - \frac{3}{2} = \frac{30}{14} - \frac{21}{14} = \frac{9}{14}$$

### M3.4

**1**  Work out and give the answer in its simplest form:

(a) $\dfrac{3}{7} + \dfrac{2}{5}$  (b) $\dfrac{8}{9} - \dfrac{2}{3}$  (c) $\dfrac{3}{8} - \dfrac{4}{5}$  (d) $-\dfrac{3}{20} - \dfrac{1}{3}$

(e) $\dfrac{1}{5} - \dfrac{4}{9}$  (f) $\dfrac{2}{3} + \dfrac{3}{4}$  (g) $\dfrac{1}{2} - \dfrac{5}{6}$  (h) $\dfrac{7}{8} - \dfrac{4}{7}$

**2**  A car is two-thirds of a mile ahead of a lorry on a long, straight motorway.
A motorbike is half a mile behind the lorry.
What is the distance between the motorbike and the car?

**3**  Work out and give the answer in its simplest form:

(a) $3\frac{3}{4} + \frac{2}{3}$  (b) $\frac{3}{4} - 1\frac{7}{8}$  (c) $2\frac{5}{8} - 3\frac{1}{2}$  (d) $3\frac{1}{6} + 1\frac{2}{5}$

**4**

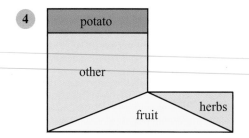

Claudia has an allotment.

$\dfrac{1}{8}$ of the allotment is used for growing potatoes.

$\dfrac{1}{5}$ is used for fruit and

$\dfrac{3}{20}$ is used for herbs.

What fraction of the allotment is used for growing other food?

**5** Work out $\frac{1}{2} + \frac{1}{3} + \frac{1}{4} + \frac{1}{5} + \frac{1}{6} + \frac{1}{7}$

**6**

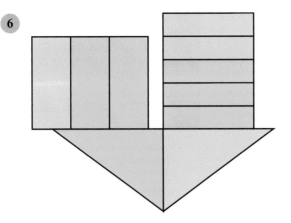

The large triangle and each of the two large rectangles have an equal area.

What fraction of the entire shape is orange?

**7** Work out $3\frac{1}{2} + 2\frac{5}{6} - 1\frac{2}{3}$

## Multiplying and dividing fractions

(a) $\frac{1}{5} \times \frac{3}{7} = \frac{3}{35}$

(b) $3\frac{1}{4} \times \frac{2}{9} = \frac{13}{\cancel{4}_2} \times \frac{\cancel{2}^1}{9} = \frac{13}{18}$

Remember: To divide two fractions, turn the second fraction upside–down and then multiply

(c) $\frac{1}{4} \div \frac{1}{3} = \frac{1}{4} \times \frac{3}{1} = \frac{3}{4}$

(d) $2\frac{2}{3} \div \frac{5}{6} = \frac{8}{\cancel{3}_1} \times \frac{\cancel{6}^2}{5} = \frac{16}{5} = 3\frac{1}{5}$

### M3.5

**1** Work out and give the answer in its simplest form.

(a) $\frac{3}{5}$ of 45

(b) $\frac{1}{6}$ of $\frac{1}{7}$

(c) $-\frac{3}{7} \times \frac{5}{6}$

(d) $-\frac{5}{8} \times \left(-\frac{4}{7}\right)$

(e) $1\frac{2}{3} \times 2\frac{3}{5}$

(f) $4\frac{1}{2} \times 1\frac{1}{4}$

(g) $\frac{5}{9} \times 15$

(h) $\frac{2}{5} \times 30$

(i) $\frac{1}{7} \div \frac{1}{9}$

(j) $\frac{3}{7} \div \left(-\frac{4}{9}\right)$

(k) $\frac{5}{8} \div 6$

(l) $-3\frac{1}{4} \div 5$

(m) $-\frac{1}{10} \div \frac{5}{9}$

(n) $\frac{3}{7} \div \frac{1}{4}$

(o) $-6\frac{1}{3} \div 4\frac{1}{2}$

(p) $5\frac{5}{6} \div 3\frac{1}{4}$

67

**2** One eighth of candidates pass an exam at the first attempt. Two-fifths of the remaining candidates pass on the second attempt. What fraction of candidates do *not* pass after two attempts?

**3** Which room below has the larger area and by how much?

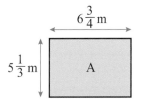

$6\frac{3}{4}$ m

$5\frac{1}{3}$ m    A

$6\frac{3}{5}$ m

B    $5\frac{2}{3}$ m

**4** Harry begins his journey with his petrol tank two-thirds full. When he stops for lunch, he notices that the amount of petrol in his tank is three-quarters of the starting amount. What fraction of the full tank is this?

**5** Carol has a lawn which measures $6\frac{1}{2}$ m by $7\frac{3}{4}$ m. She digs a new flower bed in the middle of the lawn which measures $1\frac{1}{4}$ m by $1\frac{1}{2}$ m. Find the new area of the lawn (as a fraction).

**6** A bottle of wine contains 0·75 litres when it is full. Ed drinks $\frac{1}{3}$ of a litre of this wine. What fraction of the 0·75 litres is now left in the bottle?

*Can you still?*

**Forming expressions and formulas**

**1** John's car has $x$ windows and his partner's car has $y$ windows. During one month he cleans his car 3 times and his partner's car 4 times. Write down an expression for the total number of windows he cleans during this month.

**2** Sarah hires a van for £40 plus £35 for each day. Write down a formula, in terms of $n$, for the total cost, $C$, of hiring the van for $n$ days.

**3** Mikhail earns £75 each day. He spends £$y$ each day. Write down a formula, in terms of $x$ and $y$, for the total amount of money, $T$, that he saves during $x$ days.

**7** Copy each square and fill in the missing numbers or symbols ($+, -, \times, \div$). The arrows act as equals signs.

| | − | $\frac{1}{6}$ | → | $\frac{1}{3}$ |
|---|---|---|---|---|
| × | | ÷ | | |
| $\frac{1}{4}$ | ÷ | $\frac{1}{5}$ | → | |
| ↓ | | ↓ | | |
| | × | | → | |

| | × | $\frac{1}{3}$ | → | $\frac{2}{9}$ |
|---|---|---|---|---|
| | | ÷ | | |
| $\frac{1}{2}$ | + | $\frac{3}{8}$ | → | |
| ↓ | | ↓ | | |
| $\frac{1}{6}$ | + | | → | |

**8** The organizer of a cup final gives three eighths of the tickets to each of the clubs playing. One club gives two thirds of their allocation to season ticket holders. The other club gives five sixths of their allocation to season ticket holders.

What fraction of the tickets at the cup final will be given to season ticket holders from the two clubs?

**9** Work out and give each answer in its simplest form.

(a) $\frac{3}{5} \times \frac{2}{3} \times \frac{5}{6}$

(b) $\frac{3}{4} \times \frac{2}{5} \times \frac{15}{16}$

(c) $\left(\frac{3}{5} + \frac{2}{3}\right) \times \frac{5}{7}$

(d) $\left(\frac{2}{5} + \frac{1}{2}\right) \times \left(\frac{1}{3} + \frac{1}{4}\right)$

(e) $\left(1\frac{3}{5} + 2\frac{2}{7}\right) \div \frac{4}{7}$

(f) $\left(\frac{3}{7} + \frac{2}{5}\right) \times \left(\frac{3}{10} + \frac{4}{5}\right)$

**10** A raw plug is $\frac{1}{2}$ inch long. A screw is $\frac{5}{8}$ inch long.

What fraction of the screw length is the raw plug length?

**11** The reciprocal of 0·1 is equal to the reciprocal of 0·2 plus an unknown number. Find the unknown number.

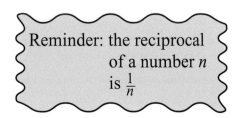

Reminder: the reciprocal of a number $n$ is $\frac{1}{n}$

Everyone wants to save money. Most people understand that saving energy will help planet earth by reducing Carbon Dioxide ($CO_2$) emissions.

More than half the money spent on energy in the home goes on:

> heating

The other main uses of energy are for:

> kitchen tasks
>
> water heating
>
> washing clothes
>
> lighting

**Task A – heating**
Loft insulation will cut down the amount of heat escaping from your home. When the savings add up to more than the cost of the insulation, you will be saving money. Look at the table opposite.

1  How long will it be before you start saving money by using loft insulation A?

2  How long before saving money with loft insulation B?

3  How many $CO_2$ savings will be made in 5 years by using loft insulation A?

4  By the time you start saving money with loft insulation B, how many $CO_2$ savings will have been made?

5  Put the five types of dwelling opposite in order according to which will have the greatest rate of average heat loss. Give a reason for your answer.

|  | Loft insulation A (0–270 mm) | Loft insulation B (50–270 mm) |
| --- | --- | --- |
| saving per year | £140 | £55 |
| cost of installing | £350 | £330 |
| $CO_2$ savings each year | 850 kg | 240 kg |

**Tip**
Turning your central heating down by one degree could save you up to 10% on your heating bill

| Types of dwelling |
| --- |
| Bungalow |
| Terrace |
| Detached |
| Flat |
| Semi-detached |

Task B – in the kitchen

If you see this energy saving logo when buying electrical goods, the machines will be amongst the most energy efficient you can buy.

1. An energy saving dishwasher costs 20% less to run and saves 24% of $CO_2$ emissions. Use the table opposite to show how much money is saved in one year and how many $CO_2$ savings are made in one year.

2. Work out the cost and $CO_2$ savings if an energy saving fridge costs 25% less to run and saves 20% of $CO_2$ emissions.

| Appliance | Average cost to run each year | $CO_2$ emissions each year |
|---|---|---|
| Fridge | £56 | 220 kg |
| Dishwasher | £60 | 230 kg |
| Fridge freezer | £175 | 645 kg |

Tip: Washing clothes at 30 °C instead of higher temperatures can save up to 40% of the energy

Energy saving bulbs use between $\frac{1}{5}$ and $\frac{1}{4}$ of the electricity of ordinary lights to produce the same amount of light.

Task C – lighting

Which energy saving bulb listed below would produce the same amount of light as an ordinary 60 watt bulb?

8–10 Watt      11–14 Watt
18–20 Watt      23–25 Watt

Explain your answer.

# TEST YOURSELF ON UNIT 3

**1. Consolidating previous fraction work**

(a) Which is larger $\frac{4}{5}$ or $\frac{5}{7}$? Explain your answer fully.

(b) Which is smaller $\frac{7}{20}$ or 0·3? Explain your answer fully.

(c) In June Mark spends £2600 in total. In July he reduces his spending by $\frac{4}{25}$. He only has £2200 to spend in July. Does Mark stay within his budget during July?

(d) Write the following decimals in order of size, starting with the smallest.

0·058, 0·07, 0·3, 0·72, 0·069, 0·29

**2. Using division to convert fractions into decimals**

(a) Convert $\frac{3}{11}$ into a recurring decimal.

(b) '$\frac{5}{6} > 0·83$' Is this true of false? Explain your answer fully.

**3. Adding and subtracting fractions**

Work out

(a) $\frac{5}{9} - \frac{3}{7}$

(b) $1\frac{1}{2} + \frac{2}{3}$

(c) $\frac{1}{4} + \frac{1}{5} - \frac{1}{6}$

(d)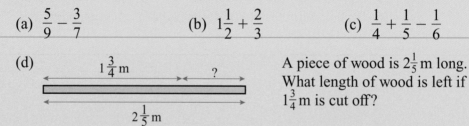
A piece of wood is $2\frac{1}{5}$ m long. What length of wood is left if $1\frac{3}{4}$ m is cut off?

**4. Multiplying and dividing fractions**

Work out

(a) $\frac{5}{6} \times \frac{3}{7}$

(b) $\frac{3}{8} \div \frac{4}{5}$

(c) $1\frac{3}{4} \div 2\frac{2}{5}$

(d)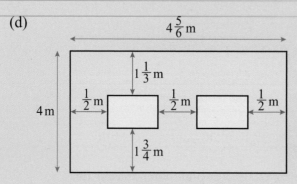
The side of a bungalow is shown opposite. The two windows are identical. Work out the area of one window.

## Mixed examination questions

**1** Which of the following fractions is nearest in value to $\frac{1}{4}$?

$$\frac{2}{10} \qquad \frac{3}{20} \qquad \frac{7}{30} \qquad \frac{11}{40}$$

**Show clearly how you reach your answer.** (CEA)

**2** Calculate $\frac{4}{9}$ of 45. (WJEC)

**3** Ben sees these adverts to hire the same car.

| Hire Deal |
|---|
| No charge for mileage |
| Normal price   £78 each day |
| **Offer**   Now $\frac{1}{3}$ off |

| Best Cars |
|---|
| £44 each day |
| 15p for each mile |

Ben wants to hire the car for 10 days.

He expects to drive 600 miles.

Should he choose Hire Deal or Best Cars to get the cheaper deal?
You **must** show your working. (AQA)

**4** Work out

(a) $\frac{3}{11} + \frac{2}{7}$     (b) $4\frac{2}{3} \div 3\frac{1}{5}$

**5** At 06:00 hours one day, the temperature in Kiev is $-8\frac{1}{4}$ °C. By 11:00 hours the temperature rises by $5\frac{3}{5}$ °C. At the same time of day the temperature in London is $3\frac{1}{6}$ °C. What is the difference in temperature between Kiev and London at 11:00 hours on this day?

**6** $\frac{2}{3}$ of Kylie's money is made up of £1 coins.

$\frac{1}{5}$ of Cameron's money is made up of £1 coins.

They put their money together. What fraction of this money is made up of £1 coins?

**7** (a) Write as a decimal.

  (i) $\dfrac{3}{50}$

  (ii) $\dfrac{2}{9}$

  (b) $3\dfrac{1}{3} - 1\dfrac{5}{6}$

  Give your answer in its simplest form. (OCR)

**8**

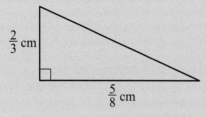 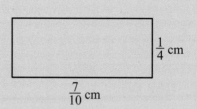

Which shape has the greater area and by how much?

**9** (i) Siobhan is putting her drill bits in order of size.

  The diameters, measured in inches, are

  $$\dfrac{1}{4} \qquad \dfrac{3}{8} \qquad \dfrac{5}{16} \qquad \dfrac{7}{32}$$

  Write these diameters in order of size, smallest first.

  Show your working.

  (ii) Siobhan is drilling a hole.

  She measures the depth of the hole and finds that it is $1\dfrac{1}{2}$ inches.

  Siobhan needs the hole to be $3\dfrac{1}{4}$ inches deep.

  How much deeper does she need to drill? (OCR)

**10** One Russian doll is $\dfrac{8}{9}$ of an inch tall.

  It is placed inside another Russian doll which is $1\dfrac{1}{3}$ inches tall.

  What fraction of the taller Russian doll's height is the smaller Russian doll's height?

74

**In this unit you will learn how to:**
- **consolidate previous geometry work**
- deal with angle proof
- prove with congruent triangles
- identify lines of reflection
- describe rotations
- find centres of enlargement
- use vectors
- USE YOUR MATHS! – who's working now?

## Previous geometry work

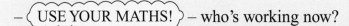 **Key Facts**

**Reminder:**

isosceles triangle

corresponding angles
are equal

alternate angles
are equal

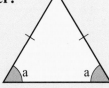

$a + b + c + d = 360°$
angles in a quadrilateral
add up to 360°

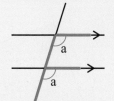

exterior angles of a
polygon add up to 360°

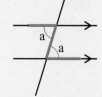

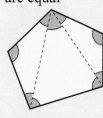

A polygon with $n$ sides
can be split into $(n - 2)$
triangles. Sum of interior
angles $= 180(n - 2)°$

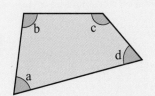

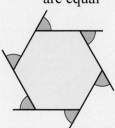

Find the angles marked with letters. Exam questions often want reasons.

Ask your teacher if you must write down all the reasons.

**1**
35°
75°
*a*

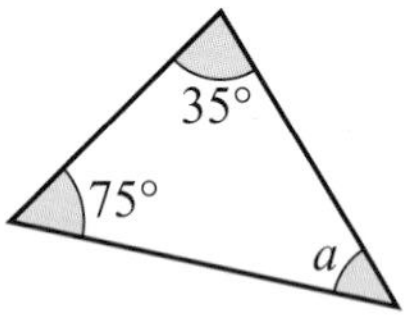

**2**
106°
*b*
*c*
38°

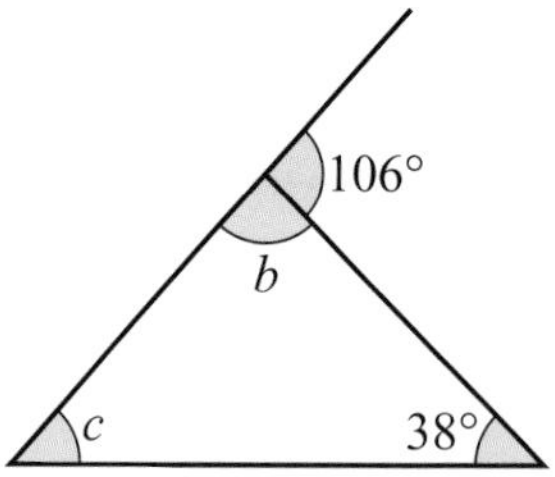

**3**
74°
*d*
82°
*e*

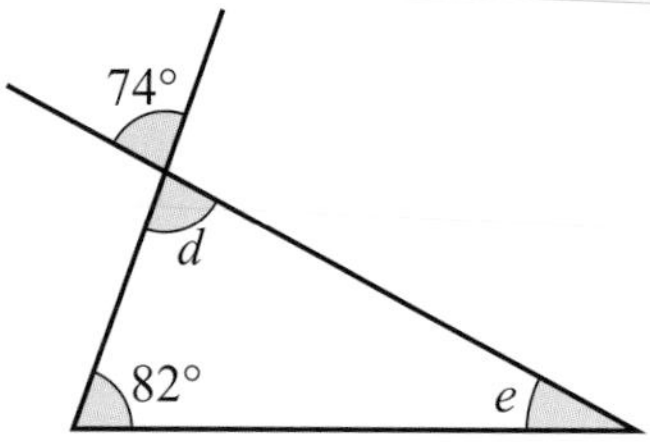

**4**
40°
*f*
*g*

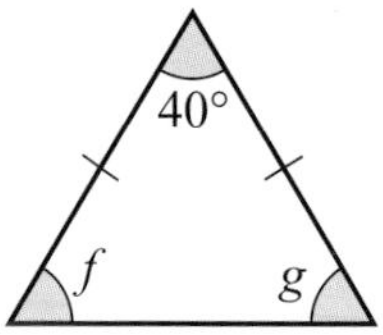

**5**
40°
*h*
*i*

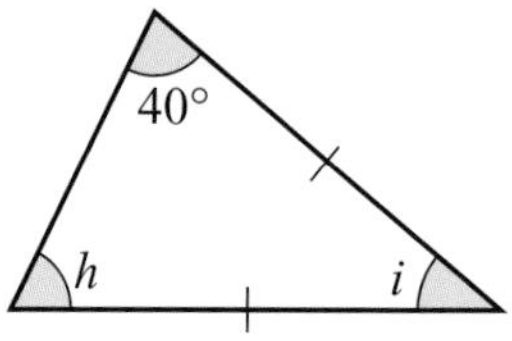

**6**
112°
*j*

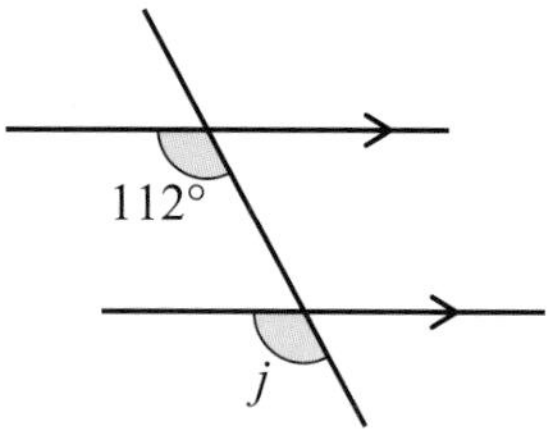

**7**
108°
*l*
*k*

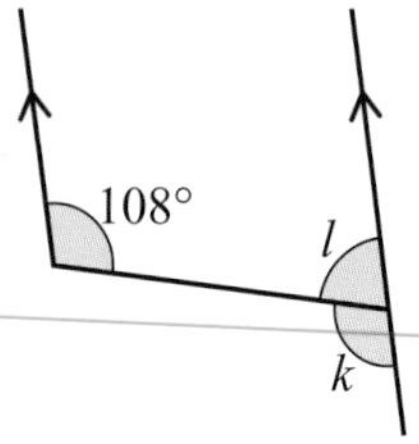

**8**
82°
125°
*m*
131°

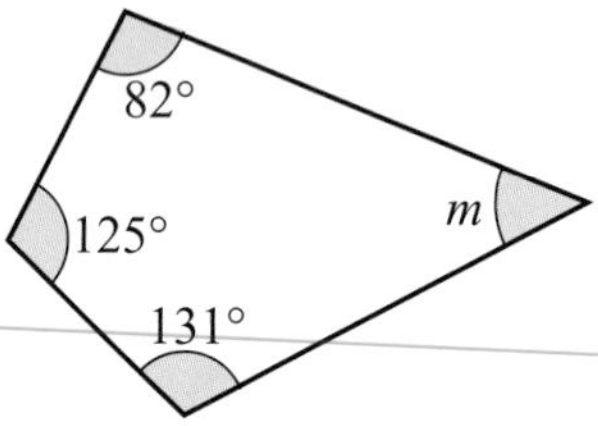

**9**
76°
*p*
*n*
85°
*o*

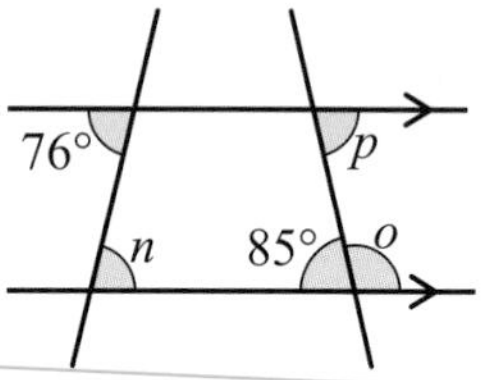

**10**
100°
*q*

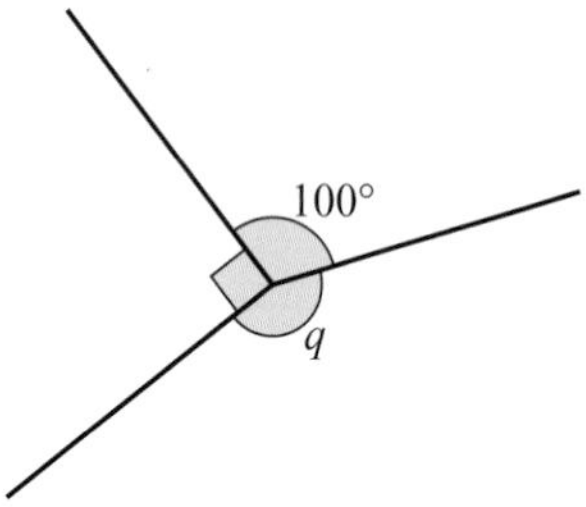

**11**
80°
72°
*r*
147°
*s*

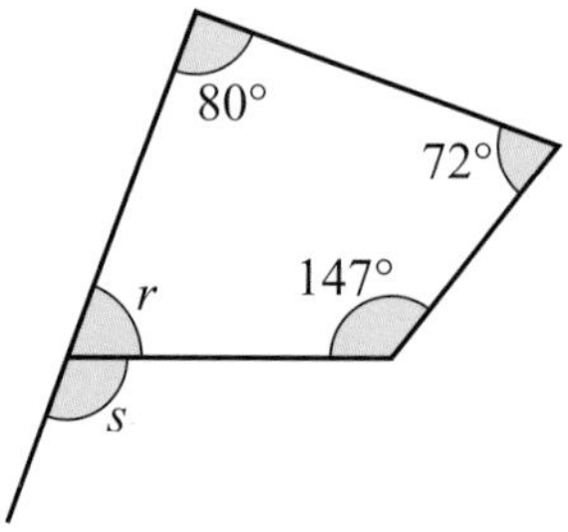

**12**
*t*

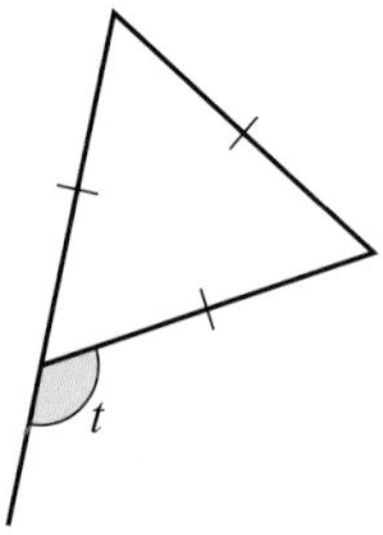

**13**
118°
*u*
*w*
*v*

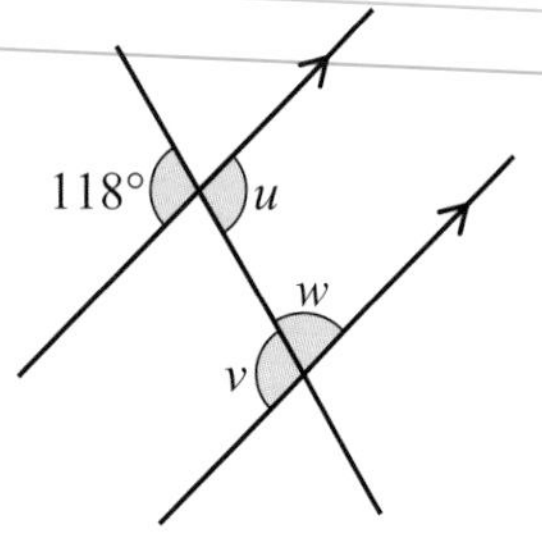

**14**
*y*
*z*
*x*
143°

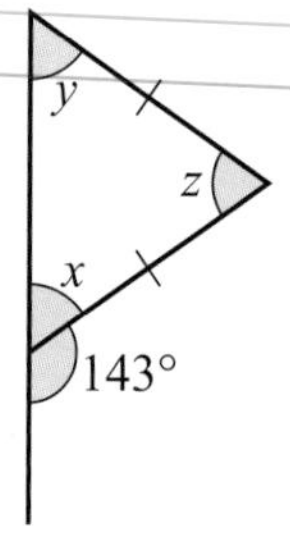

**15**
83°
97°
*a*
*b*
30°

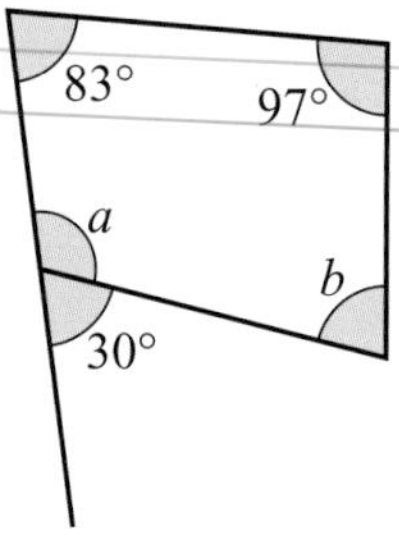

**16** (a) Find the size of an exterior angle of a regular octagon.

(b) Find the size of an interior angle of a regular octagon.

**17**

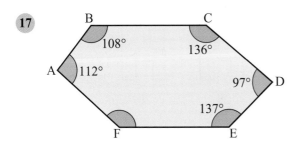

(a) Split this hexagon into triangles and find the sum of the interior angles.

(b) Work out the value of AF̂E.

**18**

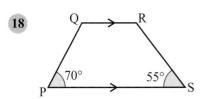

Find the values of PQ̂R and QR̂S in the trapezium opposite.

**19** PQ̂S is the exterior angle of a regular polygon. How many sides does the polygon have?

---

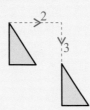 **Key Facts**

**Reminder:**

**Congruent** shapes have exactly the same size and shape.

If a shape fits onto itself three times when rotated through a complete turn, it has **rotational symmetry** of **order 3**.

A **vector** is used to describe a **translation** (movement in a straight line).

$\begin{pmatrix} 2 \\ -3 \end{pmatrix}$ means the shape moves 2 units to the right and 3 units down.

**1**   Which shapes are congruent to shape *P*?

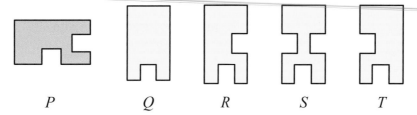

P          Q          R          S          T

**2**   Which 2 shapes are congruent?

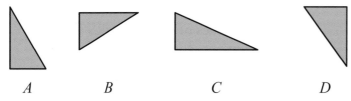

A              B                  C                  D

**3**   Copy the shape and the mirror line.

(a)  Reflect the shape in the mirror line.

(b)  Rotate the image 90° clockwise about the point C.

In questions **4** to **9** , find the angles marked with letters.

**4**

65°
p
q
r

**5**

a          a
84°
118°

**6**

u
65°   40°   t   s

**7**

c   d
65°        b

**8**

w   76°
x
v

**9**

39°
e

78

**10** (a) Draw $x$ and $y$ axes with values from $-5$ to $5$.

Draw rectangle $A$ with vertices (corners) at $(0, 2), (0, 5), (-2, 5), (-2, 2)$.

(b) Rotate rectangle $A$ $180°$ about $(-2, 2)$. Label the image $B$.

(c) Rotate rectangle $B$ $90°$ clockwise about $(0, -1)$. Label the image $C$.

(d) Rotate rectangle $C$ $180°$ about $(2, 0)$. Label the image $D$.

(e) Rotate rectangle $D$ $90°$ clockwise about $(3, -2)$. Label the image $E$.

**11** Write down the order of rotational symmetry of each shape shown below.

(a)

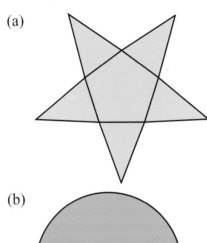

(b)

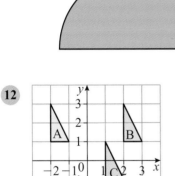

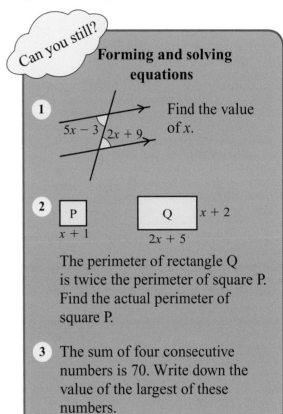

Can you still?

**Forming and solving equations**

**1** Find the value of $x$.

$5x - 3$  $2x + 9$

**2** P $\quad$ $x + 1$ $\qquad$ Q $\quad$ $x + 2$ $\quad$ $2x + 5$

The perimeter of rectangle Q is twice the perimeter of square P. Find the actual perimeter of square P.

**3** The sum of four consecutive numbers is 70. Write down the value of the largest of these numbers.

**12**

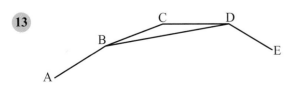

Write down the translation vector which maps

(a) $\Delta$A to $\Delta$C

(b) $\Delta$B to $\Delta$C

(c) $\Delta$B to $\Delta$A

**13**

ABCDE is part of a regular polygon with 15 sides.

Calculate angle BDC.

**14** 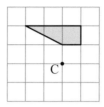 PQRS is a parallelogram.
Calculate angle RQS giving reasons for
your answer.

**15** Copy the diagram opposite.
Enlarge the shape by scale
factor 2 about the centre
of enlargement C.

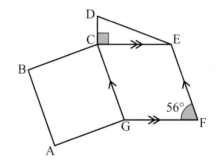

**16** ABCG is a square.
CEFG is a rhombus.
Calculate angle BCD.
Give reasons for your
answer.

## Angle proof

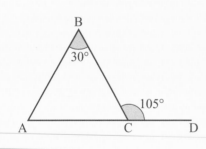

Prove that triangle *ABC* is isosceles.
Give all your reasons clearly.

$A\hat{C}B = 180° - 105° = 75°$     (angles on a straight line)

$B\hat{A}C = 180° - 30° - 75° = 75°$   (angles in a triangle
add up to 180°)

$A\hat{C}B = B\hat{A}C$ so triangle *ABC* is isosceles.

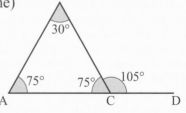

**1**

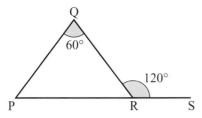

Prove that triangle *PQR* is equilateral.

**2**

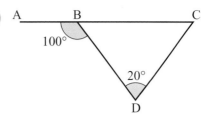

Prove that triangle *BCD* is isosceles.

**3** Copy and complete this proof for the sum of the angles in a triangle.

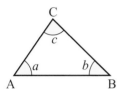

Here is triangle *ABC*.

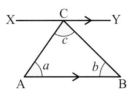

Draw line *XCY* parallel to *AB*.

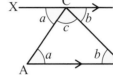

$A\hat{B}C = Y\hat{C}B$ (alternate angles)

$B\hat{A}C = \boxed{\phantom{xx}}$ (alternate angles)

$a + b + c = \boxed{\phantom{xx}}$ (angles on a straight line). Angles in a triangle $a + b + c = 180°$

**4**

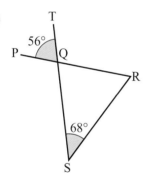

Prove that triangle *QRS* is isosceles.

Give all your reasons clearly.

**5** Copy and complete this proof for the sum of the angles in a quadrilateral.

Draw any quadrilateral *ABCD* with diagonal *BD*.

Now $a + b + c = \boxed{\phantom{xx}}$ (angles in a triangle add up to 180°)

and $d + e + f = \boxed{\phantom{xx}}$ (angles in a triangle add up to 180°)

so $a + b + c + d + e + f = \boxed{\phantom{xx}}$

This proves the result.

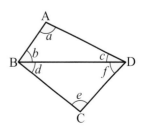

81

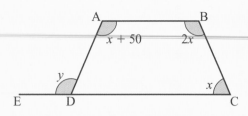

Express $y$ in terms of $x$

$A\hat{D}C = 360 - (x + 50) - 2x - x$      (angles in a quadrilateral add up to 360°)

$A\hat{D}C = 360 - x - 50 - 2x - x = 310 - 4x$

$y = 180 - A\hat{D}C$               (angles on a straight line add up to 180°)

$y = 180 - (310 - 4x) = 180 - 310 + 4x$

$y = 4x - 130$

**E4.1**

**1**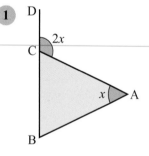

Prove that triangle ABC is isosceles.

**2**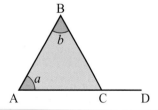

Prove that $B\hat{C}D = a + b$ (ie. 'an exterior angle of a triangle is equal to the sum of the two opposite interior angles')

**3**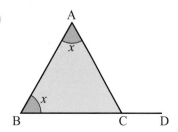

$A\hat{C}D$ is double the size of $A\hat{C}B$.

Prove that triangle ABC is equilateral.

82

**4** Express angle DEF in terms of $x$.

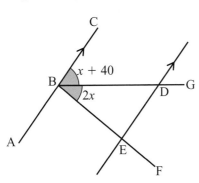

**5** Express angle RTU in terms of $x$.

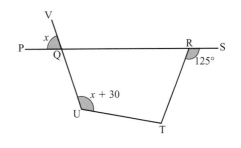

**6** Express $y$ in terms of $x$ for the hexagon shown.

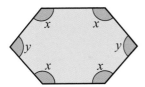

**7** Express $y$ in terms of $x$.

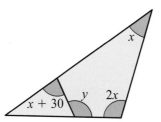

**8**

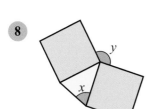

The diagram above shows two identical squares and a triangle. Express $y$ in terms of $x$.

**9** Write down an expression, in terms of n, for the exterior angle of a regular polygon with $n$ sides.

Can you still?

**Fractions**

Work out

**1** $3\frac{2}{3} - 1\frac{7}{8}$

**2** $\frac{4}{7} \times 3\frac{1}{2}$

**3** $\frac{8}{9} \div 1\frac{3}{5}$

**4** $\frac{5}{9} \times 12$

**5** $\frac{2}{7} - \frac{1}{3} \times \frac{5}{14}$

**6** 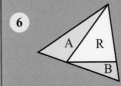 A farm is split into 3 parts. Area A is $\frac{1}{3}$ and area B is $\frac{1}{5}$.

The remaining area is divided equally between the farmer's 3 children. What fraction of the farm does one child receive?

**Key Facts**

Two shapes are congruent if they are exactly the same size and shape.

There are four ways of proving that two triangles are congruent:

1. SSS (side, side, side)
   All 3 sides are equal.

2. SAS (side, angle, side)
   Two sides and the angle between them are equal.

3. AAS (angle, angle, side)
   Two angles and a corresponding side are equal.

4. RHS (right angle, hypotenuse, side)
   Each triangle has a right angle.
   The hypotenuse and one other side are equal.

**Example**

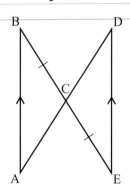

AB is parallel to ED. C is the midpoint of BE.

Prove that AC = CD.

$\hat{ABC} = \hat{CED}$    (alternate angles)

$\hat{BCA} = \hat{ECD}$    (vertically opposite angles)

$BC = CE$    (C is midpoint of BE)

3 conditions AAS proves congruence

**proof** requires reasons to be given

so Δ's ABC DEC are congruent (AAS)

write the triangles underneath each other so that each angle corresponds to its equal angle in the other triangle

so AC = CD because the triangles are congruent (we can see that the letters A and C correspond to the letters D and C in the 'congruent triangles' statement above).

---

**M4.4**

In questions ①  to ④ , state whether the pair of triangles are congruent.

Give the reason (eg. SAS) if they are congruent.

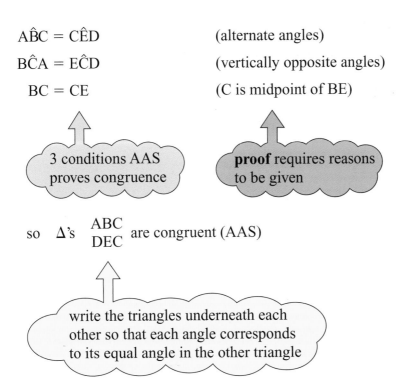

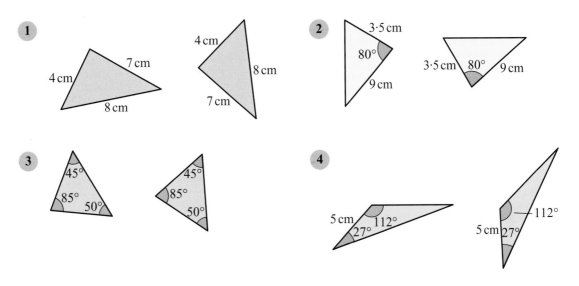

**5**

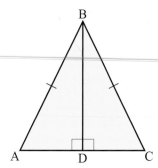

ABC is an isosceles triangle.

(a) Prove that △ABD is congruent to △CBD.

(b) Explain why $A\hat{B}D = C\hat{B}D$ (this proves that the perpendicular bisector BD cuts $A\hat{B}C$ in half).

**6** Draw a quadrilateral ABCD in which AB = AD and BC = CD (ie. a kite). Draw a line AC and state which two triangles are congruent. Hence prove that the angle at B is equal to the angle at D.

**7**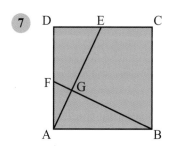

ABCD is a square. E is the midpoint of DC and F is the midpoint of AD. Prove that triangles ADE and BAF are congruent.

**8** ABCD is a rectangle.

(a) Prove that triangles ABX and DCX are congruent.

(b) Hence prove that DXA is an isosceles triangle.

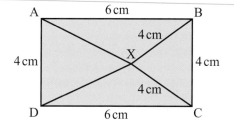

**9** Draw a quadrilateral ABCD (not a rectangle) such that AB is parallel to CD and AD is parallel to CB. Draw a line AC. Use congruent triangles to prove that opposite sides of this shape are equal.

**10** In the diagram below ABCD is a rhombus, E is the midpoint of DC and F is the midpoint of AD. Show that triangles AFB and ECB are congruent.

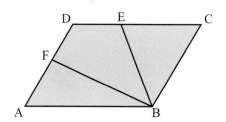

**11** PRSU is a rectangle.
Triangle PTU is isosceles.
Triangle QRS is isosceles.
Prove that triangles PQS
and PTS are congruent.

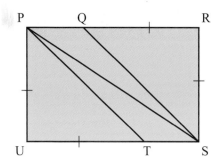

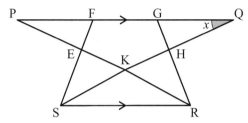

In the diagram, PK = QK, PF = QG and the lines PQ and SR are parallel.
The angle PQS is $x$.

(a) Find, with reasons, the following angles:

    (i) QP̂R

    (ii) QŜR

    (iii) PR̂S

(b) Explain why SK = RK.

(c) Hence show that PR = QS.

(d) State, with reasons, which triangle is congruent to QSF.

---

*Can you still?*

**Mixed algebra**

Expand

**1** $3n(2n + 1)$    **2** $(a + 6)(a - 4)$    **3** $(4n - 1)(5n + 3)$    **4** $(m - 6)^2$

Solve these equations

**5** $5(2n - 3) = 35$    **6** $9m + 10 = 4(3m - 2)$    **7** $\frac{1}{5}(2n + 1) = 3$

Factorise

**8** $a^2 + 6a + 8$      **9** $n^2 - 5n - 14$      **10** $m^2 + 8m - 20$

**11** $x^2 - 25$      **12** $n^2 - 8n + 15$

### Mirror line

The mirror line is sometimes called the *line of reflection*.
We can find the equation of the line of reflection.

**Horizontal lines**          **Vertical lines**

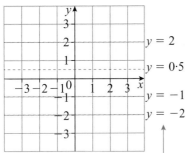

All horizontal
lines have the equation
'$y$ = number'

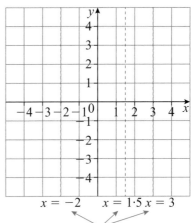

All vertical lines have the
equation '$x$ = number'

A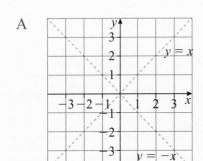

B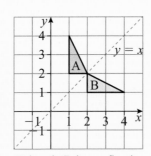

Triangle B is a reflection of
triangle A in the sloping line $y = x$

---

**M4.5**

**1**  (a)  Draw $x$ and $y$ axes then draw the line $x = 2$.

(b)  Draw any triangle then reflect it in the line $x = 2$.

**2**

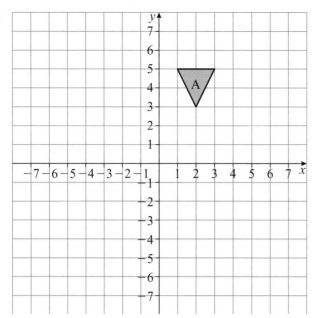

Copy this grid and shape opposite.

(a) Reflect shape $A$ in the $x$-axis. Label the image $B$.

(b) Reflect shape $B$ in the line $y = -2$. Label the image $C$.

(c) Reflect shape $C$ in the line $x = -1$. Label the image $D$.

(d) Reflect shape $D$ in the line $y = 1$. Label the image $E$.

(e) Reflect shape $E$ in the $y$-axis. Label the image $F$.

(f) Reflect shape $F$ in the line $y = 3$. Label the image $G$.

**3** (a) Draw an $x$-axis from $-4$ to $4$ and a $y$-axis from $-4$ to $4$.

(b) Draw the line $y = -x$.

(c) Draw any triangle then reflect it in the line $y = -x$.

**4**

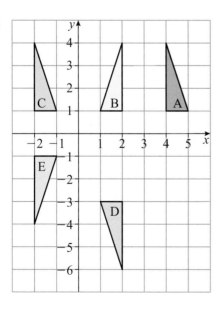

For each pair of triangles below, write down the equation of the *line of reflection*.

(a) $A$ to $B$

(b) $B$ to $C$

(c) $B$ to $D$

(d) $C$ to $E$

**5**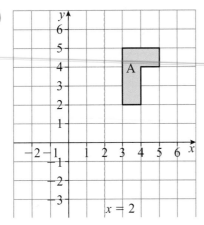

Copy this grid and shape opposite.

(a) Reflect shape $A$ in the line $x = 2$. Label the image $B$.

(b) Reflect shape $B$ in the line $y = 1$. Label the image $C$.

(c) Rotate shape $C$ 90° clockwise about $(1, -3)$. Label the image $D$.

**6** (a) Draw an $x$-axis from $-5$ to 6 and a $y$-axis from $-6$ to 5.

(b) Draw a rectangle $A$ with vertices (corners) at $(3, 1)$, $(3, 3)$, $(4, 3)$ and $(4, 1)$.

(c) Reflect rectangle $A$ in the line $y = x$. Label the image $B$.

(d) Reflect shape $B$ in the $y$-axis. Label the image $C$.

(e) Reflect shape $C$ in the line $y = -x$. Label the image D.

(f) Describe the transformation which maps (sends) shape $D$ back onto shape $A$.

(g) Draw a rectangle $E$ with vertices at $(3, -1)$, $(3, -2)$, $(6, -2)$ and $(6, -1)$.

(h) Reflect shape $E$ in the line $y = -x$. Label the image $F$.

*Can you still?*

**Number work**

**Do not use a calculator**

**1** Express 1638 as a product of its prime factors in index form.

**2** $735 = 3 \times 5 \times 7^2$ and $600 = 2^3 \times 3 \times 5^2$

(i) Find the HCF of 735 and 600

(ii) Find the LCM of 735 and 600

**3** Which is greater $\boxed{4^{-1}}$ or $\boxed{10^{-2}}$ ? By how much?

**4** Evaluate $\sqrt{(\sqrt[3]{8} + 3^2 + 5)}$

**5** $3^n \times 3^4 = 3^8$. Write down the value of $n$.

**6** How many factors does a prime number have?

**7** Work out $0{\cdot}8^2 \times 0{\cdot}3$

**M4.6**

**1**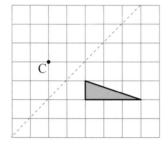

Copy the shape and the mirror line.

(a) Reflect the shape in the mirror line.

(b) Rotate the image 90° anticlockwise about the point $C$.

In questions **2** to **7** copy each diagram. Draw the shaded shape on tracing paper. Place the tip of a pencil on different points until the shape can be rotated onto the other shape. Mark the centre of rotation with a dot.

**2**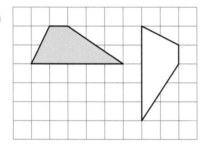

**3**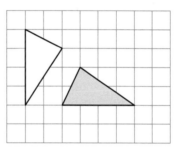

**4**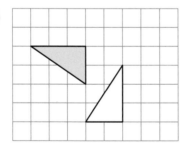

**5**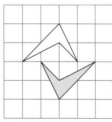

**6**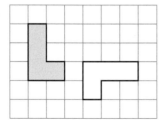

**7**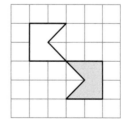

**8**

Find the co-ordinates of the centres of the following rotations:

(a) triangle $A$ onto triangle $B$

(b) triangle $A$ onto triangle $C$

(c) triangle $A$ onto triangle $D$

(d) triangle $C$ onto triangle $E$

🔑 # Key Facts

**Note**   The point $(0, 0)$ is called the **'origin'**.

We need 3 things to *describe fully* a rotation:

1.   the angle

2.   the direction (clockwise or anticlockwise)

3.   the centre of rotation

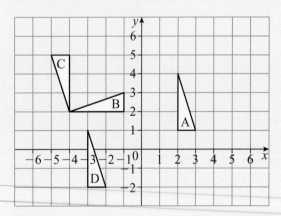

Describe fully the rotation which transforms:

(a) triangle $A$ onto triangle $B$

(b) triangle $B$ onto triangle $C$

(c) triangle $B$ onto triangle $D$

For each answer, we must write down the angle, direction and centre of rotation.

(a) rotates $90°$ anticlockwise about $(0, 0)$

(b) rotates $90°$ anticlockwise about $(-4, 2)$

(c) rotates $90°$ clockwise about $(-4, 1)$

**1**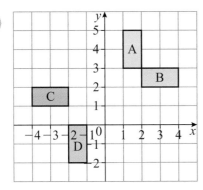

Describe *fully* the rotation which transforms:

(a) shape *A* onto shape *B*

(b) *B* onto *C*

(c) *C* onto *D*

**2** (a) Draw *x* and *y* axes with values from −6 to 6. Draw triangle *A* with vertices (corners) at (−5, 2), (−5, 6) and (−3, 5).

(b) Rotate triangle *A* 90° clockwise about (−4, −2). Label the image *B*.

(c) Rotate triangle *B* 90° clockwise about (6, 0). Label the image *C*.

(d) Rotate triangle *C* 180° about (1, 1). Label the image *D*.

(e) Rotate triangle *D* 90° anticlockwise about (−5, 1). Label the image *E*.

(f) Describe *fully* the rotation which transforms triangle *E* onto triangle *A*.

**3** Copy the shape

(a) Rotate the shape 180° about the point *C*. Label the image *Q*.

(b) Describe *fully* the rotation which sends shape *Q* back onto shape *P*.

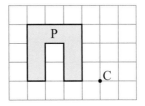

**4**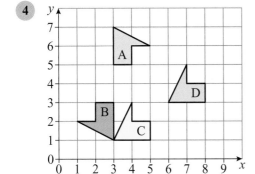

(a) Describe *fully* the rotation which moves shape *A* onto shape *B*.

(b) Describe *fully* the rotation which moves shape *B* onto shape *C*.

(c) Describe *fully* the translation which moves shape *C* onto shape *D*.

**5** (a) Draw the x axis from −4 to 4.
Draw the y axis from −3 to 3.
Draw triangle A with vertices at (−1, −2), (−2, −2), (−2, 0).

(b) Rotate triangle A 90° clockwise about (0, −1). Label the image B.

(c) Rotate triangle B 180° about (1, 1). Label the image C.

(d) Reflect triangle C in the x-axis. Label the image D.

(e) Reflect triangle D in the line $y = -2$. Label the image E.

(f) Translate triangle E through $\begin{pmatrix} -5 \\ 1 \end{pmatrix}$. Label the image F.

(g) Describe *fully* the rotation which transforms triangle F onto triangle A.

Can you still?

**Standard Form**

**1** Write the numbers below in standard form.
(a) 146000    (b) 0·000146

**2** Which number below is greater?
$5·6 \times 10^{11}$ or $7·3 \times 10^{10}$

**3** Give each answer below in standard form
(a) $(9 \times 10^{15}) \div (3 \times 10^6)$
(b) $(7 \times 10^{12}) \times (6 \times 10^8)$
(c) $(3 \times 10^{10}) - (8 \times 10^9)$

**4**
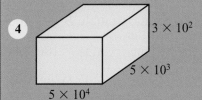

Find the total volume of four of these boxes.
All lengths are given in cm.

# Finding centres of enlargement

An **enlargement** makes the shape larger (or smaller).

Enlarge this shape by a scale factor $\frac{1}{2}$

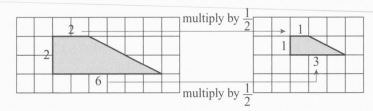

The shape gets smaller when the scale factor is a fraction between 0 and 1.

94

# Key Facts

The centre of enlargement is formed by drawing a broken line through a corner of the new shape and the same corner of the old shape.

Do this for each pair of points as shown in the diagram.

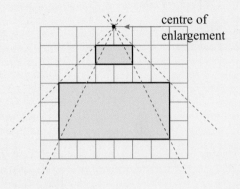

centre of enlargement

The centre of enlargement is the point where all the broken lines meet (intersect).

> We need 2 things to describe fully an enlargement:
> 1. the scale factor
> 2. the centre of enlargement

## M4.8

For questions 1 to 5, draw the grid and the 2 shapes then draw broken lines through pairs of points in the new shape and the old shape. Describe *fully* the enlargement which transforms shape *A* onto shape *B*.

 1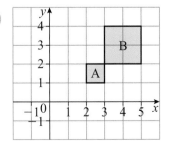

2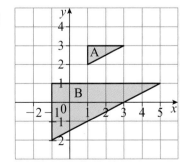

**3**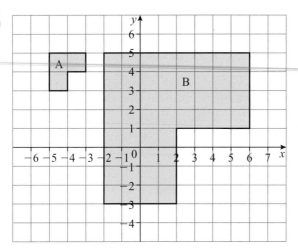

**4**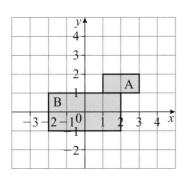

**5**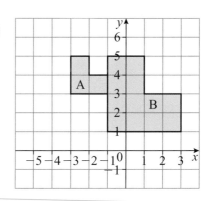

For questions **6** to **8** , copy the diagram and then draw an enlargement using the scale factor and centre of enlargement (C) given.

**6**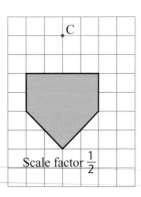

**7**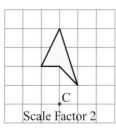

**8**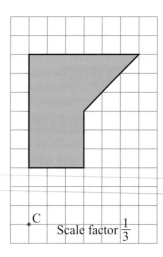

**9** (a) Draw an $x$-axis from $-2$ to 5 and a $y$-axis from $-5$ to 2.

  (b) Draw a square $A$ with vertices $(2, -2)$, $(4, -2)$, $(4, -4)$ and $(2, -4)$.

  (c) Enlarge square $A$ by scale factor $\frac{1}{2}$ about $(0, 0)$. Label the image $B$.

**10** (a) Draw the *x*-axis from −6 to 6. Draw the *y*-axis from −7 to 7.
   Draw the triangle *A* with vertices at (2, 2), (2, 6), (4, 6).

   (b) Enlarge triangle *A* by scale factor $\frac{1}{2}$ about (0, 0). Label the image *B*.

   (c) Reflect triangle *B* in the *y*-axis. Label the image *C*.

   (d) Enlarge triangle *C* by scale factor 3 about (−1, 4). Label the image *D*.

   (e) Rotate triangle *D* 90° clockwise about (−1, −5). Label the image *E*.

   (f) Enlarge triangle *E* by scale factor $\frac{1}{3}$ about (5, 1). Label the image *F*.

## Mixed transformations

**M4.9**

**1**

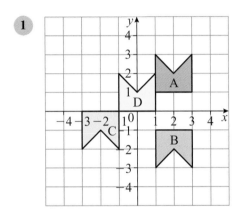

(a) Describe *fully* the transformation which transforms shape *A* onto shape *B*.

(b) Describe *fully* the transformation which transforms shape *B* onto shape *C*.

(c) Describe *fully* the transformation which transforms shape *C* onto shape *D*.

(d) Describe *fully* the transformation which transforms shape *D* onto shape *A*.

**2** (a) Draw the *x*-axis from −4 to 8.
   Draw the *y*-axis from −5 to 5.
   Draw triangle *A* with vertices of (1, 1), (1, 2), (3, 2).

   (b) Enlarge triangle *A* by scale factor 2 about (0, 0). Label the image *B*.

   (c) Rotate triangle *B* 90° anticlockwise about (6, 4). Label the image *C*.

   (d) Translate triangle *C* through $\begin{pmatrix} -1 \\ -4 \end{pmatrix}$. Label the image *D*.

   (e) Reflect triangle *D* in the line *x* = 3. Label the image *E*.

   (f) Rotate triangle *E* 90° clockwise about (1, 0). Label the image *F*.

**3**

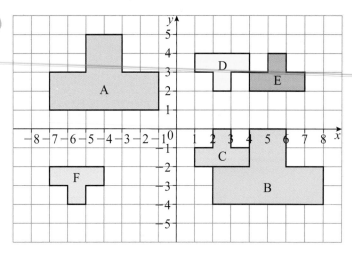

Describe *fully* the transformation which moves:

(a) shape *A* onto shape *B*

(b) shape *B* onto shape *C*

(c) shape *C* onto shape *D*

(d) shape *D* onto shape *E*

(e) shape *E* onto shape *F*

**4** (a) Draw the *x*-axis from $-5$ to 10.
Draw the *y*-axis from $-8$ to 5.
Draw shape *A* with vertices at
(2, 2), (2, 4), (3, 3), (5, 3), (5, 2).

(b) Rotate shape *A* 180° about (3, 1).
Label the image *B*.

(c) Enlarge shape *B* by scale factor 3
about (1, 1). Label the image *C*.

(d) Reflect shape *B* in the *y*-axis.
Label the image *D*.

(e) Reflect shape *D* in the line $y = 1$.
Label the image *E*.

(f) Describe *fully* the translation which
moves shape *E* onto shape *A*.

Can you still?

**Forming expressions
and equations**

**1** Avery has *m* children and gives
each one £*n*. Avery also gives
£25 to a charity.

Write down an expression for
the total amount of money
Avery has given away.

**2** $y = 6x - 20$.
Find the value of *x* when *y* is
equal to *x*.

**3**

circumference = 18 cm

$3x + 1$

$x + 2$

The perimeter of the rectangle
above is three times the
circumference of the circle.

Find the actual dimensions of
the rectangle.

**5** (a) Draw the $x$-axis from $-8$ to 4.

Draw the $y$-axis from $-5$ to 5.

Draw shape $A$ with vertices at $(-1, 2)$, $(-1, 5)$, $(-2, 5)$, $(-2, 3)$, $(-3, 3)$ $(-3, 5)$, $(-4, 5)$, $(-4, 2)$.

(b) Rotate shape $A$ 90° anticlockwise about $(-4, 1)$. Label the image $B$.

(c) Reflect shape $B$ in the line $x = -2$. Label the image $C$.

(d) Reflect shape $C$ in the $x$-axis. Label the image $D$.

(e) Rotate shape $D$ 90° clockwise about $(0, 0)$. Label the image $E$.

(f) Describe *fully* the transformation that would move shape $E$ onto shape $A$.

## Vectors

A quantity which has **both magnitude** (size) and **direction** is called a **vector**.

A vector quantity may be represented by a line because a line has a length (magnitude) and a direction.

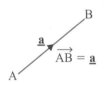

The vector begins at A and ends at B. We can write this vector as $\overrightarrow{AB}$. The arrow above the AB indicates that the vector begins at A and finishes at B.

A vector can be identified with a single lower-case letter with a line underneath it. In books this is shown by using a bold letter (the line is omitted).

If the vector is on a grid, it can be represented by a **column vector**.

$$\mathbf{a} = \begin{pmatrix} 2 \\ 3 \end{pmatrix} \qquad \overrightarrow{AB} = \begin{pmatrix} -4 \\ -2 \end{pmatrix}$$

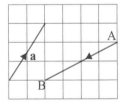

### Common vectors

Force, velocity, acceleration and displacement (eg. 9 km due south).

### Scalar quantities

A quantity which has magnitude (size) only.

**1** Write each vector as a column vector, eg. $\mathbf{a} = \begin{pmatrix} 1 \\ 3 \end{pmatrix}$ or $\overrightarrow{AB} = \begin{pmatrix} -1 \\ 2 \end{pmatrix}$.

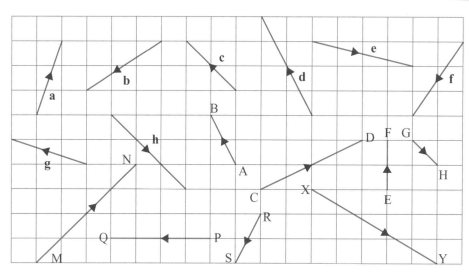

**2** Draw and label each vector below on squared paper.

$\mathbf{a} = \begin{pmatrix} 2 \\ 1 \end{pmatrix}$ $\qquad \mathbf{b} = \begin{pmatrix} -3 \\ 1 \end{pmatrix}$ $\qquad \mathbf{c} = \begin{pmatrix} 5 \\ -2 \end{pmatrix}$ $\qquad \mathbf{d} = \begin{pmatrix} 0 \\ 3 \end{pmatrix}$ $\qquad \mathbf{e} = \begin{pmatrix} -1 \\ -1 \end{pmatrix}$

$\overrightarrow{AB} = \begin{pmatrix} -4 \\ 2 \end{pmatrix}$ $\qquad \overrightarrow{CD} = \begin{pmatrix} 6 \\ -1 \end{pmatrix}$ $\qquad \overrightarrow{EF} = \begin{pmatrix} 3 \\ -4 \end{pmatrix}$ $\qquad \overrightarrow{GH} = \begin{pmatrix} -2 \\ 0 \end{pmatrix}$ $\qquad \overrightarrow{MN} = \begin{pmatrix} 4 \\ -5 \end{pmatrix}$

**3**

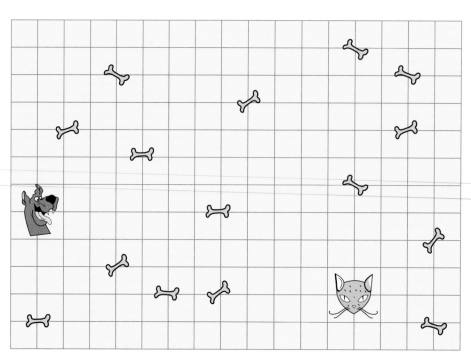

(a)  Minnie is searching for bones. She follows a route described by these vectors:

$$\begin{pmatrix} 2 \\ -3 \end{pmatrix} \text{ then } \begin{pmatrix} 3 \\ 0 \end{pmatrix} \text{ then } \begin{pmatrix} 1 \\ 5 \end{pmatrix} \text{ then } \begin{pmatrix} 2 \\ 2 \end{pmatrix} \text{ then } \begin{pmatrix} 5 \\ -4 \end{pmatrix} \text{ then } \begin{pmatrix} 2 \\ -1 \end{pmatrix} \text{ then } \begin{pmatrix} -1 \\ -4 \end{pmatrix}.$$

How many bones might Minnie have found?

(b)  Meg also wants bones. She follows this route:

$$\begin{pmatrix} -3 \\ 2 \end{pmatrix} \text{ then } \begin{pmatrix} -2 \\ 1 \end{pmatrix} \text{ then } \begin{pmatrix} -7 \\ -4 \end{pmatrix} \text{ then } \begin{pmatrix} 1 \\ 7 \end{pmatrix} \text{ then } \begin{pmatrix} 7 \\ 1 \end{pmatrix} \text{ then } \begin{pmatrix} 3 \\ 2 \end{pmatrix} \text{ then } \begin{pmatrix} 1 \\ -5 \end{pmatrix} \text{ then } \begin{pmatrix} 3 \\ -2 \end{pmatrix}.$$

How many bones might Meg have found?

 # Key Facts

**Equal vectors**

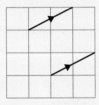

Both vectors shown are equal to $\begin{pmatrix} 2 \\ 1 \end{pmatrix}$.

Two vectors are equal if they have the same length and the same direction (the position on the diagram is not important).

$-\mathbf{a}$ is a vector equal in length to $\mathbf{a}$ but in the opposite direction.

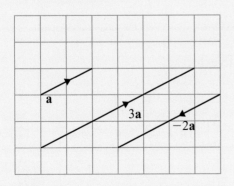

$3\mathbf{a}$ is a vector in the same direction as $\mathbf{a}$ but three times the length of $\mathbf{a}$.

$-2\mathbf{a}$ is a vector in the opposite direction to $\mathbf{a}$ but twice the length of $\mathbf{a}$.

$3\mathbf{a}$ and $-2\mathbf{a}$ are parallel to each other (both parallel to $\mathbf{a}$).

**Note**

If $\mathbf{a} = \begin{pmatrix} 2 \\ 1 \end{pmatrix}$ then $3\mathbf{a} = 3\begin{pmatrix} 2 \\ 1 \end{pmatrix} = \begin{pmatrix} 6 \\ 3 \end{pmatrix}$

## Adding vectors

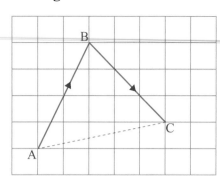

$$\overrightarrow{AB} = \begin{pmatrix} 2 \\ 4 \end{pmatrix} \text{ and } \overrightarrow{BC} = \begin{pmatrix} 3 \\ -3 \end{pmatrix}$$

Movement from A to B then B to C is the same result as movement from A to C.

We have $\overrightarrow{AC} = \begin{pmatrix} 5 \\ 1 \end{pmatrix}$

$$\overrightarrow{AB} + \overrightarrow{BC} = \begin{pmatrix} 2 \\ 4 \end{pmatrix} + \begin{pmatrix} 3 \\ -3 \end{pmatrix} = \begin{pmatrix} 5 \\ 1 \end{pmatrix}$$

so $\overrightarrow{AB} + \overrightarrow{BC} = \overrightarrow{AC}$

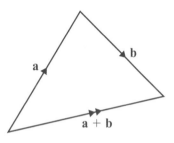

In general, adding 2 vectors shows the result of moving along one vector followed by the other.
**a** + **b** is known as the resultant vector.

## Subtracting vectors

**a** − **b** is the same **a** + −**b**.

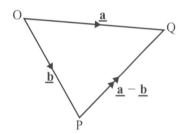

To move from P to Q, travel from P to O then from O to Q.

$\overrightarrow{PO}$ is −**b** (opposite direction to **b**).

$$\overrightarrow{PQ} = \overrightarrow{PO} + \overrightarrow{OQ} = -\mathbf{b} + \mathbf{a} = \mathbf{a} - \mathbf{b}$$

(a)  If $\mathbf{p} = \begin{pmatrix} 3 \\ -4 \end{pmatrix}$ and $\mathbf{q} = \begin{pmatrix} 2 \\ 7 \end{pmatrix}$, find as a column vector

(i)  **q** − **p**          (ii)  5**p**          (iii)  2**p** + **q**

(i)  $\mathbf{q} - \mathbf{p} = \begin{pmatrix} 2 \\ 7 \end{pmatrix} - \begin{pmatrix} 3 \\ -4 \end{pmatrix}$   (ii)  $5\mathbf{p} = 5\begin{pmatrix} 3 \\ -4 \end{pmatrix}$   (iii)  $2\mathbf{p} + \mathbf{q} = 2\begin{pmatrix} 3 \\ -4 \end{pmatrix} + \begin{pmatrix} 2 \\ 7 \end{pmatrix}$

$\qquad = \begin{pmatrix} -1 \\ 11 \end{pmatrix}$ $\qquad\qquad = \begin{pmatrix} 15 \\ -20 \end{pmatrix}$ $\qquad\qquad = \begin{pmatrix} 6 \\ -8 \end{pmatrix} + \begin{pmatrix} 2 \\ 7 \end{pmatrix}$

$\qquad\qquad\qquad\qquad\qquad\qquad\qquad\qquad\qquad\qquad = \begin{pmatrix} 8 \\ -1 \end{pmatrix}$

**1** Give each of the following as a single column vector.

(a) $\begin{pmatrix} 4 \\ 3 \end{pmatrix} + \begin{pmatrix} 5 \\ 1 \end{pmatrix}$

(b) $\begin{pmatrix} 4 \\ 3 \end{pmatrix} + 2\begin{pmatrix} 5 \\ 1 \end{pmatrix}$

(c) $\begin{pmatrix} 6 \\ 3 \end{pmatrix} - \begin{pmatrix} 3 \\ 2 \end{pmatrix}$

(d) $\begin{pmatrix} 5 \\ 4 \end{pmatrix} + \begin{pmatrix} 3 \\ -2 \end{pmatrix}$

(e) $\begin{pmatrix} 7 \\ 8 \end{pmatrix} - 3\begin{pmatrix} 2 \\ 3 \end{pmatrix}$

(f) $\begin{pmatrix} 1 \\ -4 \end{pmatrix} - 2\begin{pmatrix} -2 \\ -3 \end{pmatrix}$

(g) $4\begin{pmatrix} 4 \\ 3 \end{pmatrix} - 2\begin{pmatrix} 1 \\ 4 \end{pmatrix}$

(h) $5\begin{pmatrix} 3 \\ -2 \end{pmatrix} - 3\begin{pmatrix} 2 \\ -4 \end{pmatrix}$

(i) $\frac{1}{2}\begin{pmatrix} 10 \\ 8 \end{pmatrix} + 3\begin{pmatrix} 1 \\ 4 \end{pmatrix}$

**2** If $\mathbf{a} = \begin{pmatrix} 3 \\ 5 \end{pmatrix}$, $\mathbf{b} = \begin{pmatrix} 2 \\ -1 \end{pmatrix}$ and $\mathbf{c} = \begin{pmatrix} -4 \\ 2 \end{pmatrix}$,

find as a column vector:

(a) $2\mathbf{a}$

(b) $3\mathbf{c}$

(c) $\mathbf{a} - \mathbf{b}$

(d) $2(\mathbf{a} - \mathbf{b})$

(e) $2\mathbf{b} + \mathbf{c}$

(f) $\frac{1}{2}\mathbf{c}$

(g) $2\mathbf{b} + 3\mathbf{a}$

(h) $\mathbf{a} + \mathbf{b} - \mathbf{c}$

(i) $\mathbf{a} - 3\mathbf{b} + 2\mathbf{c}$

(j) $\mathbf{b} - 3\mathbf{c} - 2\mathbf{a}$

**3** (a) Draw an $x$-axis from $-2$ to 5 and a $y$-axis from $-2$ to 5.

(b) Mark a cross at each of the points A(2, 5), B(4, −2) and C(−1, 1).

(c) Write the following as column vectors:

(i) $\overrightarrow{AB}$

(ii) $\overrightarrow{BC}$

(iii) $\overrightarrow{BA}$

(iv) $\overrightarrow{AC}$

(d) Find the co-ordinates of the point D where $\overrightarrow{AD} = \begin{pmatrix} 3 \\ -2 \end{pmatrix}$

(e) Find the co-ordinates of the point E where $\overrightarrow{BE} = \begin{pmatrix} -2 \\ 4 \end{pmatrix}$

(f) Caleb says that point E is the midpoint of line CD. Is this true or false?

---

*Can you still?*

**Fractions and decimals**

**1** Write each set of numbers below in order of size, starting with the smallest.

(a) 0·3, 0·038, 0·32, 0·04

(b) $\frac{2}{5}, \frac{3}{10}, \frac{7}{20}, \frac{1}{2}$

(c) $0·8, \frac{7}{10}, 0·79, \frac{3}{4}$

**2** Lucy has £540. She hands over $\frac{1}{3}$ of this money for her rent. She puts $\frac{5}{9}$ of the remaining money in her savings account. The remaining money is to live on for the week. She spends £136 during the week. How much money did she have left at the end of the week?

**3** Work out $\frac{1}{6} + \left(\frac{1}{3} \times \frac{1}{6}\right) - \frac{5}{9}$

**4** If $\mathbf{m} = \begin{pmatrix} 1 \\ -4 \end{pmatrix}$, $\mathbf{n} = \begin{pmatrix} 3 \\ 4 \end{pmatrix}$ and $\mathbf{r} = \begin{pmatrix} -2 \\ 2 \end{pmatrix}$, find as a column vector:

(a) $\mathbf{m} + \dfrac{1}{2}\mathbf{r}$  (b) $4\mathbf{n} - 3\mathbf{r}$  (c) $\dfrac{1}{2}\mathbf{m} + 2\mathbf{n} - \dfrac{1}{3}\mathbf{r}$

**5** $\mathbf{a} = \begin{pmatrix} 6 \\ 5 \end{pmatrix}$ and $\mathbf{b} = \begin{pmatrix} 9 \\ 3 \end{pmatrix}$

(a) Find $\mathbf{x}$ if $\mathbf{x} + \mathbf{a} = \mathbf{b}$

(b) Find $\mathbf{m}$ if $\mathbf{x} - 2\mathbf{a} = \mathbf{b}$

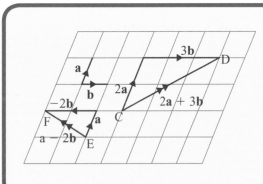

Based on the given vectors $\mathbf{a}$ and $\mathbf{b}$, $\overrightarrow{CD}$ has been drawn so that $\overrightarrow{CD} = 2\mathbf{a} + 3\mathbf{b}$ and $\overrightarrow{EF}$ has been drawn so that $\overrightarrow{EF} = \mathbf{a} - 2\mathbf{b}$.

**E4.2**

**1**

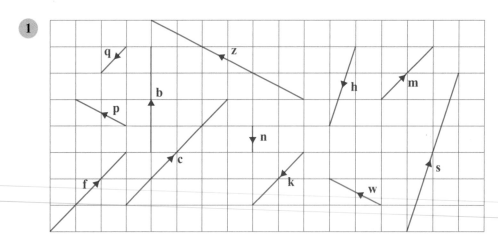

Name a vector equal to

(a) $\mathbf{p}$  (b) $2\mathbf{m}$  (c) $3\mathbf{w}$  (d) $-\mathbf{k}$

(e) $-2\mathbf{h}$  (f) $-\dfrac{1}{4}\mathbf{b}$  (g) $-\dfrac{1}{2}\mathbf{m}$  (h) $-\dfrac{1}{3}\mathbf{f}$

(i) $2\mathbf{q}$  (j) $\dfrac{1}{3}\mathbf{z}$  (k) $\dfrac{2}{3}\mathbf{f}$

**2**

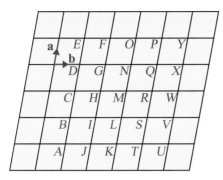

Use this diagram to express the vectors below in terms of **a** and **b**, for example:

$\overrightarrow{LN} = 2\mathbf{a}$ and $\overrightarrow{WK} = -2\mathbf{a} - 2\mathbf{b}$.

(a) $\overrightarrow{HM}$     (b) $\overrightarrow{PR}$     (c) $\overrightarrow{SP}$

(d) $\overrightarrow{CG}$     (e) $\overrightarrow{BN}$     (f) $\overrightarrow{BG}$

(g) $\overrightarrow{LW}$     (h) $\overrightarrow{XS}$     (i) $\overrightarrow{JQ}$

(j) $\overrightarrow{WI}$     (k) $\overrightarrow{PK}$     (l) $\overrightarrow{CX}$

**3** Using the same diagram as question **2**, express the following vectors in terms of the capital letters.
Start at L each time, for example, $2\mathbf{b} = \overrightarrow{LV}$ and $\mathbf{a} - 2\mathbf{b} = \overrightarrow{LC}$.

(a) $\mathbf{a} + 2\mathbf{b}$     (b) $3\mathbf{a} + \mathbf{b}$     (c) $2\mathbf{a} - 2\mathbf{b}$     (d) $\mathbf{b} - \mathbf{a}$

(e) $2\mathbf{b} - \mathbf{a}$     (f) $\mathbf{a} - \mathbf{b}$     (g) $-\mathbf{a} - 2\mathbf{b}$     (h) $3\mathbf{a} - 2\mathbf{b}$

**4**

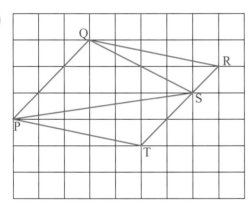

Write down a column vector equal to:

(a) $\overrightarrow{QR}$

(b) $\overrightarrow{RT}$

(c) $\overrightarrow{PQ} + \overrightarrow{QR}$

(d) $\overrightarrow{RS} + \overrightarrow{SQ}$

(e) $\overrightarrow{PS} + \overrightarrow{SQ}$

(f) $\overrightarrow{SP} + \overrightarrow{PT}$

**5** Check that your teacher wants you to try this question?

(a) Draw the vector $\overrightarrow{AB} = \begin{pmatrix} 3 \\ 4 \end{pmatrix}$ on grid paper like question **4**.

(b) *Calculate* the length of vector $\overrightarrow{AB}$.

**6** Only try this if you have done question **5**.

*Calculate* the length of vector $\overrightarrow{PQ}$ if $\overrightarrow{PQ}$ equals:

(a) $\begin{pmatrix} 8 \\ 6 \end{pmatrix}$      (b) $\begin{pmatrix} 5 \\ 12 \end{pmatrix}$      (c) $\begin{pmatrix} 9 \\ 12 \end{pmatrix}$      (d) $\begin{pmatrix} 7 \\ 24 \end{pmatrix}$

**1** Express each vector in terms of **a** and **b** (ABCD is a parallelogram).

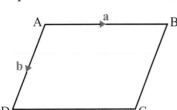

(a) $\overrightarrow{BC}$

(b) $\overrightarrow{CD}$

(c) $\overrightarrow{DB}$

(d) $\overrightarrow{AC}$

**2** Express each vector in terms of **p** and **q**.

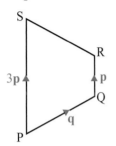

(a) $\overrightarrow{SP}$

(b) $\overrightarrow{PR}$

(c) $\overrightarrow{RS}$

(d) $\overrightarrow{SQ}$

**3** Express each vector in terms of **m** and **n**.

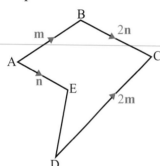

(a) $\overrightarrow{CD}$

(b) $\overrightarrow{AC}$

(c) $\overrightarrow{CE}$

(d) $\overrightarrow{BD}$

(e) $\overrightarrow{DE}$

**4** M is the midpoint of AC.

Express the following vectors in terms of **a** and **b**:

(a) $\overrightarrow{AC}$     (b) $\overrightarrow{AM}$     (c) $\overrightarrow{BM}$

**5** PQRS is a parallelogram.

$\overrightarrow{PQ} = 3\mathbf{a}$ and $\overrightarrow{PS} = 4\mathbf{b}$

M is the midpoint of QR and N is the midpoint of PS. Express the following vectors in terms of **a** and **b**.

(a) $\overrightarrow{QM}$          (b) $\overrightarrow{PM}$          (c) $\overrightarrow{PN}$          (d) $\overrightarrow{QN}$

A manager has six people willing to work one weekend at the 'Dog and Elephant' pub.

At any one time he needs two people behind the bar, one person serving food and one person in the kitchen. This is not the case towards the end of the evening when food is no longer served.

This table shows what the six people can do which depends on their age and experience.

| Name | Bar | Serving food | Kitchen |
|------|-----|--------------|---------|
| Joe | ✓ | ✓ | |
| Kate | ✓ | ✓ | ✓ |
| Ben | | ✓ | ✓ |
| Penny | | ✓ | ✓ |
| Nazrul | ✓ | ✓ | |
| Milly | ✓ | ✓ | ✓ |

On Saturday the six people can work the hours shown below.

| Name | Joe | Kate | Ben | Penny | Nazrul | Milly |
|------|-----|------|-----|-------|--------|-------|
| Hours | 8 | 9 | 5 | $3\frac{1}{2}$ | 9 | 8 |

Task A

*No person can work more than 3 hours without taking a break of at least $\frac{1}{2}$ hour.*

Make a copy of the Saturday schedule below then fill in who works where and when. It may be better to use a pencil and have a rubber handy.

Saturday schedule

| | 12 pm | 1 pm | 2 pm | 3 pm | 4 pm | 5 pm | 6 pm | 7 pm | 8 pm | 9 pm | 10 pm | 11 pm | 12 am |
|---|---|---|---|---|---|---|---|---|---|---|---|---|---|
| Bar | | | | | | | | | | | | | |
| Bar | | | | | | | | | | | | | |
| Serving food | | | | | | | | | | | | | |
| Kitchen | | | | | | | | | | | | | |

107

On Sunday five people can work the hours shown below.

| Name | Joe | Kate | Ben | Penny | Milly |
|------|-----|------|-----|-------|-------|
| Hours | 6 | 5 | 2 | 6 | 6 |

**Task B**

On Sunday the pub is shut between 3 pm and 7 pm. Make a copy of the Sunday schedule below and then fill in who works where and when.
*Remember no person can work more than 3 hours without taking a break of at least $\frac{1}{2}$ hour.*

Sunday schedule

| | 12 pm | 1 pm | 2 pm | 3 pm | 4 pm | 5 pm | 6 pm | 7 pm | 8 pm | 9 pm | 10 pm | 11 pm | 12 am |
|---|---|---|---|---|---|---|---|---|---|---|---|---|---|
| Bar | | | | | | | | | | | | | |
| Bar | | | | | | | | | | | | | |
| Serving food | | | | | | | | | | | | | |
| Kitchen | | | | | | | | | | | | | |

| Rate of pay per hour | |
|------|------|
| Bar | £8·20 |
| Serving food | £7·40 |
| Kitchen | £7·40 |

**Task C**

Using your schedules, work out how much each of the six people earn during this weekend.

Their total pay should add up to £529·90

**Task D**

Get a partner to check through your two schedules to make sure you have not broken any rules.

## TEST YOURSELF ON UNIT 4

**1.** Consolidating previous geometry work

Find the angles marked with letters.

(a)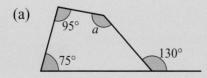

(b)

(c)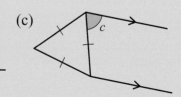

(d) Write down the size of each exterior angle in a regular pentagon.

(e) Each interior angle of a regular polygon is 165°.
How many sides has the polygon?

(f)

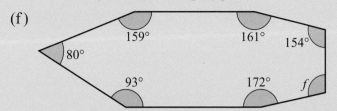

Find the value of angle *f*.

(g) Write down the order of rotational symmetry of a parallelogram.

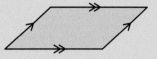

(h) Triangle P is translated onto triangle Q.
Write down the translation vector.

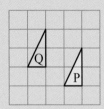

---

**2.** Dealing with angle proof

(a) Prove that the exterior angle of a triangle is equal to the sum of the two opposite interior angles.

(b)

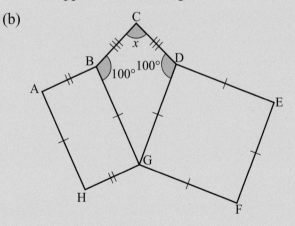

BCDG is a kite.

DEFG is a square.

ABGH is a rectangle.

Prove that angle FGH is equal to ($x + 20$).

Explain fully.

109

**3.** Proving with congruent triangles

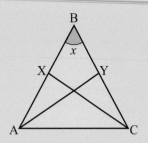

ABC is an isosceles triangle with AB = BC.

X and Y lie on AB and BC respectively so that AX = CY.

Label the angle ABC as *x*.

(a) Show, with reasons, which triangle is congruent to ABY.

(b) Hence prove that CX = AY.

**4.** Identifying lines of reflection

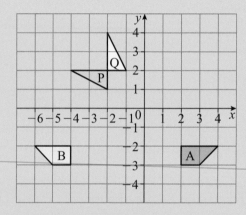

(a) Shape A is reflected onto shape B.
    Write down the equation of the mirror line.

(b) Describe *fully* the transformation that sends triangle P to triangle Q.

**5.** Describing rotations

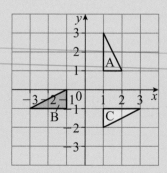

Describe *fully* the rotation which transforms:

(a) shape *A* onto *B*

(b) shape *A* onto *C*

**6.** Finding centres of enlargement

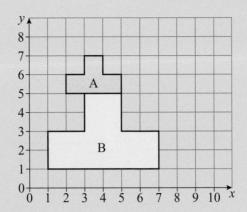

Describe *fully* the enlargement which transforms shape *A* onto shape *B* (draw the grid and 2 shapes if you need to).

**7.** Using vectors

If $\mathbf{a} = \begin{pmatrix} 3 \\ 4 \end{pmatrix}$ and $\mathbf{b} = \begin{pmatrix} 5 \\ -7 \end{pmatrix}$, find as a column vector:

(a) $2\mathbf{b}$  (b) $\mathbf{b} - \mathbf{a}$  (c) $3\mathbf{a} - 2\mathbf{b}$  (d) $3(\mathbf{b} - \mathbf{a})$

(e) If the co-ordinates of a point A are (4, 1) and $\overrightarrow{AB} = \begin{pmatrix} 2 \\ -3 \end{pmatrix}$,

what are the co-ordinates of B?

(f)

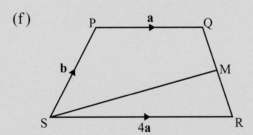

PQRS is a parallelogram.

M is the midpoint of QR.

Express each vector below in terms of **a** and **b**:

(i) $\overrightarrow{QR}$  (ii) $\overrightarrow{SQ}$  (iii) $\overrightarrow{QM}$  (iv) $\overrightarrow{SM}$

(g)
$\overrightarrow{AB} = \begin{pmatrix} 2 \\ 3 \end{pmatrix}$ and $\overrightarrow{BC} = \begin{pmatrix} 4 \\ 1 \end{pmatrix}$

Express $\overrightarrow{AC}$ as a column vector.

111

1. The diagram shows 2 identical rectangles and 2 identical parallelograms.
   The coordinates of four vertices are shown on the diagram.

   Find the coordinates of the vertices marked *A*, *B* and *C*.

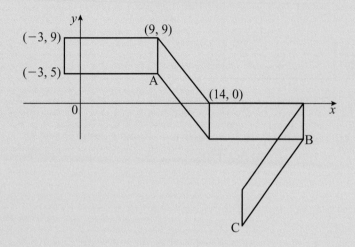

(WJEC)

2. $\mathbf{m} = \begin{pmatrix} 4 \\ -7 \end{pmatrix}$ and $\mathbf{n} = \begin{pmatrix} -3 \\ 1 \end{pmatrix}$

   Write down the following column vectors:

   (a) $\mathbf{m} - \mathbf{n}$

   (b) $2\mathbf{m} + 3\mathbf{n}$

3.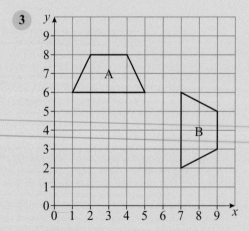

   Describe fully the **single** transformation that takes
   shape *A* to shape *B*.

(AQA)

4 (a) Calculate the size of the interior angle of a regular pentagon.

(b) Three regular pentagons are placed together as shown below.

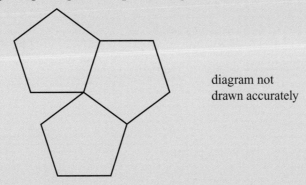

diagram not
drawn accurately

Explain why you cannot cover a floor with regular pentagonal tiles.    (CEA)

5

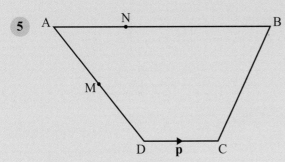

AB is parallel to DC.

$$\overrightarrow{AB} = 5\mathbf{p} \qquad \overrightarrow{DC} = \mathbf{p} \qquad \overrightarrow{DA} = 2\mathbf{q} - \mathbf{p}$$

Show that $\overrightarrow{CB} = 2\mathbf{q} + 3\mathbf{p}$    (AQA)

6 The perpendicular from a vertex to the opposite side of a triangle bisects this side. Prove by using congruent triangles that the triangle must be isosceles.

7 The four vertices of parallelogram *ABCD* lie on the sides of triangle *PQR* as shown in the diagram.

The sides *PD*, *AD*, *BC* and *CR* are equal.

Given that $A\hat{D}C = 50°$, find the value of *x*.

**You must show full details of how you obtained your answer.**

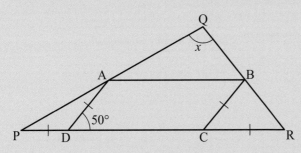

(WJEC)

113

**8** ABC is a triangle.

M is the midpoint of AB and N is the midpoint of BC.

$\overrightarrow{AB} = 2\mathbf{p}$ and $\overrightarrow{AC} = 3\mathbf{q}$.

Find, in terms of **p** and **q**.

(i) $\overrightarrow{BC}$

(ii) $\overrightarrow{AN}$ 

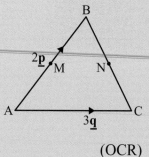

(OCR)

**9** The diagram shows part of a pattern made from tiles.

The pattern is made from two types of tiles, tile A and tile B.

Both tile A and tile B are regular polygons.

Work out the number of sides tile A has.

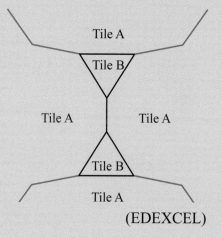

(EDEXCEL)

**10** 

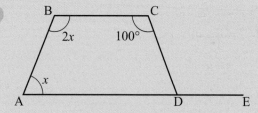

Express angle CDE in terms of *x*.

**11** 

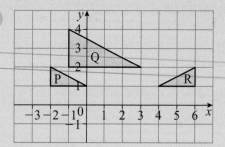

Describe *fully* the transformation that maps

(a) triangle P onto triangle Q

(b) triangle P onto triangle R

# NUMBER 3

# 5

## Previous number work

 **Key Facts**

**Remember:**

$$- \times - = +$$

$$\left.\begin{array}{l} - \times + \\ + \times - \end{array}\right\} = -$$

$$- \div - = +$$

$$\left.\begin{array}{l} - \div + \\ + \div - \end{array}\right\} = -$$

The product of prime factors for 60 is $2 \times 2 \times 3 \times 5$

### M5.1

**1** Answer true or false:

(a) $7 \times -3 = -21$     (b) $-6 - 2 = -4$     (c) $-8 \times -4 = -32$

(d) $-2 + 6 = 4$     (e) $-10 \div -5 = 2$     (f) $-24 \div 3 = -8$

(g) $-6 \times -5 = 30$     (h) $(-7)^2 = -49$     (i) $18 \div -9 = -2$

**2** If $a = -3$, $b = 5$ and $c = -4$, find the values of:

(a) $bc$      (b) $a + c$      (c) $4b - a$      (d) $c^2$      (e) $ab - c$

(f) $4a + 2b$      (g) $(b + c)^2$      (h) $\dfrac{3c}{2a}$      (i) $\dfrac{2b}{a - c}$      (j) $a^2 + b^2 + c^2$

**3** Hayden works as a chef.
He earns £184 for 16 hours work.
How much will he earn for
21 hours work?

**4** Which factors of 36 are square numbers?

**5** (a) Copy and complete the two factor trees below:

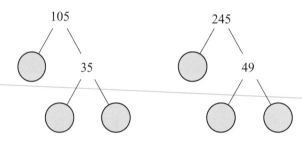

(b) Write down 105 as a product of its prime factors.

(c) Write down 245 as a product of its prime factors.

(d) Write down the Highest Common Factor (HCF) of 105 and 245.

**6** Work out

(a) $268 \times 47$      (b) $888 \div 24$      (c) $3107 - 1490$

**7** Lena hires a stall which costs
£28 for the day. She sells 14 pairs
of colourful Wellington boots
at £18 each and 9 pairs of plain
Wellington boots at £14 each.
She keeps half the sale price of
each boot. What is her profit for
the whole day?

**8**  Last year Aiden used 4250 units of gas at 16p per unit.

This year the price per unit of gas increased to 19p per unit.

Aiden managed to use less gas by reducing the number of units by one tenth compared to last year.

In which year did he pay more for his gas and by how much?

**9**  Find the number which belongs in the box below:

$$3 \times (-7 - \boxed{\phantom{0}}) = -15$$

**10**  The following tickets are sold for a tennis match in the USA.

15000 tickets at $50 each.

4500 tickets at $65 each.

3800 tickets at $75 each.

A further $5 million is taken from television rights.

How much money is taken in total from the ticket sales and the television rights?

---

 **Key Facts**

**BoDMAS – Brackets, Divide, Multiply, Add then Subtract**

Standard Form:     $A \times 10^n \leftarrow$ integer (whole number)

$$1 \leqslant A < 10$$

$$\left. \begin{array}{l} 3 \times 10^{10} \times 2 \times 10^{13} \\ = 6 \times 10^{23} \end{array} \right\}$$  'multiplying standard form numbers'
– multiply the numbers, add the powers

**M5.2**

**1**  Answer true or false:

(a)  $6 + 2 \times 4$
(b)  $4 + 6 \div 2 - 3$
(c)  $5 \times 3 + 2 \times 6$
(d)  $5 \times (6 + 3) - 10$
(e)  $(9 - 2) \times (4 + 6)$
(f)  $1 + 5 \times (4 - 2)$

**2** Each fraction has an equivalent decimal value.
Write down each pair.

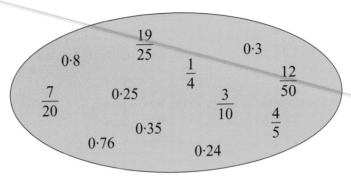

$\frac{19}{25}$   0·3

0·8   $\frac{1}{4}$   $\frac{12}{50}$

$\frac{7}{20}$   0·25   $\frac{3}{10}$

0·35   $\frac{4}{5}$

0·76   0·24

**3** Copy the sum below. Put in one pair of brackets to make the sum correct.

$$6 + 2 \times 5 - 1 = 14$$

**4** Ashley says that

$$\frac{4}{5} + \frac{1}{2} = \frac{5}{7}$$

Explain fully whether Ashley
is correct or not.

**5** A teacher has 60 bars of chocolate.
She gives $\frac{1}{3}$ of these bars to her tutor group.
She uses $\frac{7}{10}$ of the remaining bars as prizes for her other classes.
She eats 2 of the bars of chocolate herself.
How many bars of chocolate does she now have?

**6** Write the following numbers in standard form.

(a)  2300          (b)  141 000          (c)  0·084          (d)  0·0028

**7** The length of each butterfly
opposite is $2\frac{4}{5}$ cm.

What is the total length of the
two butterflies if they are placed
together, one behind the other?

**8** On the day before Valentine's day,
Sophia sells red roses.

She buys 4 crates of roses,
each containing 50 roses.

Each crate costs £45.

She sells $\frac{3}{5}$ of the roses at £3 each.

She sells $\frac{3}{4}$ of the remaining roses at £1·50 each.

She then sells the leftover roses for £1 each.

How much profit does Sophia make in total?

**9** A Lottery win is £$(1·43 \times 10^7)$.

It is shared equally between 500 people.

How much money is received by each person?

**10** Work out

(a) $\frac{5}{9}$ of 54     (b) $\frac{1}{4} - \frac{3}{5}$     (c) $-\frac{3}{8} \times \frac{2}{7}$     (d) $3\frac{1}{4} - 1\frac{2}{3}$

---

 # Key Facts

---

**Remember:**     $0·\underline{4} \times 0·\underline{0}\,\underline{6} = 0·\underline{0}\,\underline{2}\,\underline{4}$

When we multiply two decimal numbers together, the answer has the same
number of figures after the decimal point as the total number of figures
after the decimal point in the question.

---

**M5.3**

**1** Work out the following *without a calculator*:

(a) $0·7 \times 0·3$     (b) $0·09 \times 0·7$     (c) $16·2 - 8·8$

(d) $24·37 + 16·9$     (e) $0·08 \times 0·03$     (f) $1·2 \times 1·2$

(g) $13 - 3·8$     (h) $1·2 \times 0·12$     (i) $0·23 \times 1·1$

**2** *Use a calculator* to work out the following.

Give each answer to 2 decimal places.

(a) $\dfrac{3 \cdot 1 + 2 \cdot 3}{8 \cdot 4 - 1 \cdot 653}$

(b) $\dfrac{4 \cdot 9^2}{6 \cdot 13 + 2 \cdot 59}$

(c) $\sqrt{(6 \cdot 2 - 1 \cdot 93)}$

(d) $\dfrac{5 \cdot 18^3}{7 \cdot 67}$

(e) $\dfrac{0 \cdot 64 + \sqrt{5 \cdot 93}}{1 \cdot 89 + 3 \cdot 6^2}$

(f) $7 \cdot 4 + \dfrac{6 \cdot 3}{\sqrt{15 \cdot 2}}$

**3** Last year there were 17 600 serious accidents in one region of the country. The number of serious accidents this year has decreased by 6%. How many serious accidents were there during this year?

**4** Polly invests £3000 for 4 years at 3% per annum simple interest.

William invests £3500 for $2\frac{1}{2}$ years at 4% per annum simple interest.

Who receives more interest and by how much?

**5** Some people are asked if they are married or not.

The information is shown below.

|  | male | female |
|---|---|---|
| married | 11 | 13 |
| not married | 7 | 9 |

(a) What percentage of the people who are not married are female?

(b) What is the ratio of males to females who were asked?

**6** A shirt costs £32 after a 20% reduction in a sale.

What was the price of the shirt before the reduction?

**7** A celebrity photographer spends 50% of his working hours one day waiting to take photos.

He spends $\frac{2}{5}$ of the working hours travelling.

The remaining 1 hour 10 minutes of his working day is spent taking photos.

How many hours and minutes made up his total working day?

**8** Round off each number below to 3 significant figures.

(a) 1289       (b) 31·6482       (c) 0·317781       (d) 53615·63

**9** Glenn and Lisa share £5000 in the ratio 7 : 13. Lisa gives 30% of her money to her mother. She spends $\frac{4}{5}$ of the remaining money. How much money has she got left?

**10** Alison changes £800 into euros at a rate of £1 = €1·15.

She travels to Rome and spends €780.

She returns home and changes her remaining money back into pounds at a rate of £1 = €1·12.

How many pounds does she get?

## Dividing by decimals

To divide by a decimal, multiply both numbers by 10, 100, 1000, … so that the decimal you are dividing by becomes a whole number. Now divide the 2 numbers to get the answer.

(a) $3·2 \div 0·\underline{4}$

multiply both numbers by 10

$= 32 \div 4$

$= 8$

(b) $5·517 \div 0·\underline{9}$

multiply both numbers by 10

$= 55·17 \div 9$

$$\begin{array}{r} 6·\,1\ 3 \\ 9\overline{)55·^11^27} \end{array}$$

(c) $3·5882 \div 0·\underline{007}$

Multiply both numbers by 1000

$= 3588·2 \div 7$

$$\begin{array}{r} 51\ 2·\,6 \\ 7\overline{)358^18·^42} \end{array}$$

**Note:**

**When a number is divided by a decimal between 0 and 1, the answer will be larger than the starting number.**

121

*Do not use a calculator.*

**1** Copy the questions below and fill in the empty boxes

    (a) $4.6 \div 0.2 = \boxed{\phantom{x}} \div 2 = \boxed{\phantom{x}}$      (b) $3.2 \div 0.04 = \boxed{\phantom{x}} \div 4 = \boxed{\phantom{x}}$

    (c) $1.65 \div 0.5 = \boxed{\phantom{x}} \div 5 = \boxed{\phantom{x}}$      (d) $2.64 \div 0.002 = \boxed{\phantom{x}} \div 2 = \boxed{\phantom{x}}$

**2** Divide the numbers below by $0.5$.

    (a) $3.5$      (b) $4$      (c) $6.5$      (d) $8$

**3** Divide the numbers below by $0.3$.

    (a) $6$      (b) $2.4$      (c) $3.6$      (d) $0.18$

**4** Divide the numbers below by $0.7$.

    (a) $2.8$      (b) $6.3$      (c) $21$      (d) $0.42$

Work out

**5** $7.2 \div 0.4$        **6** $3.8 \div 0.2$        **7** $1.84 \div 0.8$

**8** $14.98 \div 0.7$        **9** $0.084 \div 0.03$        **10** $0.496 \div 0.08$

**11** $0.444 \div 0.06$        **12** $3.25 \div 0.05$        **13** $26.6 \div 0.7$

**14** $0.075 \div 0.003$        **15** $0.144 \div 0.04$        **16** $0.065 \div 0.002$

**17** A large pot of paint contains $1.5$ litres. How many $0.25$ litre pots of paint can be filled from this large pot?

**18** A bottle of lemonade holds 1 litre. How many glasses can be filled from this bottle if each glass holds $0.2$ litres?

**19** A box of sweets contains $2.4$ kg. How many packets can be filled from this box if each packet holds $0.15$ kg?

In questions **20** to **22**, find the odd answer out.

**20** (a) $0.63 \div 0.7$        (b) $0.57 \div 0.6$        (c) $0.72 \div 0.8$

**21** (a) $7.02 \div 0.09$        (b) $5.18 \div 0.07$        (c) $2.96 \div 0.04$

**22** (a) $8.82 \div 0.6$        (b) $7.4 \div 0.5$        (c) $11.84 \div 0.8$

**23** Each empty square below contains either a number or an operation
(+, −, ×, ÷). Copy each square and fill in the missing details.
The arrows are equal signs.

(a)
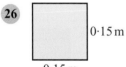

| 22·4 | ÷ | 7 | → | |
|---|---|---|---|---|
| × | | + | | |
| 0.1 | × | | → | 0.01 |
| ↓ | | ↓ | | |
| | + | | → | |

(b)

| 6·52 | ÷ | 0·2 | → | |
|---|---|---|---|---|
| × | | × | | |
| 10 | × | | → | 1 |
| ↓ | | ↓ | | |
| | + | | → | |

**24** 147 × 382 = 56154   Use this to work out:

(a) 1470 × 382

(b) 147 × 38200

(c) 14·7 × 38·2

(d) 1·47 × 3820

**25** 64·848 ÷ 28 = 2·316   Use this to work out:

(a) 64848 ÷ 28

(b) 6484·8 ÷ 280

(c) 0·64848 ÷ 0·028

(d) 2316 × 28

**26**

0·15 m

0·15 m

The square floor tile above
measures 0·15 m by 0·15 m.
The floor shown below
measures 2·1 m by 2·4 m.
How many tiles will fit:

(a) along the 2·1 m side?

(b) along the 2·4 m side?

(c) to cover the whole floor?

2·1 m

2·4 m

**Can you still?**

**Mixed algebra**

**1** Expand $(x + 3)(x − 6)$

**2** Expand $(2x − 7)(3x − 1)$

**3** Solve $2(x − 4) = x − 3$

**4** Solve $3(2x + 5) = 4x + 21$

**5** Solve $4(3x − 2) = 5(2x + 4)$

**6**
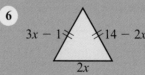

$3x − 1$      $14 − 2x$

$2x$

Find the actual perimeter of this
triangle. All lengths are in cm.

**7** Factorise $x^2 − 4x + 4$

**8** Factorise $x^2 + 7x − 18$

**9** Factorise $x^2 − 16$

## Percentage change

A holiday firm reduces its prices of a holiday from £1740 to £1479.

Find the percentage decrease.

actual decrease $= 1740 - 1479$

$= 261$

percentage decrease $= \left(\dfrac{261}{1740}\right) \times 100$

$= 15\%$

or we can find 1479 as a percentage of 1740

$\left(\dfrac{1479}{1740}\right) \times 100 = 85\%$

so 1479 is $\dfrac{85}{100}$ or 0·85 of £1740

so percentage decrease $= 15\%$

Notice that in both calculations we divide by the *original value*.

### M5.5

*Use a calculator* when needed. Give answers to the nearest whole number when needed.

1. Tai's wages were increased from £240 to £259·20 per week. What was the percentage increase?

2. The population of a country increases from 2,374,000 to 2,445,220. What is the percentage increase?

3. The value of a bike drops from £240 to £160 in one year. What is the percentage decrease in that year?

4. 'Dobbs Autos' has to reduce its workforce from 120 people to 93 people. What is the percentage decrease?

5. Copy and complete the table below:

| original price (£) | final price (£) | actual increase or decrease (£) | percentage increase or decrease |
|---|---|---|---|
| 524 | 550·20 | | |
| 780 | 897·00 | | |
| 310 | 170·50 | | |
| 96 | 62·40 | | |

**6**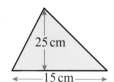

25 cm

15 cm

The base and height are both increased by 20%.
What is the percentage increase in the area of the triangle?

**7** The cost of a first-class stamp is increased from 28p to 29p. What is the percentage increase?

**8** The value of a car drops from £8000 to £6560. What fraction of the starting value is the current value of £6560?

---

Roger buys a box of shirts for £180 and sells them for £232·20.

Find the percentage profit.

actual profit = 232·20 − 180

$$= 52·20$$

percentage profit $= \left(\dfrac{52·20}{180}\right) \times 100$

$$= 29\%$$

or we can find 232·20 as a percentage of 180

$$\left(\dfrac{232·20}{180}\right) \times 100 = 129\%$$

so 232·20 is $\dfrac{129}{100}$ or 1·29 of 180

so percentage profit $= 29\%$

---

### M5.6

**1** Kevin bought a car for £7350 and sold it quickly for £8100.
Calculate the percentage profit.

**2** Carla buys a house for £221,000. She sells it 3 years later for £247,520.
What percentage profit does Carla make?

**3** The 'King's Arms' pub buys some of its items at the costs shown below and sells them at the prices shown below.
Find the percentage profit on each item.

| Item | cost price | selling price |
|---|---|---|
| pint of lager | £1·20 | £2·70 |
| packet of crisps | 25p | 60p |
| pint of bitter | £1·15 | £2·50 |
| packet of nuts | 27p | 75p |

**4**  Simon buys 300 cans of drink at 30p for each can. The cans are sold at a school disco for 36p a can. What is the percentage profit if all the cans are sold?

**5**  A clock is bought for £60 and sold for £69. What is the percentage profit?

**6**  Lloyd buys a painting for £2500 and a year later sells it for £2900. Work out

    (a) the selling price as a percentage of the buying price.

    (b) the percentage profit that Lloyd makes.

**7**  Arnie the grocer bought 100 cabbages at 30p each. He sold 80 of the cabbages at 65p each. The other 20 cabbages went rotten and had to be thrown away. Find the percentage profit Arnie made on the 100 cabbages.

**8**  On average $2\frac{1}{2}$ days out of every 60 working days are missed through ill health at the Henton factory. $\frac{3}{20}$ of the missed days are due to back problems. What percentage of all the working days at the factory are missed due to back problems?

**9**  In 2014 a company makes a profit which is 25% higher than in 2013. In 2015 the profit drops back to the level of 2013. What was the percentage decrease from 2014 to 2015?

*Can you still?*

**Vectors**

**1**  If $\mathbf{m} = \begin{pmatrix} 3 \\ 4 \end{pmatrix}$ and $\mathbf{n} = \begin{pmatrix} 1 \\ -2 \end{pmatrix}$, find the values of the vectors

    (a) $3\mathbf{m}$   (b) $\mathbf{m} - \mathbf{n}$   (c) $2\mathbf{m} + \mathbf{n}$

**2**  Express the following vectors in terms of $\mathbf{a}$ and $\mathbf{b}$:

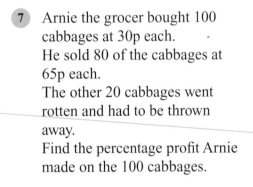

M is the midpoint of AC

    (a) $\overrightarrow{AC}$  (b) $\overrightarrow{AM}$  (c) $\overrightarrow{BM}$  (d) $\overrightarrow{CM}$

**3**  If $\overrightarrow{AB} = \begin{pmatrix} 10 \\ 24 \end{pmatrix}$, find the length of the line AB.

**4**  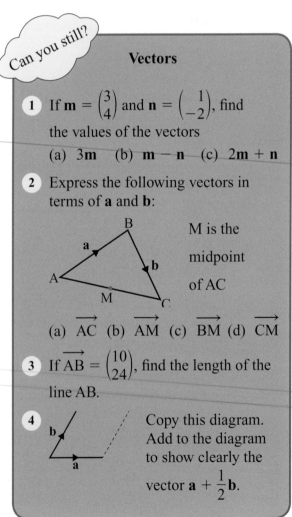 Copy this diagram. Add to the diagram to show clearly the vector $\mathbf{a} + \frac{1}{2}\mathbf{b}$.

# Key Facts

Any percentage increase or decrease refers to the *original* (old) amount *not* the new amount.

---

Rose reduces her hours at work a little and takes an 8% pay cut. She now earns £202·40 each week. What was her weekly pay before she reduced her hours?

8% decrease so £202·40 is 92% of original pay
                    (100% − 8%)

$\dfrac{202 \cdot 40}{92}$ is 1% of original pay

$\dfrac{202 \cdot 40}{92} \times 100$ is 100% of original pay

original pay = £220

> or £202·40 is 0·92 of original pay
>
> REVERSE THE PERCENTAGE
>
> original pay = $\dfrac{202 \cdot 40}{0 \cdot 92}$
>
>             = £220

---

**M5.7**

*You may use a calculator when needed.*

**1** Martin works out and increases his muscle mass. His weight therefore increases by 8%. If he now weighs 73·44 kg, how much did he weigh originally?

**2** Harry earns £27 300 each year after a 5% pay rise. How much did he earn before the pay rise?

**3** A garden table is selling for £48 with a sign saying *'Reduction of 20%.'* What was the price before the sale?

**4** In a sale all items are reduced by 15%. A carpet is selling for £15·30 per square metre. What was it before the sale?

**5** A train ticket costs £38·76 after a 14% increase in prices. How much would the train ticket have cost before the price increase?

**6** A drill costs £67·68 after VAT has been added at 20%. How much would the drill cost a builder who did not have to pay VAT?

**7** A TV costs £748·80 including 20% VAT. How much did the TV cost before VAT was added?

**8** Colin buys a car for £1500 and sells it a year later for a 22% loss. How much did Colin sell the car for?

**9** Aaliyah earns £30 797 in 2015 which is 3% more than her salary in 2014. Owen earned £28 500 in 2013. The following year he received a 4% pay rise. Who earns more money in 2014 and by how much?

**10** Joe and Tania have saved £31500 as a 15% deposit towards buying a house. What is the total cost of the house?

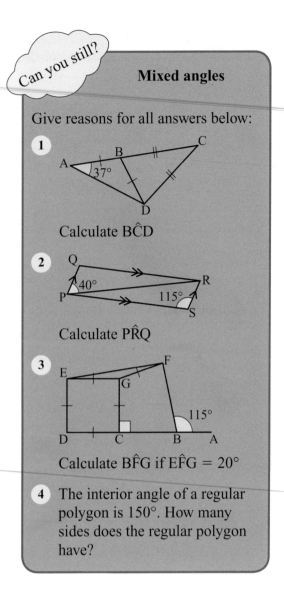

*Can you still?*

**Mixed angles**

Give reasons for all answers below:

**1**

Calculate BĈD

**2**

Calculate PR̂Q

**3**

Calculate BF̂G if EF̂G = 20°

**4** The interior angle of a regular polygon is 150°. How many sides does the regular polygon have?

**11** Jackie has £663 stolen from her whilst on holiday. This is 65% of her total holiday money. What was her total holiday money?

**E5.1**

**1** The price of a computer drops each year by 5% of its value at the start of the year. If the computer now costs £415·15, how much did it cost two years ago?

**2** A school claims that the pupils' average mark in an exam has increased by 15% over 5 years. Two pupils are told that the average mark in now 85·1. George thinks that the average mark five years ago was 72·335 but Jane thinks it was 74. Who is right and how is the correct answer obtained?

**3** The Chambers Company is made up of three departments – factory, office and sales. The number of people working in the factory and office this year is shown in the table below.

| factory | 1248 |
|---------|------|
| office  | 517  |

There are 4% more workers in the factory than one year ago. The number of people in the office has decreased by 6% compared to one year ago.

One year ago the size of the sales department was 30% of the number of workers in the factory.

Work out the total number of people in the three departments one year ago.

**4** An aeroplane has 41 069 litres of fuel which is 35% of its maximum capacity.

When it leaves London Heathrow it has its maximum load of fuel. It uses up 42% of its fuel before it lands again. How much fuel does the aeroplane have when it lands again?

**5** A chef uses $\frac{4}{5}$ kg and $\frac{31}{100}$ kg of sugar when making cakes.

This is 60% of the chef's sugar supply at the start of the day.

How much sugar did the chef have at the start of the day?

**6** Maria invests some money which makes 1% interest in the 1st year, 2% in the 2nd year, 3% in the 3rd year, 4% in the 4th year and 5% in the 5th year. Maria then has £2085·71. How much did she invest?

# Compound interest-type problems

Suppose £2000 is invested at 10% per annum (year) compound interest. How much money will there be after 2 years.

'**compound**' interest here means that the interest must be worked out separately for each year.

After 1 year:    interest = 10% of 2000 = 200

        total money = 2000 + 200 = £2200

            ↗        ↑

    money at start of year    interest

Do a new calculation for the interest in the second year.

After 2 years:    interest = 10% of 2200 = 220

                     ↑

              money at start of year

       total money = 2200 + 220 = £2420

             ↗      ↑

   money at start of 2nd year    interest

## M5.8

*Use a calculator* when needed. Give answers to the nearest penny when needed.

**1**  £5000 is invested at 10% per annum (year) compound interest. How much money will there be after 2 years?

**2**  A bank pays 6% per annum compound interest. How much will the following people have in the bank after the numbers of years stated?
(a)  Kim: £9000 after 2 years.    (b)  Freddie: £4000 after 3 years
(c)  Les: £2500 after 2 years.    (d)  Olive: £600 after 2 years.

**3**  A computer loses 30% of its value every year. Tim bought it for £800. How much would it be worth after:
(a)  2 years?                  (b)  3 years?

**4**  The number of fish in a lake is decreasing by 5% each year. There are 10 000 fish in the lake at the start of 2015. How many fish are there in the lake
(a)  at the end of 2015?      (b)  at the end of 2016?

**5** A new car is bought for £23 000. Each year, its value depreciates (goes down) by 15% of its value at the start of the year.
How much is the car worth after 3 years?

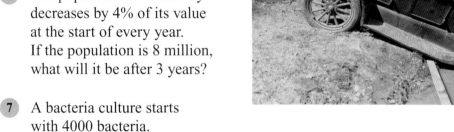

**6** The population of a country decreases by 4% of its value at the start of every year.
If the population is 8 million, what will it be after 3 years?

**7** A bacteria culture starts with 4000 bacteria.
Each hour the number of bacteria increases by 20%. How many bacteria will there be after 3 hours?

**8** Mohammed puts £200 in a bank at 6% p.a. (per annum) compound interest.
Genna puts £210 in a bank at 4% p.a. compound interest.

   (a) Who will have more money in the bank after 2 years?

   (b) By how much?

**9** Savannah has a choice of two accounts into which she can put her money.

| **Account 1** |
| --- |
| 4·5% per annum compound interest |

| **Account 2** |
| --- |
| 4·65% per annum simple interest |

Savannah invests £2000. Which account will produce more money for her after 3 years and by how much more?

## Using percentage multipliers

£500 is invested in a bank at 14% per annum compound interest.
How much money is in the bank after 5 years?

Use a *percentage multiplier* 1·14 (100% + 14% = 114%)

Now multiply by 1·14 every year to get the new amount.

Start with £500:

after 1 year:      $500 \times 1·14 = 570$

after 2 years:      $\times 1·14 = 649·80$ and so on

after 5 years:    total money $= 500 \times \underbrace{1·14 \times 1·14 \times 1·14 \times 1·14 \times 1·14}_{5 \text{ years}}$

$$= 962·70|729 \ldots$$
$$= £962·71 \text{ (to the nearest penny)}$$

---

### E5.2

*Use a calculator.* Give answers to the nearest penny when needed.

**1** £800 is put in a bank with 10% p.a. (per annum) compound interest.

  (a) Work out the total money in the bank after 3 years (use *percentage multiplier* 1·1).

  (b) How much money is in the bank after 5 years?

  (c) How much money is in the bank after 10 years? ( just multiply £800 by 1·1 ten times)

**2** Another bank pays 7% p.a. compound interest.
If you put in £400, how much money
would be in the bank after:

  (a) 2 years?    (b) 3 years?    (c) 5 years?

**3** (a) What is the percentage multiplier to
find a 15% decrease?
(Hint: what percentage would you have left after
you have taken off 15%?)

  (b) The value of a car depreciates (goes down) by 15% of its value each
year. Sally buys the car for £16 000.

     How much will the car be worth after 7 years?

**4** Inflation is how much more expensive things in the shop get each year. Assume the average inflation rate is 3%.

If a pair of shoes costs £50, how much will the pair of shoes cost after 15 years?

**5** If a 15-year old person put £500 in a bank at 9% p.a. compound interest and left it in the bank for 50 years until retirement, how much money would be in the bank?

**6** Misha invests £400 in a bank with a compound interest of 3·75% per annum.

At the end of each year Misha has to pay 20% tax on the interest made during that year. After 4 years Misha finds a ruby stone valued at £4500. Has he got enough money in the bank to afford to buy the ruby stone? If not, how much more would he need to save?

**7** Callow Bank offers two 3 year Savings accounts.

| Simple Save: | 2% per annum compound interest |
|---|---|

| Changer Save: | 1% for first year |
| | 2% for second year |
| | 3% for third year |

If you invest £3500 in each account, which will give you more money after 3 years and by how much?

**8** Imran invests some money in a bank at 8% p.a. compound interest. After how many years will his money have doubled?

**9** The number of burglaries in a certain country rose by 8% for two years in a row from 2013 to 2015. If there were 20,000 burglaries in 2013 then:

(a) How many burglaries were there in 2014?

(b) How many burglaries were there in 2015?

(c) What was the overall percentage increase in burglaries over the two years?

(note: the answer is *not* 16%).

**10** Arnav invests £500 at a compound interest rate of 4% per annum. At the same time Simone invests £600 at a compound interest rate of 2% per annum.

At the end of which year will Arnav have more money than Simone for the first time?

Can you still?

**Describing transformations**

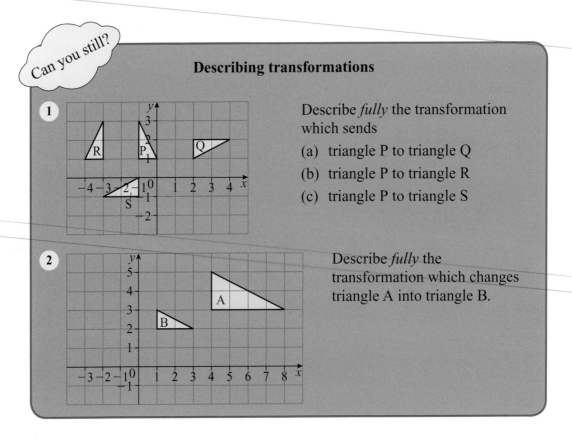

**1** Describe *fully* the transformation which sends

(a) triangle P to triangle Q

(b) triangle P to triangle R

(c) triangle P to triangle S

**2** Describe *fully* the transformation which changes triangle A into triangle B.

Share £480 between Carol, Maggie and Peter in the ratio 5 : 3 : 4.

Carol : Maggie : Peter
= 5 : 3 : 4
Total of 12 shares

£480
so each share = 480 ÷ 12
= £40

Most important:
find the value
of 1 share

Carol gets 5 shares
= 5 × £40 = £200
Maggie gets 3 shares
= 3 × £40 = £120
Peter gets 4 shares
= 4 × £40 = £160

**M5.9**

1.  (a) Divide 180 kg in the ratio 5 : 3 : 2    (b) Divide £450 in the ratio 3 : 1 : 5
    (c) Divide 375 g in the ratio 4 : 3 : 8    (d) Divide £680 in the ratio 7 : 3 : 10

2.  Some money is shared between Omar, Molly and Sachin in the ratio 5 : 2 : 7.
    Molly got £90 less than Sachin. How much money did Omar get?

3.  The recipe below is for 8 chocolate buns.

    220 g butter
    240 g sugar
    2 tablespoons of boiling water
    4 eggs
    200 g self-raising flour
    2 tablespoons of cocoa

    Jordan has:
    1·1 kg of butter
    840 g of sugar
    24 eggs
    1·5 kg of self-raising flour
    10 tablespoons of cocoa

    Work out the maximum number of chocolate buns that Jordan can make.

4.  P is $\frac{4}{7}$ of Q. Write down the ratio P : Q.

**5**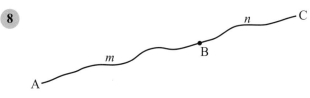

The angles $a$, $b$ and $c$ in the pentagon opposite are in the ratio $8 : 3 : 6$.

Find the values of angles $a$, $b$ and $c$.

**6** A coin is made of copper and nickel in the ratio $19 : 5$.

What fraction of the coin is

(a) copper
(b) nickel?

**7** £8000 is shared between Carl and Anna in the ratio $11 : 5$.

Carl then divides his share between himself and his two brothers in the ratio $5 : 3 : 3$ respectively.

How much money does Carl keep?

**8**

AB if $\frac{5}{8}$ of AC.

Write down the ratio $m : n$ in its simplest form.

**9** Grannie Ann eats $\frac{3}{8}$ of a chocolate cake.

Her dear son eats $\frac{1}{10}$ of the cake.

Grannie Ann then eats another $\frac{1}{3}$ of the cake.

What is the final ratio of the amount of cake eaten by Grannie Ann compared to that eaten by her son?

**10** The ratio of plain to milk chocolates in a box is $12 : 13$.

All the chocolates are plain or milk.

Hannah says that $\frac{12}{13}$ of the chocolates are plain.

Explain clearly whether she is correct or not?

**11** Express each of the following ratios in the form $m : n$ where $m$ and $n$ are integers (whole numbers).

(a) $\frac{3}{10} : \frac{2}{3}$

(b) $\frac{5}{7} : \frac{2}{9}$

(c) $\frac{5}{8} : \frac{3}{5}$

**12** This year Maya and Ishaan were given a bonus payment of £3360 in the ratio 7 : 5.

Maya's bonus payment was a 96% increase on last year.

Ishaan's bonus was $\frac{1}{6}$ more than last year's payment.

Work out the bonus payment ratio for last year.

**13** Some sweets are shared between Jan and Dom in the ratio 6 : 5.

If Jan gets $y$ sweets, how many sweets does Dom get?

(Give your answer in terms of $y$).

**14** If $\frac{x}{y}$ of the students in Year 10 play a musical instrument, what is the ratio of the number of students who play an instrument to the number who do not?

**Can you still?**

**Congruent triangles**

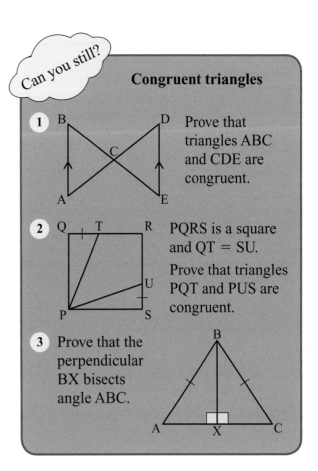

**1** Prove that triangles ABC and CDE are congruent.

**2** PQRS is a square and QT = SU.

Prove that triangles PQT and PUS are congruent.

**3** Prove that the perpendicular BX bisects angle ABC.

---

**Direct proportion**

🔑 # Key Facts

Two quantities are 'directly proportional' if one quantity is a multiple of the other.

This means that if one quantity is doubled so is the other.

If $x$ is directly proportional to $y$ then $x$ plotted against $y$ will always produce a straight line graph *passing through the origin*.

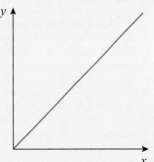

1. The voltage $V$ in a circuit is directly proportional to the current $I$.
   Sketch a graph of $V$ against $I$.

2. A force $F$ on an object is directly proportional to its acceleration $a$.

   This is shown in the graph opposite.

   We can see that $a = 2$ when $F = 10$.

   This means $a = 1$ gives $F = 5$.

   This means $F = 5a$.

   (a) Work out the value of $F$ when $a = 10$.

   (b) Work out the value of $a$ when $F = 35$.

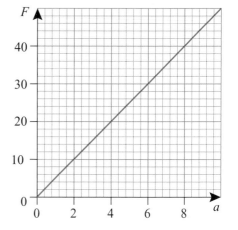

3. The distance $d$ travelled on a cycle rickshaw is directly proportional to the time $t$ spent on it.

   $d = 15$ km when $t = 2$ hours.

   Work out the value of $d$ when $t = 3$ hours.

4. Which graph below shows that $y$ is directly proportional to $x$?

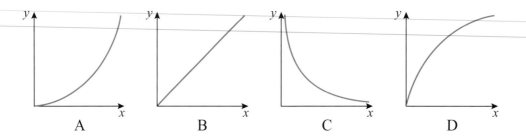

   A          B          C          D

5. £1 = \$1·26

   Convert \$81·90 into pounds.

138

**6** Use the graph opposite.

(a) Are inches and cm directly proportional?

(b) How many cm are equal to 1 inch?

(c) Complete the formula

number of cm = ☐ × number of inches

(d) How many cm are equal to 7 inches?

(e) How many inches are equal to 30 cm?

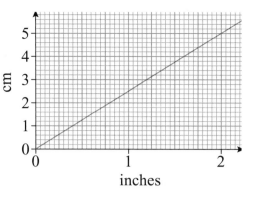

**7**

If $y$ is 'directly proportional' to $x$, we write $y \propto x$.

If $y \propto x$ then $\boxed{y = kx}$

where $k$ is any $y$-value divided by the corresponding $x$-value ($k$ is the gradient of the graph).

$y$ is directly proportional to $x$.
$y = 12$ when $x = 4$.

(a) $y = kx$. Find the value of $k$.

(b) Find $y$ when $x = 8$.

(c) Find $x$ when $y = 42$.

(d) Find $y$ when $x = 3\cdot5$.

**8** When a car is accelerating from rest at a constant rate its speed, $v$, is directly proportional to time, $t$.

(a) $v = kt$. The car is travelling at 2 m/s after 5 seconds. Find the value of $k$.

(b) How fast will the car be travelling after 6 seconds?

(c) After how long will the car be travelling at 3·2 m/s?

**9** Which equation below shows that $m$ is directly proportional to $V$?

(a) $m = 4V^2$     (b) $m = \dfrac{4}{V}$     (c) $m = 4V$     (d) $m = 4V^3$

**10** Carter returns from New York to London. He still has $213·72 and changes them back into pounds. He is charged 2% of his money to do this.

The following week he is going to Paris to watch the Marathon so changes all the above money into euros. Again he is charged 2%.

How many complete euros will he take to Paris if the exchange rates below are used?

£1 = $1·37
£1 = €1·19

**11** Jocelyn says that two of the equations below indicate that $y$ is directly proportional to $x$.

Is she correct?

Explain your reasons fully.

(a) $y = 9x$

(b) $y = 3x^2$

(c) $2y = x$

(d) $y^2 = x$

(e) $y = 4\sqrt{x}$

(f) $y = x + 2$

**12** $m$ is directly proportional to $p$. When $m = 8$, $p = 12$.

Work out the value of $p$ when $m = 11$.

*Can you still?*

**Finding formulas**

**1** Landen buys $n$ packets of crisps at 65p each. He also buys $m$ bottles of water at 90p each.

Write down an expression for the total amount of money he spends.

**2**

$PS$ is twice the length of $QR$.

Write down a formula for the perimeter $P$ in terms of $a$.

**3** Isabella is paid a weekly wage of £$y$ plus £$n$ for every bed she sells.

Write down a formula for the wage $W$ she gets if she sells 8 beds during one week.

## Key Facts

Two quantities are 'inversely proportional' if one increases at the same rate as the other decreases.

This means that if one quantity is doubled, the other is halved.

We say that one quantity $y$ is directly proportional to the reciprocal of the other quantity $x$

('reciprocal' of $x$ is $\frac{1}{x}$)

Their graph is shown opposite.

### M5.11

**1** If 4 men can build a wall in 12 hours, how long will it take 2 men?

**2** If 3 people can paint a room in 8 hours, how long will it take 6 people?

**3** If it takes Adam and one friend 3 hours to hand wash his clothes, how long will it take Adam and two friends to hand wash his clothes?

**4** The volume $V$ of a gas is inversely proportional to its pressure $P$.

Sketch a graph of $V$ against $P$.

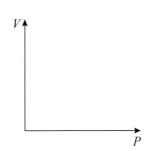

**5** A farmer has enough hay to feed 15 horses for two weeks and a day.

How long would the hay last for 9 horses?

141

**6** Arianna has enough food for her 4 dogs for 30 days. She then looks after her parents' dog also. How many days will the dog food last for now?

**7** Which graph below shows that $m$ is inversely proportional to $l$?

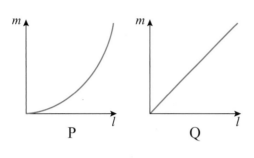
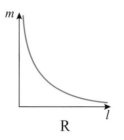
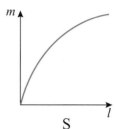

P    Q    R    S

**8**

If $y$ is 'inversely proportional' to $x$, we write $y \propto \dfrac{1}{x}$.

If $y \propto \dfrac{1}{x}$ then $\boxed{y = \dfrac{k}{x}}$

where $k$ is any $y$-value multiplied by the corresponding $x$-value.

$y$ is inversely proportional to $x$. When $y = 3, x = 16$.

(a) If $y = \dfrac{k}{x}$, find the value of $k$.

(b) Work out the value of $y$ when $x = 12$.

**9** The resistance $R$ is inversely proportional to the current $I$. $R = 40$ when $I = 2$.

(a) If $R = \dfrac{k}{I}$, find the value of $k$.

(b) Work out the value of $R$ when $I = 5$.

**10** A car uses 25 litres of petrol to travel 225 km. How many litres of petrol are needed for a journey of 153 km?

**11** $y$ is inversely proportional to $x$ such that one of the equations below is true.

(a) $y = 5x^2$    (b) $y = \dfrac{5}{x}$    (c) $y = 5x$

Which of these equations describes the inverse proportion graph shown opposite?

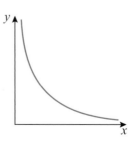

142

**12** The speed $S$ of an object is inversely proportional to the time taken, $t$.

$S = 5$ m/s when $t = 6$ s.

(a) Find $S$ when $t = 2$ s.

(b) Find $S$ when $t = 120$ s.

(c) Find $t$ when $S = 2$ m/s.

**13** The wavelength $w$ of sound waves is inversely proportional to the frequency $f$.

$f = 350$ when $w = 0\cdot6$.

(a) Find $f$ when $w = 1\cdot5$.

(b) Find $w$ when $f = 1050$.

(c) Find $f$ when $w = 0\cdot125$.

**14** Five people each read the same book at the same time. It takes them 9 hours. If 10 people each read the same book at the same time, how long will it take them?

Comment on the reason for your answer.

**15** How many equations below show that $M$ is inversely proportional to $H$?

(a) $M = \dfrac{4}{H^2}$

(b) $M = \dfrac{4}{H}$

(c) $M = \dfrac{7}{H}$

(d) $M^2 = \dfrac{7}{H}$

(e) $H = \dfrac{4}{M}$

**16** 8 workers take 3 hours to make 11 tents. 2 of the workers resign. The remaining workers have to make 22 tents. How long will this take them?

---

*Can you still?*

## Number Work

**1** Write the numbers below in order of size, starting with the smallest.

$4\cdot2 \times 10^{-6}$    $4\cdot3 \times 10^{-5}$

$4\cdot3 \times 10^{-6}$    $4\cdot2 \times 10^{-4}$

**2** If $s = at^2$, find the value of $s$ in standard form if $a = 5 \times 10^8$ and $t = 3 \times 10^5$.

**3** $150 = 2 \times 3 \times 5^2$ and $495 = 3^2 \times 5 \times 11$.

Find the HCF and LCM of 150 and 495.

**4** Ellen says the product of 2 square numbers is always a square number.

Is Ellen correct?

Justify your answer.

**5** Which is greater:-

$3^{-3}$ or $\dfrac{1}{3^2} \times 3^{-2}$?

**6**

$\sqrt{3}$ cm

$4\sqrt{3}$ cm

Work out the area of this triangle.

143

Some bread rolls have the following information printed on the packet.

| How to store and bake | |
|---|---|
| | **Freezable**<br>If freezing, freeze on the day of purchase and consume within 1 month.<br>Defrost thoroughly and use within 24 hours.<br>Once thawed do not re-freeze. |
| | Oven bake |
| | Oven bake from frozen |

| Electric | 200°C |
|---|---|
| Gas | 6 |

10 mins

| Electric | 190°C |
|---|---|
| Gas | 5 |

13 mins

| Nutrition information | | | |
|---|---|---|---|
| Typical values | Per 100 g | Per roll | % of GDA for women |
| Energy | 975 kJ<br>230 kcal | 487 kJ<br>115 kcal | —<br>5·8% |
| Protein | 8·3 g | 4·2 g | 9·3% |
| Carbohydrate<br>of which sugars<br>of which starch | 49·4 g<br>3·2 g<br>46·2 g | 24·7 g<br>1·6 g<br>23·1 g | 10·7%<br>1·8%<br>— |
| Fat<br>of which saturates | 1·4 g<br>0·4 g | 0·7 g<br>0·2 g | 1·0%<br>1·0% |
| Fibre | 3·0 g | 1·5 g | 6·3% |
| Salt | 1·08 g | 0·54 g | 9·0% |

| Guideline daily amounts (GDA) | | |
|---|---|---|
| Women | Men | Children (5–10 years) |
| —<br>2000 kcal | —<br>2500 kcal | —<br>1800 kcal |
| 45 g | 55 g | 24 g |
| 230 g<br>90 g<br>— | 300 g<br>120 g<br>— | 220 g<br>85 g<br>— |
| 70 g<br>20 g | 95 g<br>30 g | 70 g<br>20 g |
| 24 g | 24 g | 15 g |
| 6 g | 6 g | 4 g |

## Task A

1. Gary needs to bake two bread rolls from frozen. What setting must he use on his gas cooker?

2. Gary puts his frozen bread rolls in the cooker at 13:55. At what time must he take the rolls out of the oven?

3. There are 30 days in June. If Gary freezes bread rolls on Tuesday, 9th June, by what date must he eat the rolls and on what day of the week would this be?

4. Sandy buys bread rolls and wants to eat them on the same day. At what time must she put the rolls in the oven if she wants to take them out at 6:35 p.m.?

5. Sandy eats two rolls. How much protein has she eaten?

6. Gary eats rolls and works out that he has eaten 2·1 g of fat. How many rolls does he eat?

7. How much fibre is in 250 g of these bread rolls?

## Task B

1. What is the guideline daily amount (GDA) of energy kcals for men?

2. Gary eats two bread rolls. Is this more or less than 10% of his energy GDA?

3. What is the *least* number of bread rolls that would give a woman more than her GDA of carbohydrate?

4. Sandy eats four bread rolls. What percentage of the GDA of fat for women has she eaten?

5. Gary eats three bread rolls in total. How much more fibre must he eat on that day if he is to reach his GDA for fibre?

## TEST YOURSELF ON UNIT 5

**1.** Consolidating previous number work

(a) Nick earns £560·50 for 38 hours work and Makayla earns £475·20 for 32 hours work. Who earns more per hour and by how much?

(b) $5 + 6 \times ?$ must give an answer greater than 42. What is the missing value if it is the lowest integer (whole number) possible?

(c) Write $2·6 \times 10^{-4}$ as an ordinary number.

(d) At work Yakov spends $\frac{1}{5}$ of his time on the phone.
He spends $\frac{1}{3}$ of his time replying to letters and $\frac{13}{60}$ of his time on the computer.
The remaining $1\frac{1}{2}$ hours are spent doing other tasks.
How long is his working day?

(e) Find the HCF and LCM of 245 and 350.

**2.** Dividing by decimals

*Do not use a calculator.*

(a) Which of the questions below gives the greater answer and by how much?

| A | 3·22 ÷ 0·7 | or | B | 1·365 ÷ 0·3 |

(b) The total weight of these lottery balls is 1·72 kg.
Each ball weighs 0·02 kg.
How many lottery balls are there?

## 3. Finding percentage changes

(a) Khloe buys a painting for £1200.
    She sells it for £1536.

    What percentage profit does she
    make on the deal?

(b) Will and Minnie are practising old
    maths exam papers. Will scores 72 on
    the first paper and 82 on the second.
    Minnie scores 81 on the first paper and
    92 on the second. Who achieved the
    greater percentage increase from their
    first mark to their second and by how
    much?

## 4. Finding reverse percentages

(a) The volume of an ice cube
    decreases by 35% as it melts.
    Its volume is now 5·85 cm³.
    What was its volume before it
    started melting?

(b) Arushi runs a business. The profit
    this year was £41 202. This was
    10% down on last year's profit.
    Last year's profit was 9% up on the
    profit two years ago. Work out the
    total profit that Arushi has made
    for the last 3 years.

## 5. Using compound interest

(a) Alison and Jocelyn each have £2500 to invest. Alison invests in an
    account which pays 2% interest in the first year and 3% interest in
    the second year. Jocelyn invests in an account which pays 2·5% p.a.
    compound interest. Who has more money after 2 years and by how
    much?

(b) Each year a population of penguins is decreasing by 2% of its value
    at the start of the year. What will the population be in 10 years time
    if it is now 12 000? Give the answer to the nearest whole number.

**6.** Sharing in a ratio

(a) Some sweets were shared between Chloe and Lewis in the ratio $7 : 2$.
Chloe got 45 more sweets than Lewis.
How many sweets did Lewis get?

(b) 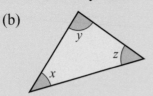 The angles $x$, $y$ and $z$ in a triangle are in the ratio $9 : 7 : 4$.

Find the sizes of angles $x$, $y$ and $z$.

(c) Write the ratio $\frac{2}{5} : \frac{3}{8}$ in the form $m : n$ where $m$ and $n$ are integers.

(d) A toad-in-the-hole is made with sausages and yorkshire pudding.
$\frac{3}{10}$ of the toad-in-the-hole is the sausages.
Write down the ratio of sausages to yorkshire pudding.

**7.** Using direct and inverse proportion

(a) $y$ is directly proportional to $x$.
$x = 2$ when $y = 7$. Find the value of $y$ when $x = 5$.

(b)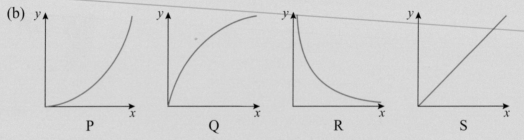

P          Q          R          S

(i) Which graph above represents inverse proportion?

(ii) Which graph above represents direct proportion?

(c) 6 machines pack 10 000 boxes in 8 hours.
How many hours and minutes would 9 machines take to pack 10 000 boxes?

(d) Which equation below represents direction proportion?

| A | $y = \dfrac{6}{x}$ | B | $y = 6x$ | C | $y^2 = 6x$ | D | $y = 6\sqrt{x}$ |

(e) Volume $V$ is inversely proportional to pressure $P$.

(i) If $V = \dfrac{k}{P}$, find the value of $k$ if $V = 4$ when $P = 15$.

(ii) Work out the value of $V$ when $P = 6$.

148

## Mixed examination questions

**1** Each day a company posts some small letters and some large letters.

The company posts all the letters by first class post.

The tables show information about the cost of sending a small letter by first class post and the cost of sending a large letter by first class post.

**Small Letter**

| Weight | First Class Post |
|--------|------------------|
| 0–100 g | 60p |

**Large Letter**

| Weight | First Class Post |
|--------|------------------|
| 0–100 g | £1·00 |
| 101–250 g | £1·50 |
| 251–500 g | £1·70 |
| 501–750 g | £2·50 |

One day the company wants to post 200 letters.

The ratio of the number of small letters to the number of large letters is 3 : 2

70% of the large letters weigh 0–100 g.

The rest of the large letters weigh 101–250 g.

Work out the total cost of posting the 200 letters by first class post.

(EDEXCEL)

**2** During a very cold winter a glacier increased in volume by 32%.

At the end of the winter its volume was found to be 6864 km$^3$.

What was its volume at the start of that winter? (CEA)

**3** Nita is making a fruit drink.
She mixes apple juice and mango juice in the ratio 3 : 1.

(a) How much of each type of juice will she need to make 1 litre of the fruit drink? Give your answer in millilitres.

(b) Apple juice costs 56p for a 1-litre carton.
Mango juice costs £1·20 for a 1-litre carton.
A pack of 80 plastic cups costs £1.

Nita sells her fruit drink at a school concert in 250 ml cups for 60p each.
She gives all the **profit** she makes to the school fund.
Nita makes 80 cups of the fruit drink and sells them all.

How much money does she give to the school fund? (OCR)

**4** Annie invests £3500 at 4% per annum compound interest. Tobias invests £3000 at 5·5% per annum compound interest. After how many years will Tobias have more money invested?

**5**

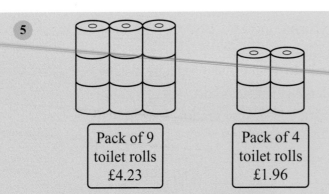

Pack of 9
toilet rolls
£4.23

Pack of 4
toilet rolls
£1.96

A pack of 9 toilet rolls costs £4·23
A pack of 4 toilet rolls costs £1·96
Which pack gives the better value for money?
You must show all your working. (EDEXCEL)

**6** The weight if a cow increases from 147 kg to 165 kg.
What is the percentage increase in the weight of the cow? (CEA)

**7** 2 workers take 15 hours to decorate a room.
How long will it take 3 workers to decorate the same room?

**8** Viv wants to invest £2000 for 2 years in the same bank.

| **The International Bank** | **The Friendly Bank** |
|---|---|
| Compound Interest | Compound Interest |
| 4% for the first year | 5% for the first year |
| 1% for each extra year | 0.5% for each extra year |

At the end of 2 years, Viv wants to have as much money as possible.
Which bank should she invest her £2000 in? (EDEXCEL)

**9**

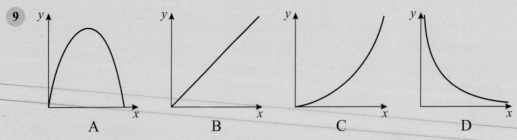

A          B          C          D

Which graph above shows that $y$ is inversely proportional to $x$?

**10** A farmer decided that he would gradually decrease the number of acres he
was using for growing wheat.
His plan was to reduce the number of acres each year by $\frac{1}{4}$ of what it was
the previous year.
He now has 450 acres for growing wheat.
How many acres did he have for growing wheat two years ago? (WJEC)

**11** The area of a shape is directly proportional to its length. The area is 28 cm² when its length is 3·5 cm.

Find the area when its length is 8·4 cm.

**12** In the top 4 football divisions, 70% of the players are under 28 years old.

25% of the under 28's play in the Premiership.

30% of the 28's or over play in the Premiership.

What percentage of the players play in the Premiership?

**13** Here is a list of ingredients for making 18 mince pies.

> **Ingredients for 18 mince pies**
> 225 g of butter
> 350 g of flour
> 100 g of sugar
> 280 g of mincement
> 1 egg

Elaine wants to make 45 mince pies.

Elaine has

> 1 kg of butter
> 1 kg of flour
> 500 g of sugar
> 600 g of mincemeat
> 6 eggs

Does Elaine have enough of each ingredient to make 45 mince pies?
You must show clearly how you got your answer.         (EDEXCEL)

**14** The speed $s$ of an object is inversely proportional to the time taken $t$.
$s = 6$ when $t = 12$.

(a) If $s = \dfrac{k}{t}$, find the value of $k$.

(b) Find $s$ when $t = 18$.

(c) Find $t$ when $s = 24$.

**15** Luke went to the USA.

He changed £650 into US dollars ($) before he left England.

Sales tax of 6% was added on to this price.

How much did Luke pay in total?         (OCR)

# WATCH YOUR MONEY

In this unit we will explore two of the taxes that most people have to pay.

## WATCH YOUR MONEY! – Income tax

Tim earns £900 each week. Before he gets his pay, he finds that £155·06 has been taken off his money already. This is *income tax*.

This does not make Tim happy but this money is used by the government to pay for things like hospitals, schools and defence.

Most people have income tax deducted from their pay *before* they receive it, by their employer, who then pays the tax to the government. This method of paying income tax is called *PAYE (Pay As You Earn)*.

**Tax allowance**
An amount of money a person may earn before paying income tax (at the time of writing this is £10 500 each year for a single person).

**Taxable income**
Taxable income = income − tax allowance
Income tax is worked out as a percentage of the taxable income.

**Percentage rate of income tax**
20% on first £32 285 of taxable income.
40% on any other taxable income.

---

If Tim earns £900 each week, that will be £46 800 in one year (assuming 52 weeks in one year).

Tax allowance = £10 500
taxable income = income − tax allowance
= 46 800 − 10 500
= £36 300

Tim pays 20% of £32 285 on first £32 285 of taxable income.

This leaves 36 300 − 32 285 = £4015 of taxable income. Tim must then pay 40% of £4015.

Income tax = 20% of £32 285 = £6457
and 40% of £4015 = £1606

Total income tax for the year = £8063 (this is £155·06 for each week if divided by 52 weeks).

---

1. Sophie earns £50 000 each year. She has a tax allowance of £10 500.
   Copy and complete the statement below to find out how much income tax
   Sophie must pay.

   Taxable income = income − tax allowance

   = 50 000 − ⬜

   = £39 500

   income tax = 20% of 32 285 = £⬜

   and 40% of ⬜ 'taxable income' − 32 285

   = 40% of ⬜ = £⬜

   total income tax = £⬜ + £⬜ = £⬜

2. Callum earns £13 400 each year. He has a tax allowance of £10 500. Copy and
   complete the statements below to find out how much income tax Callum must pay.

   Taxable income = income − tax allowance

   = ⬜ − ⬜

   = ⬜

   income tax = 20% of ⬜

   total income tax = £⬜

3. Wendy earns £28 500 each year. She has a tax allowance of £10 500.
   (a) What is Wendy's taxable income?
   (b) How much income tax will Wendy have to pay?

4. Alex earns £3950 each month. He has a tax allowance of £10 500.
   (a) What is his annual (yearly) taxable income?
   (b) How much income tax will he have to pay for one year?
   (c) How much income tax will he have to pay each month?

5. Angus earns £60 000 each year. How much income tax will he pay?
   (He has a tax allowance of £10 500).

6. Millie earns £320 each week. She has a tax allowance of £10 500.
   (a) Find her annual salary (assuming 52 weeks in one year).
   (b) What is her taxable income?
   (c) How much income tax will she have to pay for one year?
   (d) How much income tax will she have to pay each week?

7. Dom earns £90 each week. His tax allowance is £10 500. Assuming 52 weeks in
   one year, how much income tax will Dom pay each week?

8. Emma earns £896 each month from her work in a shop. She also works in a pub,
   earning £30 each week. Her tax allowance is £10 500. Assuming 52 weeks in one
   year, how much income tax will Emma pay each week?

153

This is tax collected by local authorities. It is a tax on domestic property. In general, the bigger the property is, the more tax will be charged.

Each property is put into a *valuation band*. At the time of writing the bands are as listed below (they are based on house values in 1991).

| valuation band | range of values |
| --- | --- |
| A | up to £40 000 |
| B | over £40 000 and up to £52 000 |
| C | over £52 000 and up to £68 000 |
| D | over £68 000 and up to £88 000 |
| E | over £88 000 and up to £120 000 |
| F | over £120 000 and up to £160 000 |
| G | over £160 000 and up to £320 000 |
| H | over £320 000 |

The council tax is used to pay for local services such as rubbish collection, schools and the fire service.

Council tax is not paid on some properties, for example any property that only students live in or property where all the people who live in it are aged under 18.

**Note**
If only one person lives in a property they will get a 25% discount on the council tax bill.

Jack lives on his own in a flat valued at £75 000. This year's council tax rates in his area are shown in the table below:

| band | A | B | C | D | E | F | G | H |
| --- | --- | --- | --- | --- | --- | --- | --- | --- |
| annual council tax (£) | 650 | 800 | 1000 | 1200 | 1350 | 1550 | 1900 | 2300 |

(a) How much council tax will Jack have to pay this year?

(b) If he spreads the council tax payment over 10 months, how much will he pay each month?

(a) Using the table at the start of this section, Jack's flat is in band D. The other table shows he must pay £1200 this year.
Jack lives on his own so gets a 25% discount.
25% of £1200 = £300
Jack pays £1200 − £300 = £900

(b) If the payment is spread over 10 months, each month Jack pays £900 ÷ 10 = £90

For this exercise use the council tax rates shown in the table below.

Use the table at the start of this section to find out which band each property belongs to.

| band | A | B | C | D | E | F | G | H |
|------|-----|-----|------|------|------|------|------|------|
| annual council tax (£) | 661 | 798 | 1109 | 1252 | 1420 | 1675 | 1910 | 2405 |

**1**  Harry and Erica Smith live in a house valued at £105 000.
How much council tax will they have to pay?

**2**  Simon and Shanice live in a house valued at £132 000.
   (a)  How much council tax will they have to pay?
   (b)  If the council tax payment is spread over 10 months, how much will the monthly payments be?

**3**  Molly lives on her own in a bedsit valued at £50 000. How much council tax will Molly have to pay this year?

**4**  The Jackson family live in a house valued at £210 000. If they spread their council tax payment over 10 months, what will the monthly payments be?

**5**  Jenny, David and Matt are all students. They live in a house valued at £90 000. How much council tax will they have to pay this year?

**6**  Mr. and Mrs. Pickford live in a flat valued at £102 000. They are allowed to pay their council tax in 4 equal (quarterly) payments. How much will each quarterly payment be?

**7**  Rhys lives on his own in a bungalow valued at £110 000. If he spreads his council tax payment over 10 months, what will his monthly payments be?

**8**  Find out what the council tax bill for a band D property in *your area* is this year. Do you think council tax is a fair way of collecting money for local services or not? Give reasons. Discuss with your teacher.

# ALGEBRA 2

**In this unit you will learn how to:**

- consolidate previous algebra work
- use and find the $n$th term formulas for sequences
- recognise more sequences
- change the subject of a formula
- deal with inequalities
- solve quadratic equations by factorising
- use a graph to find roots of quadratic equations
- solve simultaneous equations graphically
- solve simultaneous equations algebraically
- draw more curves from equations
- find rates of change
- find straight line equations and identify parallel lines
- ⟨USE YOUR MATHS!⟩ – the school prom

## Previous algebra work

**M7.1**

1. Complete the table below then draw $y = 2x - 1$.

| $x$ | $-2$ | $-1$ | 0 | 1 | 2 |
|-----|------|------|---|---|---|
| $y$ |      |      |   |   |   |

2. Complete the table below then draw $y = -2x$.

| $x$ | $-2$ | $-1$ | 0 | 1 | 2 |
|-----|------|------|---|---|---|
| $y$ |      |      |   |   |   |

156

**3** Write down the gradient of the line $y = 5x + 3$.

**4** Which of the graphs below shows:

(A) steady speed     (B) car that speeds up     (C) car that slows down

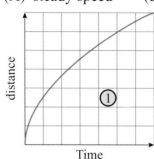 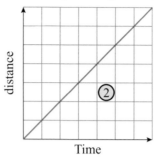 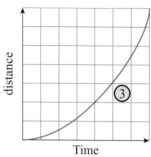

**5** Complete the table then draw $y = x^2 + 3$.

| x | −3 | −2 | −1 | 0 | 1 | 2 | 3 |
|---|---|---|---|---|---|---|---|
| y |  |  |  |  |  |  |  |

**6** Jennifer walked 18 km between 9 a.m. and 2 p.m. The graph below shows how far she had walked at various times.

 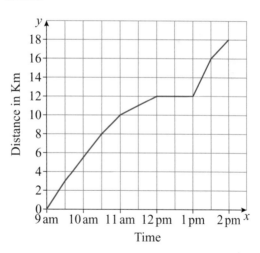

What distance had Jennifer walked by the following times?

(a) 9:30 a.m.        (b) 11:30 a.m.        (c) 1:30 p.m.

(d) 9:45 a.m.        (e) 1:15 p.m.        (f) 1:45 p.m.

(g) Between what times did Jennifer stop for a rest?

(h) During which half-hour interval did Jennifer walk the furthest?

     What distance was this?

**7** Find the gradient of each line shown opposite.

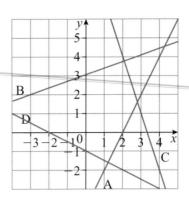

**8** Write down the co-ordinates of the point where the line $y = 3x + 2$ cuts the $y$-axis.

**9**

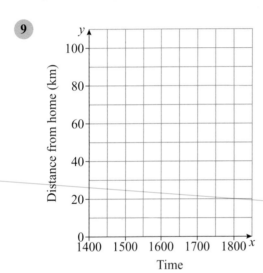

Copy the axes and draw a travel graph to show the journey below.

'At 1400 Jason leaves home and drives 60 km in 1 hour at a steady speed. He stops at a café for $\frac{1}{2}$ hour.

He travels another 40 km in $\frac{1}{2}$ hour.

He then stops for 1 hour before returning home in 1 hour at a steady speed.'

---

## 🔑 Key Facts

2, 7, 12, 17 … is an *arithmetic* sequence because the same number is added on each time.

Expand $(x + 3)(x - 5)$       Use FOIL

     multiply   First terms

$(x + 3)(x - 5)$          Outer terms

$= x^2 - 5x + 3x - 15$    Inner terms

$= x^2 - 2x - 15$       Last terms

Factorise $4n^2 - 6n$     Take out *common factor* 2n

Answer $= 2n(2n - 3)$

**1** For each *arithmetic* sequence below *only,* write down the next 2 numbers.

(a) 3, 6, 12, 24, …

(b) 1, 7, 13, 19, …

(c) 3000, 300, 30, 3, …

(d) 26, 23, 20, 17, …

(e) 1, 4, 9, 16, …

(f) 0, 3, 8, 15, …

**2** Expand

(a) $3(x + 4)$

(b) $5(x - 2)$

(c) $n(n - 3)$

(d) $n(m + 4n)$

(e) $m(3n - 2m)$

(f) $2n(4n - 1)$

(g) $3m(4n + m)$

(h) $4(2m - n + 3p)$

**3** Make $x$ the subject of each formula given below:

(a) $y = x - 6$

(b) $m = 7x$

(c) $n = 4x + 1$

(d) $y = \dfrac{x}{3}$

(e) $m = 2x - 6$

(f) $y = \dfrac{x}{4} - 3$

(g) $\dfrac{x}{6} + 5 = n$

(h) $y = 3x + 2$

**4** Toni builds a pyramid of cards. The top layer has 1 triangle, the second layer has 3 triangles and the third layer has 5 triangles.

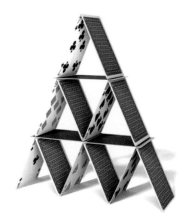

(a) She builds a larger pyramid. How many triangles does the fifth layer have?

(b) What kind of sequence do the number of cards in each layer form?

(c) Explain clearly why the number of triangles in each layer will always be odd.

**5** Factorise (take out the common factor)

(a) $n^2 + 5n$

(b) $8m - 12n$

(c) $9xy - 15xz$

(d) $x^2 - 6xy$

(e) $2x^2 + 8xy$

(f) $10n^2 - 15mn$

(g) $6ab - 18a^2$

(h) $9a^2 - 3a$

**6** 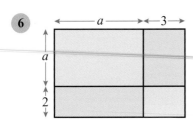 Find an expression for the area of the whole shape shown opposite. Give the answer in its simplest form.

**7** Solve

(a) $5x - 3 = 2x + 18$    (b) $4(2x + 1) = 3x + 34$    (c) $2 - 4x = x - 13$

(d) $\dfrac{2x - 1}{3} = 7$    (e) $\dfrac{3x}{2} + 7 = 13$    (f) $2 = 3(2x - 1)$

**8** Expand

(a) $(x + 5)(x + 2)$    (b) $(x + 6)(x - 3)$    (c) $(p + 4)(p - 7)$

(d) $(m - 4)(m - 5)$    (e) $(x - 8)(x + 3)$    (f) $(n - 4)^2$

## *n*th term formulas for sequences

 **Key Facts**

Each term in a sequence can be found by using a formula which gives the *n*th term.

For example: *n*th term $= n^2 + n$

$n = 1$ gives 1st term $= 1^2 + 1 = 2$

$n = 2$ gives 2nd term $= 2^2 + 2 = 6$

$n = 3$ gives 3rd term $= 3^2 + 3 = 12$

so the sequence is 2, 6, 12, …

For an arithmetic sequence (difference between successive terms is always the same number),

$$n\text{th term} = a + (n - 1)d$$ where $a$ is the first term in the sequence and $d$ is the common difference between each pair of terms.

---

32, 27, 22, 17, …        $a = 32$        $d = -5$ (note the negative sign)

*n*th term $= a + (n - 1)d = 32 + (n - 1) \times (-5)$

$n$th term $= 32 - 5n + 5 = 37 - 5n$

1. Which sequence below has the $n$th term $= n^2 + 3$?

   (a) 5, 8, 13, 20, ...　　　(b) 4, 7, 12, 19, ...　　　(c) 4, 7, 10, 13, ...

2. Which sequence below has the $n$th term $= 4n - 3$?

   (a) 1, 5, 9, 13, ...　　　(b) 3, 7, 11, 15, ...　　　(c) 16, 13, 10, 7, ...

3. For each sequence below, write down the first term and common difference then use them to find the $n$th term.

   (a) 5, 11, 17, 23, ...

   (b) 2, 9, 16, 23, ...

   (c) 36, 31, 26, 21, ...

   (d) 50, 43, 36, 29, ...

4. (a) Find the $n$th term of 6, 15, 24, 33, ...

   (b) Find the 40th term of 6, 15, 24, 33, ...

   (c) Which term of 6, 15, 24, 33, ... is equal to 582?

5. (a) Find the $n$th term of 3, 10, 17, 24, ...

   (b) Find the 71st term of 3, 10, 17, 24, ...

   (c) Which term of 3, 10, 17, 24, ... is equal to 710?

*Can you still?*

### Fractions

1. Evan manages to increase his savings by $\frac{4}{5}$ during the first year and by $\frac{1}{3}$ again during the second year. How much were his savings at the start if he has £7200 at the end?

2. Write down the largest number from below:

   $\frac{7}{11}$　　0·63　　$\frac{16}{25}$　　0·615　　$\frac{5}{7}$?

3. A shop is $\frac{7}{8}$ km from Chloe's house. Chloe has walked $\frac{3}{5}$ km from her house towards the shop. How far is she from the shop?

4. Work out $7\frac{2}{3} \div \left(-4\frac{1}{2}\right)$

6. Write down the first four terms of the sequence which has an $n$th term equal to:

   (a) $6n - 1$

   (b) $n^2 - 1$

   (c) $n^2 + 8$

   (d) $2^n$

   (e) $\dfrac{2n - 1}{2n + 1}$

   (f) $\dfrac{1}{2} n(n - 1)$

   (g) $n^2 + 2n$

   (h) $n^2 - n$

   (i) $n^2 + 3n - 2$

# Key Facts

**Quadratic sequence**

Consider $n$th term $= n^2 + n$ (this is a quadratic formula).

This gives sequence 2, 6, 12, 20, 30, ...

Look at differences:

```
          2    6    12    20    30
              ⌣    ⌣    ⌣    ⌣
1st differences =   4    6    8    10
                      ⌣    ⌣    ⌣
2nd differences =      2    2    2
```

If *all* 2nd differences are equal, the sequence is quadratic.

**Fibonacci sequence**

Consider 1, 1, 2, 3, 5, 8, ...

New terms are formed by adding previous terms.

---

## M7.4

**1** Find the next 2 numbers in each sequence below:

(a) 6, 7, 10, 15, 22, ...

(b) 4, 9, 19, 34, 54, ...

**2** Which sequences below are quadratic?

(a) 3, 5, 12, 24, 41, ...

(b) 1, 4, 10, 19, 31, ...

(c) 12, 17, 22, 27, 32, ...

(d) 2, 3, 7, 14, 24, ...

(e) 4, 12, 36, 108, 324, ...

(f) 1, 9, 25, 49, 81, ...

**3** (a)

| 3 | 7 |  |  |  |
|---|---|---|---|---|

The numbers in the two previous boxes are added to find the number in the next box (forming a Fibonacci sequence).
Copy the above and fill in the empty boxes.

(b) Copy and complete each set of boxes below.

(i)

| 3 |  | 11 |  |  |
|---|---|---|---|---|

(ii)

|  |  |  | 20 | 33 |
|---|---|---|---|---|

(iii)

|  |  | 13 | 22 |  |
|---|---|---|---|---|

(iv)

|  |  | $m$ | $n$ |  |
|---|---|---|---|---|

**4**

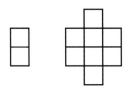 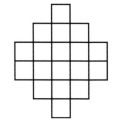

(a) Draw the next pattern in this sequence.

(b) Is the sequence formed by the number of squares 'arithmetic' or 'quadratic'?

$n = 1$      $n = 2$      $n = 3$

**5** Find the next 2 numbers in the sequence 0, 0, 1, 1, 2, 4, 7, 13, …

**6** This is Pascal's triangle.

```
            1
          1   1
        1   2   1
      1   3   3   1
    1   4   6   4   1
  1   5   10   10   5   1
1   6   15   20   15   6   1
```

(a) Look carefully at how the triangle is made. Write down the next row. It starts: 1, 7, …

(b) Work out the *sum* of the numbers in each row of Pascal's triangle. What do you notice?

(c) 1, 3, 6, 10, 15 are known as triangular numbers. Explain why.

---

 **Key Facts**

---

**Geometric progressions** – each term is obtained by multiplying the previous term by a constant number.

This constant number is called the common ratio, $r$.

4, 12, 36, 108, … Geometric progression with common ratio 3

24, 12, 6, 3, … Geometric progression with common ratio $\frac{1}{2}$

---

**M7.5**

**1** Write down the common ratio for each geometric progression below.

(a) 405, 135, 45, 15, …

(b) $\frac{1}{2}$, 2, 8, 32, …

(c) 2, −6, 18, −54, …

(d) $\frac{2}{25}$, $\frac{2}{5}$, 2, 10, …

**2** Find the 6th term in the geometric progression 3, 12, 48, …

**3** The 3rd term of a geometric progression is 18 and the 4th term is 108. Find the common ratio and the first term of the series.

**4** Which sequences below are arithmetic and which are geometric?

(a) $6, 3, 0, -3, \ldots$

(b) $\dfrac{1}{2}, 1, \dfrac{3}{2}, 2, \ldots$

(c) $18, 9, \dfrac{9}{2}, \dfrac{9}{4}, \ldots$

(d) $-0.6, -0.2, 0.2, 0.6, \ldots$

(e) $8, 24, 72, 216, \ldots$

(f) $100, -50, 25, -25/2$

**5** On each day from Monday to Friday, Ken likes to spend time sitting inside a bottle. The time spent each day increases by 10% on the day before. The daily times therefore form a geometric progression. Ken spends 2 hours inside the bottle on Monday. Work out, to the nearest minute, the total amount of time spent in the bottle from Monday to Friday.

**6** The 4th term of a geometric progression is 49. The 5th term is 245. Find the common ratio.

**7** The first two terms of a geometric progression are 2 and 12.

Find   (a)   the 3rd term

        (b)   the 6th term

**8** The expression $n^2 + n - 12$ can be used to generate a sequence of numbers. Work out the difference between the 4th term and the 1st term of this sequence.

**9** The 7th term of a geometric progression is 72 and the 8th term is 216. Work out the value of the 6th term.

**10** The $n$th term of a sequence is $n^2 + 3n$. Is 28 a number in the sequence? *Explain* your answer fully.

> *Can you still?*
>
> **Ratio and proportion**
>
> **1** Express $\dfrac{3}{7} : \dfrac{2}{9}$ as a ratio using whole numbers only.
>
> **2** Half of Joe's money is pound coins and one third of Marie's money is pound coins. What fraction of all their money is pound coins?
>
> **3** The voltage V is directly proportional to the resistance R. V = 6 when R = 4. Find the value of V when R = 13.
>
> **4** Simplify the ratio $50\,\text{g} : 2\,\text{kg} : 0.4\,\text{kg}$.

## Changing the subject of a formula

$c(x - d) = y$          Make $c$ the subject of the formula

$c(x - d) = y$          *multiply out the bracket first*

$\boxed{cx} \;\; \boxed{-cd} = \boxed{y}$     add $cd$ onto *both* sides of the equation

$\boxed{cx} \;\; \boxed{-cd} + cd = \boxed{y} + cd$

$cx = y + cd$      divide *both* sides of the equation by $c$

$\dfrac{\cancel{c}x}{\cancel{c}} = \dfrac{y + cd}{c}$     the $c$ cancels down

$x = \dfrac{y + cd}{c}$

### M7.6

**1** Copy and fill each box below:

(a) $y = ax - b$

$\quad y + \boxed{\phantom{x}} = ax - b + \boxed{\phantom{x}}$

$\quad y + \boxed{\phantom{x}} = ax$

$\quad \dfrac{y + \boxed{\phantom{x}}}{\boxed{\phantom{x}}} = x$

(b) $v = at + u$

$\quad v - \boxed{\phantom{x}} = at + u - \boxed{\phantom{x}}$

$\quad v - \boxed{\phantom{x}} = at$

$\quad \dfrac{v - \boxed{\phantom{x}}}{\boxed{\phantom{x}}} = t$

**2** Make $x$ the subject of each formula given below:

(a) $y = px + q$        (b) $y = cx - h$        (c) $y = rx - 2p$

(d) $q = cx + 3s$      (e) $bx + 5c = 2f$     (f) $y = ax + b - c$

**3** Copy and fill each box below:

(a) $y = \dfrac{fx - g}{h}$

$\quad \boxed{\phantom{x}} = fx - g$

$\quad \boxed{\phantom{x}} + g = fx - g + g$

$\quad \boxed{\phantom{x}} + g = fx$

$\quad \dfrac{\boxed{\phantom{x}} + g}{\boxed{\phantom{x}}} = x$

(b) $\dfrac{px + 2h}{c} = y$

$\quad px + 2h = \boxed{\phantom{x}}$

$\quad px + 2h - 2h = \boxed{\phantom{x}} - \boxed{\phantom{x}}$

$\quad px = \boxed{\phantom{x}} - \boxed{\phantom{x}}$

$\quad x = \dfrac{\boxed{\phantom{x}} - \boxed{\phantom{x}}}{\boxed{\phantom{x}}}$

**4** Make $x$ the subject of each formula given below:

(a) $c(x + d) = y$      (b) $m(x - n) = q$      (c) $r(x + 5) = y$

(d) $a(x + 7) = 3b$      (e) $y = f(x - g)$      (f) $4b = s(x - t)$

**5** Make $x$ the subject of each formula given below:

(a) $\dfrac{ax + d}{4} = e$      (b) $\dfrac{bx + 3c}{y} = p$      (c) $\dfrac{ax - r}{5} = q$

(d) $y = \dfrac{cx - 2d}{7}$      (e) $y = \dfrac{ax - 3c}{b}$      (f) $\dfrac{px + qr}{8} = y$

**6** $h = 3g + m$    Make $g$ the subject of the formula.

**7** $v = u + fy$    Make $y$ the subject of the formula.

**8** Make $x$ the subject of the formula $y = \dfrac{cx - 3}{a}$

---

**Powers**

(a) Make $w$ the subject of the formula $w^2 = a + 6$

$w^2 = a + 6$    [square root both sides of the equation]

$w = \sqrt{(a + 6)}$

(b) Make $x$ the subject of the formula $\sqrt[3]{(x - b)} = c$

$\sqrt[3]{(x - b)} = c$    [cube both sides of the equation to remove the cube root]

$x - b = c^3$    [add $b$ onto both sides of the equation]

$x = c^3 + b$

---

**E7.1**

**1** Copy and complete:

(a) $x^2 - w = z$

$x^2 = z + \boxed{\phantom{x}}$

$x = \sqrt{\left(z + \boxed{\phantom{x}}\right)}$

(b) $3c = p - m^3$

$\boxed{\phantom{x}} + m^3 = p$

$m^3 = p - \boxed{\phantom{x}}$

$m = \sqrt[3]{\left(p - \boxed{\phantom{x}}\right)}$

(c) $m\sqrt{y} = 4n$

$\sqrt{y} = \dfrac{4n}{\boxed{\phantom{x}}}$

$y = \left(\dfrac{4n}{\boxed{\phantom{x}}}\right)^2$

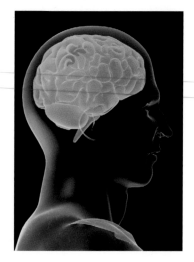

166

**2** Make $x$ the subject of each formula given below:

(a) $x^2 + 7 = b$        (b) $z = x^2 - t$

(c) $q + x^2 = 4p$      (d) $x^3 - a = c$

(e) $r = qx^3$          (f) $bx^2 = n$

(g) $\dfrac{x^2}{b} = c$        (h) $\sqrt{x} = m - n$

(i) $p + 2q = \sqrt[3]{x}$

**3** Make $n$ the subject of each formula given below:

(a) $\sqrt{(n - r)} = p$

(b) $\sqrt{(n + 2r)} = 3q$

(c) $b = \sqrt[3]{(n + 5c)}$

(d) $(n + t)^2 = w$

(e) $w = \sqrt{(y - n)}$

(f) $s = \dfrac{1}{2} an^2$

(g) $\dfrac{\sqrt{n}}{5} + c = d$

(h) $w = \dfrac{1}{4} mn^3$

**4** Make $w$ the subject of each formula given below:

(a) $\dfrac{m}{w} = q$

(b) $c = \dfrac{n}{w}$

(c) $3a = \dfrac{2m}{w}$

(d) $\dfrac{x}{w} - z = m$

(e) $q = \dfrac{r}{w} + 5n$

(f) $3r = q - \dfrac{t}{w}$

**5** Make $v$ the subject of the formula $\sqrt{(v^2 + n)} = m$

**Transformations**

**1**

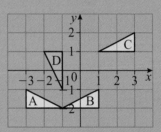

Describe each transformation which sends

(a) $\triangle A \to \triangle B$     (b) $\triangle B \to \triangle C$

(c) $\triangle C \to \triangle D$

**2**

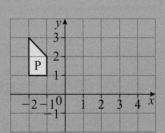

(a) Copy the grid and shape above.

(b) Enlarge shape P by scale factor $\dfrac{1}{2}$ about $(3, 0)$.

(c) Rotate shape P 90° clockwise about $(0, -1)$.

**Required subject appears more than once**

Collect all the terms containing the required subject on the same side of the equation and all the other terms on the other side of the equation.

The required subject usually has to be extracted as a *common factor* before it is finally isolated.

---

(a)  Make $m$ the subject of the formula $km + n = p - qm$

$km + n = p - qm$    [add $qm$ onto both sides of the equation and subtract $n$ from both sides of the equation]

$km + qm = p - n$    [take out $m$ as a common factor]

$m(k + q) = p - n$    [divide both sides of the equation by $(k + q)$]

$m = \dfrac{p - n}{k + q}$

(b)  Make $x$ the subject of the formula $\dfrac{mx - ny}{fx} = k$

$\dfrac{mx - ny}{fx} = k$    [multiply both sides of the equation by $fx$]

$mx - ny = kfx$    [subtract $kfx$ from both sides of the equation and add $ny$ onto both sides of the equation]

$mx - kfx = ny$    [take out $x$ as a common factor]

$x(m - kf) = ny$    [divide both sides of the equation by $(m - kf)$]

$x = \dfrac{ny}{m - kf}$

---

**E7.2**

**1**  Continue the working to make $t$ the subject of the formula.

$vt = p - mt$

$vt + mt = p$

$t(v + m) = p$

$t = \ldots$

**2**  Continue the working to make $m$ the subject of the formula.

$4m + 6y = x + am$

$4m - am = x - 6y$

$m(\ldots\ldots) = \ldots\ldots$

**3** Make $x$ the subject of each formula given below:

(a) $fx + g = dx + e$               (b) $xy - wx = wz + y$

(c) $ax - b = 3c - bx$          (d) $m(x - y) = n(x + z)$

(e) $c(d - x) = b + fx$          (f) $y^2x = 3z - wx$

**4** Will tries to make $x$ the subject of the formula as shown below:

$$m + cx = n - ax$$

$$cx + ax = n - m$$

$$x + x = \frac{n - m}{ca}$$

$$2x = \frac{n - m}{ca}$$

$$x = \frac{n - m}{2ca}$$

(a) Which line down does Will make his mistake?

(b) Rearrange the formula yourself to make $x$ the subject.

**5** Make $m$ the subject of the formula $P = \dfrac{m + n}{mn}$

**6** Make $a$ the subject of the formula $Y = \dfrac{b - a}{ab}$

**7** Make $x$ the subject of the formula $px - q + qx = r(q - x)$

**8** Make $x$ the subject of each formula given below:

(a) $z = \dfrac{yx - 4}{x}$        (b) $3mx = 5 + x$

(c) $\dfrac{ax + b}{cx} = m$        (d) $t + sx = p(x - r)$

(e) $\dfrac{f - x}{g + x} = m$        (f) $a(x + m) = cx$

(g) $n(x - y) = abx$        (h) $mn = \dfrac{ax - b}{x}$

**9** Mia tries below to make $x$ the subject of the formula.

$$abx = mx + c$$

$$abx - mx = c$$

$$x = \frac{c}{abm}$$      Explain clearly what Mia has done incorrectly.

# Inequalities

Show on a number line the range of values of $x$ for the inequalities shown.

(a)      $x > 2$

     ↑

'$x$ is greater than 2'

The circle at the left hand end of the range is open. This means $x$ *cannot* equal 2.

(b)      $x \leqslant -1$

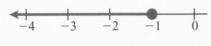

     ↑

'$x$ is less than or equal to $-1$'

The circle at $-1$ is filled in. This means $x$ *can* equal $-1$.

(c)   $-2 \leqslant x < 1$

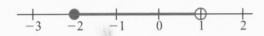

$x$ is greater than $-2$ and *can equal* $-2$.

$x$ is also less than 1 and *cannot equal* 1.

## M7.7

**1**   Write down the inequalities shown below:

(a)     (b)   (c)

(d)   (e)   (f)

(g)   (h)   (i)

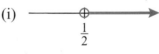

(j)   (k)   (l)

**2**   Draw a number line to show the following inequalities.

(a) $x \geqslant 3$          (b) $x < 6$          (c) $x \leqslant -3$

(d) $3 < x < 8$     (e) $-6 < x \leqslant 2$     (f) $n > -1$

(g) $-7 \leqslant n < -3$   (h) $2 \leqslant t \leqslant 4$     (i) $-2 < p \leqslant 0$

170

**3** If $\boxed{\phantom{x}} < 120$, write a possible number for $\boxed{\phantom{x}}$

**4** If $\boxed{\phantom{x}} > 50$, write a possible number for $\boxed{\phantom{x}}$

**5** Write a possible number for $\boxed{\phantom{x}}$ in each of the following:

(a) $\boxed{\phantom{x}} > 820$      (b) $\boxed{\phantom{x}} < 175$      (c) $300 < \boxed{\phantom{x}}$

(d) $1100 < \boxed{\phantom{x}}$      (e) $185 < \boxed{\phantom{x}}$      (f) $\boxed{\phantom{x}} < 362$

**6** Write a possible number for $\boxed{\phantom{x}}$ in each of the following:

(a) $150 < \boxed{\phantom{x}} < 250$    (b) $730 < \boxed{\phantom{x}} < 750$    (c) $1241 < \boxed{\phantom{x}} < 1243$

(d) $428 < \boxed{\phantom{x}} < 430$    (e) $-6 < \boxed{\phantom{x}} < 0$    (f) $-8 < \boxed{\phantom{x}} < -4$

**7** Copy and fill each box below with $<$ or $>$

(a) $17 \boxed{\phantom{x}} 13$     (b) $228 \boxed{\phantom{x}} 241$     (c) $7{\cdot}5 \boxed{\phantom{x}} 7{\cdot}05$     (d) $-6 \boxed{\phantom{x}} -5$

**8** Answer true or false:

(a) $-4 > 3$      (b) $3{\cdot}6 < 3{\cdot}17$      (c) $5{\cdot}23 > 5{\cdot}1$      (d) $6\frac{1}{4} < 6{\cdot}5$

---

Solve the inequalities:

(a) $x + 6 > 14$     (b) $x - 3 \leqslant 6$     (c) $4x < 320$     (d) $\frac{x}{7} \geqslant -3$

       $x > 8$            $x \leqslant 9$         $x < \dfrac{320}{4}$       $x \geqslant -3 \times 7$

                                                $x < 80$          $x \geqslant -21$

---

### M7.8

**1** Copy and fill in the boxes below:

(a) $x - 5 > 3$      (b) $\dfrac{x}{4} \leqslant 9$      (c) $2x + 4 < 10$

    $x > 3 + \boxed{\phantom{x}}$       $x \leqslant 9 \times \boxed{\phantom{x}}$       $2x < 10 - \boxed{\phantom{x}}$

    $x > \boxed{\phantom{x}}$            $x \leqslant \boxed{\phantom{x}}$             $2x < \boxed{\phantom{x}}$

                                            $x < \boxed{\phantom{x}}$

Solve the inequalities in questions **2** to **13**.

**2** $x + 8 < 15$      **3** $x - 2 \geqslant 9$      **4** $n - 8 < 1$

**5** $n + 6 \geqslant -2$      **6** $a - 7 > -2$      **7** $b - 6 \geqslant -4$

**8** $5 + x \leqslant 17$      **9** $4n \leqslant 20$      **10** $6y > 42$

**11** $\dfrac{b}{3} \geqslant 8$      **12** $\dfrac{x}{5} < -9$      **13** $3x \geqslant -12$

Find the range of values of $x$ which satisfy each inequality in questions **14** to **19** and show each answer on a number line.

**14** $5x \leqslant 30$

**15** $9x > -27$

**16** $2 + x \geqslant 6$

**17** $\dfrac{x}{2} \geqslant 1$

**18** $x + 3 < 0$

**19** $\dfrac{x}{4} \leqslant -2$

In questions **20** to **25** write down all the *integer* values (*whole numbers*) of $x$ which satisfy the given inequalities.

**20** $0 < x < 4$

**21** $2 \leqslant x \leqslant 4$

**22** $1 \leqslant x < 7$

**23** $-2 \leqslant x \leqslant 2$

**24** $-4 < x \leqslant 0$

**25** $-5 \leqslant x < 4$

**26** Write down the smallest integer $x$ for which $2x > 5$.

**27** Write down the largest integer $x$ for which $10x < 56$.

Solve the inequalities in questions **28** to **39**.

**28** $2x + 7 > 19$

**29** $3x - 1 \leqslant 14$

**30** $6n - 5 \geqslant 43$

**31** $4b + 12 \leqslant 28$

**32** $3 + 7x > -4$

**33** $4n - 8 < 0$

**34** $3(a - 2) < 15$

**35** $4(x + 3) \leqslant 20$

**36** $\dfrac{a}{6} - 4 \geqslant 2$

**37** $5x + 3 \geqslant 2x + 21$

**38** $8n - 2 > 3n + 33$

**39** $6x + 8 < 38 - 4x$

**40** In each case below find all the *integer* values of $x$ which satisfy both the inequalities.

(a) $x - 3 < 4$ and $x + 2 \geqslant 6$

(b) $x + 5 > 3$ and $3x - 2 < 1$

**41**

The perimeter of this rectangle has a maximum possible value of 92 cm. Find the range of possible values for $x$.

$2x$

$3x + 1$

**42** In each case below, find the range of values of $x$ which satisfy both the inequalities and show this answer on a number line.

(a) $4x + 3 \leqslant 11$ and $5x + 1 \geqslant -9$

(b) $2(x + 3) > 14$ and $3x - 14 \leqslant 4$

(c) $5x - 3 > 3x + 9$ and $\dfrac{x + 2}{3} < 4$

172

# Key Facts

Solve $x^2 - 3x - 18 = 0$

Factorise by taking out a common factor, using the difference of 2 squares or factorising into 2 brackets.

$(x - 6)(x + 3) = 0$

Consider the equation $A \times B = 0$.
The only way $A \times B$ can equal 0
is if $A = 0$ or $B = 0$ or both $A$ and $B = 0$

Consider $(x - 6) \times (x + 3) = 0$

$x - 6 = 0$    or    $x + 3 = 0$

$x = 6$    or    $x = -3$

---

Solve the following equations:

(a) $x^2 - 7x + 12 = 0$
$(x - 3)(x - 4) = 0$
$x - 3 = 0$ or $x - 4 = 0$
$x = 3$ or $x = 4$

(b) $2y^2 = 4y$
$2y^2 - 4y = 0$
$2y(y - 2) = 0$
$2y = 0$ or $y - 2 = 0$
$y = 0$ or $y = 2$

(c) $n^2 - 10n + 25 = 0$
$(n - 5)(n - 5) = 0$
$n - 5 = 0$ or $n - 5 = 0$
$n = 5$ or $n = 5$
so $n = 5$ only

---

**M7.9**

Copy and complete:

**1**   $x^2 + 9x + 20 = 0$
$(x + 5)(x + \boxed{\phantom{0}}) = 0$
$x + 5 = 0$ or $x + \boxed{\phantom{0}}$
$x = \boxed{\phantom{0}}$

**2**   $m^2 - 6 = 5m$
$m^2 - \boxed{5m} - 6 = 0$
$\ldots = 0$
$\ldots + \boxed{1} = 0$

**3**   $r^2 - 6r = 0$
$r(\boxed{r} - \boxed{6}) = 0$
$r = 0$ or $\boxed{r} - \boxed{6} = 0$
$r = 0$ or $r = \boxed{\phantom{0}}$

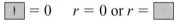

Solve the

**4**   $x^2 +$

**6**   $n^2 + 8$

**8**   $p^2 - 6$

**10**   $m^2 - 1$

**12**   $n^2 - n$

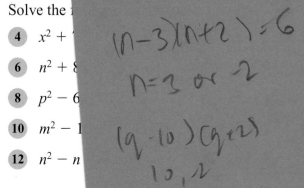

$(n - 3)(n + 2) = 6$

$n = 3 \text{ or } 2$

$(q - 10)(q + 2)$

$10, 2$

Solve these equations:

**1** $x^2 - x - 20 = 0$ **2** $(n + 9)(n - 1) = 0$ **3** $(p - 3)(p - 8) = 0$

**4** $(a - 8)(a + 7) = 0$ **5** $y^2 + 2y = 0$ **6** $w^2 - 3w = 0$

**7** $(b - 2)(b + 10) = 0$ **8** $z^2 + 2z + 1 = 0$ **9** $k^2 + k = 0$

Rearrange then solve these equations:

**10** $x^2 - 3x = -2$ **11** $a^2 + 30 = 11a$ **12** $n^2 + 6n = 7$

**13** $r^2 = 2r$ **14** $c^2 + 15c = -36$ **15** $z^2 - 12 = 4z$

**16** $h(h - 4) + 1 = 6$ **17** $t(t - 4) - 14 = t$ **18** $x^2 = x$

**19** The width of a rectangle is $x$ cm.
The length of the rectangle is 5 cm
more than its width.

(a) Write down an expression for the
length of the rectangle in terms
of $x$.
(b) Write down an expression for
the area of the rectangle in terms
of $x$.
(c) If the area of the rectangle is
36 cm², write down a quadratic
equation involving $x$.
(d) Solve this equation to find $x$.

**20** (a) A triangle of area 30 cm² is such
that its height is 4 cm greater than
its base. If its base is $x$ cm then
show that $x^2 + 4x - 60 = 0$.
(b) Solve this equation to find the
base of the triangle.

*Can you still?* **Percentages**

**1** Firm A employs 756 people which
is 8% more than last year. Firm
B employs 720 people which is a
20% increase on last year. How
many more people did Firm A
employ than Firm B last year?

**2** Lucy invests £6000 at 6% per
annum compound interest. In
which year will she first have
more than £10 000?

**3** Jackson buys 60 books at £3 each.
He sells 35 of these at £8 each and
the remainder at £4 each. What
percentage profit does he make
(give the answer to the nearest
whole number).

# Key Facts

Solve   $x^2 - 3x + 2 = 0$

$(x - 1)(x - 2) = 0$

$x - 1 = 0$ or $x - 2 = 0$

$x = 1$ or $x = 2$

These answers are known as the *roots* of the equation.

These can be found graphically by drawing $y = x^2 - 3x + 2$ then looking where $y = 0$ which is where the curve meets the $x$-axis, ie. $x = 1$ and $x = 2$

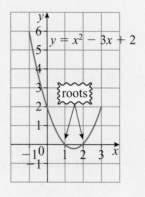

## M7.10

**1**

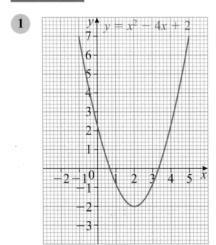

Use this graph to find the roots of

$$x^2 - 4x + 2 = 0$$

Give your answers to one decimal place.

**2**  (a)  Copy and complete the table below for $y = x^2 + x$

| $x$ | −2 | −1 | 0 | 1 | 2 |
|-----|----|----|---|---|---|
| $y$ |    |    |   |   |   |

(b)  Draw the graph of $y = x^2 + x$

(c)  Use the graph to find the roots of $y = x^2 + x$

175

**3**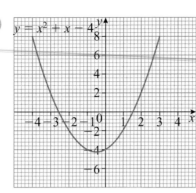

$y = x^2 + x - 4$

Use this graph to find the roots of

$$x^2 + x - 4 = 0$$

Give your answers to one decimal place.

**4** (a) Copy and complete the table below for $y = x^2 - 5$

| $x$ | $-3$ | $-2$ | $-1$ | $0$ | $1$ | $2$ | $3$ |
|-----|------|------|------|-----|-----|-----|-----|
| $y$ |      |      |      |     |     |     |     |

(b) Draw the graph of $y = x^2 - 5$

(c) Use the graph to find the roots of $x^2 - 5 = 0$.
Give the roots to one decimal place.

**5** (a) Copy and complete the table below for $y = x^2 + 4x + 3$

| $x$ | $-6$ | $-5$ | $-4$ | $-3$ | $-2$ | $-1$ | $0$ | $1$ | $2$ |
|-----|------|------|------|------|------|------|-----|-----|-----|
| $y$ |      |      |      |      |      |      |     | $8$ |     |

(b) Draw the graph of $y = x^2 + 4x + 3$

(c) Use the graph to find the roots of $x^2 + 4x + 3 = 0$

## 'Cover-up' method for drawing straight lines

Draw $2x + 3y = 6$

use $\boxed{x = 0}$   so $2x = 0$   'Cover up' $2x$ in the equation.

$2x + 3y = 6$ becomes $\boxed{\ }\, + 3y = 6$ so $\boxed{y = 2}$

use $\boxed{y = 0}$   so $3y = 0$   'Cover up' $3y$ in the equation.

$2x + 3y = 0$ becomes $2x + \boxed{\ } = 6$ so $\boxed{x = 3}$

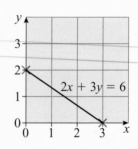

**Always use $x = 0$ then $y = 0$**

Plot the points $x = 0$, $y = 2$ and $x = 3$, $y = 0$ on the graph and join them up to get your straight line.

**1** (a) Draw these axes.

(b) If $x + 2y = 4$, find the value of $y$ when $x = 0$.

(c) If $x + 2y = 4$, find the value of $x$ when $y = 0$.

(d) Plot 2 points from (b) and (c) and join them up to make the straight line $x + 2y = 4$.

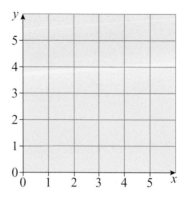

**2** (a) Draw the same axes as in question **1**.

(b) Use $x = 0$ then $y = 0$ to find 2 points for $3x + y = 3$.

(c) Draw the straight line $3x + y = 3$.

**3** Draw each line below with the 'cover-up' method. You need to find the 2 points first then draw the axes big enough.

(a) $5x + 3y = 15$     (b) $2x + 5y = 10$     (c) $9x + y = 18$

(d) $3x + 4y = 12$     (e) $6x + 5y = 30$     (f) $2x + 7y = 28$

## Simultaneous equations on a graph

Solve the simultaneous equations:

$3x + y = 6$     $x + y = 4$

(a) Draw the line $3x + y = 6$

when $x = 0$, $y = 6$

when $y = 0$, $3x = 6$, so $x = 2$

(b) Draw the line $x + y = 4$

when $x = 0$, $y = 4$

when $y = 0$, $x = 4$

(c) The lines intersect at $(1, 3)$

The solutions of these simultaneous equations are $x = 1$, $y = 3$

This is the only pair of values of $x$ and $y$ which satisfy both equations at the same time (*simultaneously*)

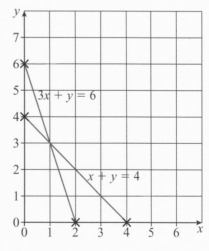

**1** Use the graph to solve the simultaneous equations:

$$x + y = 7$$
$$2x - y = -1$$

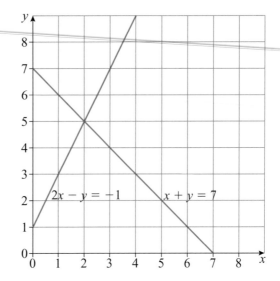

**2** Use the graph to solve the simultaneous equations:

(a) $2x + y = 8$
  $x + y = 5$

(b) $x - y = -5$
  $x + y = 5$

(c) $2x + y = 8$
  $x - y = -5$

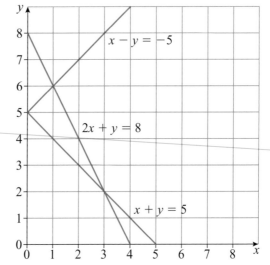

**3** (a) Draw $x$ and $y$ axes from 0 to 9.

(b) Use the cover-up method to draw the line $3x + 4y = 24$.

(c) Use the cover-up method to draw the line $3x + 2y = 18$.

(d) Write down the solutions of the simultaneous equations $3x + 4y = 24$
$$3x + 2y = 18$$

**4** (a) Draw $x$ and $y$ axes from 0 to 6.

(b) Draw the lines $x + y = 6$ and $y = x + 3$.

(c) Solve the simultaneous equations $x + y = 6$
$$y = x + 3$$

**5** (a) Draw $x$ and $y$ axes from 0 to 5.

(b) Solve graphically the simultaneous equations $x + y = 5$
$$y = x + 2$$

**6** (a) Draw $x$ and $y$ axes from 0 to 13.

(b) Solve graphically the simultaneous equations $x + 2y = 11$
$$2x + y = 13$$

**7** Use the graph to solve the simultaneous equations:

(a) $x + y = 11$
$x + 3y = 13$

(b) $2x - y = -2$
$x + y = 11$

(c) $x + 3y = 13$
$2x - y = -2$

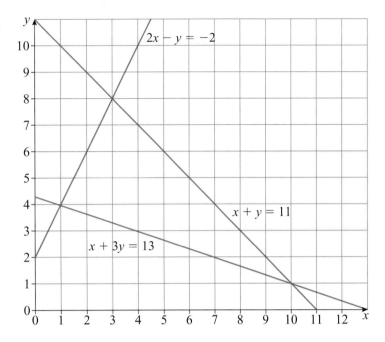

---

# Using algebra to solve simultaneous equations

Solve the simultaneous equations

$5x + y = 17$ ... (1)

$3x + y = 11$ ... (2)

> Label the equations (1) and (2) and use these to explain the working out

(1) − (2)

$$5x + y - (3x + y) = 17 - 11$$

$$5x + y - 3x - y = 6$$

$$2x = 6$$

$$x = 3$$

> Subtracting equation (2) from equation (1) *eliminates* the $y$ terms

Substitute $x = 3$ in (1)

$$(5 \times 3) + y = 17$$

$$15 + y = 17$$

$$y = 2$$

Check in (2)

$$3x + y = (3 \times 3) + 2 = 11 \checkmark$$

> The solution $x = 3$, $y = 2$ works in equation (2) so is likely to be correct

Solution: $x = 3$, $y = 2$.

> **Note**
> If the signs in front of the letter to be eliminated are the same we subtract but if the signs are different we add

Solve the simultaneous equations:

**1**   $4x + y = 13$
         $2x + y = 7$

**2**   $7x + 3y = 26$
         $3x + 3y = 18$

**3**   $2x + 4y = 18$
         $2x + 2y = 8$

In questions **4** to **6**, add the equations to eliminate the $y$ terms.

**4**   $5x - y = 17$
         $2x + y = 11$

**5**   $8x + 3y = 19$
         $3x - 3y = 3$

**6**   $7x - 4y = 22$
         $4x + 4y = 0$

Solve the simultaneous equations:

**7**   $3x + 2y = 24$
         $x + 2y = 12$

**8**   $2x + 6y = 14$
         $2x - 2y = -2$

**9**   $7x - 2y = 31$
         $5x - 2y = 21$

**10**  $5x - y = -16$
         $3x - y = -10$

**11**  $3x - 4y = 20$
         $6x - 4y = 32$

**12**  $4x - 3y = -3$
         $4x + 5y = -27$

**Can you still?**

**Angles**

**1**

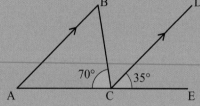

Find the values of AB̂C.

**2**

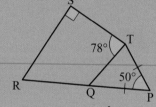

Find the value of QR̂S.

**3**

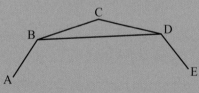

ABCDE is part of a regular polygon with 12 sides. Calculate BĈD.

**4**

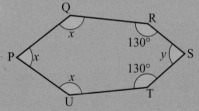

Express $y$ in terms of $x$.

Solve   $2x + 5y = -2$   ... (1)
         $3x - 4y = 20$   ... (2)

> Multiply both equations to get the same number of $x$'s in both equations

(1) × 3 and (2) × 2

   $6x + 15y = -6$   ... (3)
   $6x - 8y = 40$    ... (4)

(3)–(4)

   $6x + 15y - (6x - 8y) = -6 - 40$
   $6x + 15y - 6x + 8y = -46$
   $23y = -46$
   $y = -2$

Substitute $y = -2$ in (2)

   $3x - (4 \times -2) = 20$
   $3x + 8 = 20$ so $x = 4$

Multiply one equation first to solve each of the simultaneous equations below.

1. $5a + 3b = 13$
$7a + 6b = 20$

2. $4c + 5d = 17$
$8c + 3d = 27$

3. $9x + 2y = 31$
$3x + y = 11$

4. $11p + 2q = 63$
$6p + 4q = 46$

5. $3u + 2v = 10$
$7u - v = 29$

6. $11p + 3q = 71$
$5p - q = 37$

7. $9a + 2b = 41$
$5a - 4b = 33$

8. $5m + 3n = 27$
$m = 7 - n$

9. $2p + 7q = 3$
$p = q + 6$

Multiply both equations first to solve each of the simultaneous equations below:

10. $5g + 3h = 27$
$4g + 5h = 32$

11. $9m + 7n = 43$
$5m + 2n = 22$

12. $8b + 3c = 46$
$5b + 2c = 29$

13. $6x + 5y = 13$
$7x + 2y = 19$

14. $8r + 5s = 41$
$9r + 11s = 30$

15. $7p - 3q = 15$
$5p + 2q = 19$

16. $13b - 7c = 47$
$7b - 9c = 41$

17. $6x - 5y = -32$
$5x + 4y = 6$

18. $9m - 2n = -23$
$5m - 9n = 3$

$r + v = 6$
$v = 3 \quad r = ?$

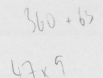

**Mixed problems involving simultaneous equation**

Brendan buys 3 'fries' and 2 hamburgers for £6·75.
for £10·55. Find the cost of one portion of 'fries' an

Let the cost of one portion of 'fries' be $x$ pence.

Let the cost of one hamburger be $y$ pence.

{ Form two equations }

$3x + 2y = 675$ ... (1)
$5x + 3y = 1055$ ... (2)

**Note:** All the money is now written in pence so that the units are the same throughout each equation.

{ Solve the simultaneous equations } ➡ $x = 85,\ y = 210$

One portion of 'fries' costs 85p and one hamburger costs £2·10 (these answers can be checked in the original paragraph of information).

181

Answer these questions by forming a pair of simultaneous equations then solving them.

**1** Ted buys three ties and two shirts which cost him £132. Keanan buys four ties and three shirts for £190. Find the cost of a tie and the cost of a shirt.

**2** A shop sells 'Gello' pens and 'Inko' pens. A 'Gello' pen costs £5 and an 'Inko' pen costs £7. One day the shop sold 17 pens and received £109. How many of each type of pen were sold?

**3** Nasser buys 3 first class tickets and 5 second class tickets for a plane journey. These cost him £1264.

Mary buys 7 first class tickets and 3 second class tickets for the same journey. These cost her £1827.

Find the cost of one first class ticket and one second class ticket.

**4** A man had £1·75 in his pocket made up of 2p and 5p coins. If he had 50 coins in his pocket then find the number of 2p coins he had.

**5** Three times one number plus the other number adds up to 45. The difference between the two numbers is 7. Find the values of the two numbers.

**6** Two sheets of metal need to be cut into 12 larger rectangles and 4 smaller rectangles.

One sheet is 3 m long and is cut into 8 larger rectangles and one smaller rectangle.

The second sheet is 2 m long and is cut into 4 larger rectangles and 3 smaller rectangles.

Calculate the width of one of the larger rectangles.

**7** Sinead buys 4 tickets in stand A and 5 tickets in stand B for a football match which cost her £144. Terri buys 6 tickets in stand A and 7 tickets in stand B and these cost her £207. Find the cost of one stand A ticket and one stand B ticket.

**8** The heights of the logos on two T-shirts are in the ratio 7 : 5. Both shirts shrink in the wash. The height of the larger logo reduces by 3 cm and the smaller one decreases by 2 cm. The heights are now in the ratio 5 : 4. Find the original height of each logo.

*Can you still?*

**Algebra**

**1** Simplify $m^3 + m^3$

**2** Factorise $6n^2 - 4mn$

**3** Expand and simplify $5(2a + 3) - 3(3a - 2)$

**4** Expand $(x + 2)^2$

**5** Simplify $(n^4)^2 \times n^3$

**6** Factorise $x^2 - 6x + 8$

**7** Solve $3(4x - 1) = 2x + 4$

---

## Drawing more curves from equations

# 🔑 Key Facts

Quadratic functions give these curves.

   × shows the *turning points*

*Intercepts* – where the curve meets the *x*-axis or the *y*-axis.

---

**M7.15**

**1** (a) Copy and complete the table then draw the curve $y = x^2 - 4$

| $x$ | −3 | −2 | −1 | 0 | 1 | 2 | 3 |
|---|---|---|---|---|---|---|---|
| $y$ | | | | | | | |

(b) Write down the co-ordinates of the *y*-intercept.

(c) Write down the co-ordinates of the turning point.

2. (a) Complete the table opposite then draw the curve $y = x^2 + x$.

| $x$ | $-3$ | $-2$ | $-1$ | $0$ | $1$ | $2$ | $3$ |
|---|---|---|---|---|---|---|---|
| $x^2$ | | | $1$ | | | | $9$ |
| $+x$ | | | $-1$ | | | | $3$ |
| $y$ | | | $0$ | | | | $12$ |

(b) Write down the co-ordinates of the intercepts with the $x$-axis.

(c) Write down the co-ordinates of the turning point.

3. (a) Using $x$-values from $-4$ to $2$, complete a table then draw $y = x^2 + 3x - 2$.

(b) Read off the value of $y$ from your curve when $x = -1\cdot5$

(c) Write down the co-ordinates of the turning point.

(d) Write down the co-ordinates of the $y$-intercept.

(e) Write down the $x$-values of the intercepts with the $x$-axis (the roots of $x^2 + 3x - 2 = 0$).

*Can you still?* **Number Work**

*Do not use a calculator.*

1 Evaluate $2^{-3}$

2 Work out $(3 \times 10^{-8}) \times (4 \times 10^{20})$, giving the answer in standard form.

3 Work out $\dfrac{\sqrt[3]{(9^2 - 4^2 - 1^2)}}{\sqrt{(5^2 - 3^2)}}$

4 Find the LCM of 825 and 1155.

5 Work out $(6 \times 10^{18}) - (5 \times 10^{17})$, giving the answer in standard form.

## Graphs of cubics and reciprocals

 **Key Facts**

A *cubic* equation has an $x^3$ term as the highest power of $x$, for example: $y = x^3 + 5x^2 + 3x + 2$    $y = x^3 + x$

A *reciprocal* equation has the $x$ term in the denominator of a fraction,

for example: $y = \dfrac{7}{x}$    $y = \dfrac{3}{x - 2}$

**Note**

$\dfrac{4}{0} = 4 \div 0$ gives *no value*. You *cannot* divide by 0. If you use '0' in the denominator, the graph will have a 'break' in it (see example on next page).

Draw the graph of $y = \dfrac{4}{x}$ for $x$-values from $-5$ to $5$.

Complete a table. Some $y$-values will have to be rounded off.

| $x$ | $-5$ | $-4$ | $-3$ | $-2$ | $-1$ | 0 | 1 | 2 | 3 | 4 | 5 |
|-----|------|------|------|------|------|---|---|---|---|---|---|
| $y$ | $-0{\cdot}8$ | $-1$ | $-1{\cdot}3$ | $-2$ | $-4$ | no value | 4 | 2 | $1{\cdot}3$ | 1 | $0{\cdot}8$ |

What happens between
$x = -1$ and $x = 1$?

Work out more $y$-values

| $x$ | $-0{\cdot}8$ | $-0{\cdot}6$ | $-0{\cdot}4$ | $0{\cdot}4$ | $0{\cdot}6$ | $0{\cdot}8$ |
|-----|------|------|------|-----|-----|-----|
| $y$ | $-5$ | $-6{\cdot}7$ | $-10$ | 10 | $6{\cdot}7$ | 5 |

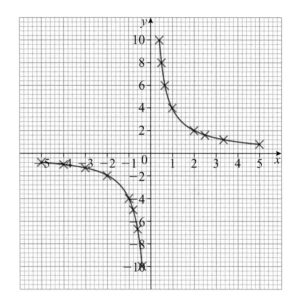

There is no value for $y$ when $x = 0$.
As $x$ gets nearer to 0, the curve
approaches the $y$-axis but never
touches it.

As $x$ gets very large or very small,
the curve approaches the $x$-axis but
never touches it.

---

**E7.5**

*Check all your graphs with a computer or graphical calculator if your teacher
wants you to.*

**1**  Complete the table below then draw $y = x^3$.

| $x$ | $-3$ | $-2$ | $-1$ | 0 | 1 | 2 | 3 |
|-----|------|------|------|---|---|---|---|
| $y$ | $-27$ | | | | | | |

> Remember to draw a
> smooth curve

**2**  (a)  Complete the table below then draw $y = x^3 + x + 1$.

| $x$ | $-3$ | $-2$ | $-1$ | 0 | 1 | 2 | 3 |
|------|------|------|------|---|---|---|---|
| $x^3$ | | $-8$ | | | | | |
| $+x$ | | $-2$ | | | | | |
| $+1$ | | 1 | | | | | |
| $y$ | | $-9$ | | | | | |

(b)  Read off the value of $y$ from your curve when $x = 1{\cdot}5$

**3** Using $x$-values from $-3$ to $3$ draw:

   (a) $y = x^3 + 1$                           (b) $y = x^3 + x$

   (c) $y = x^3 + 3x - 4$               (d) $y = x^3 + x^2 + 1$

   (e) For each graph in parts (a) to (d), write down the co-ordinates of the turning points where they exist.

   (f) For each graph in parts (a) to (d), write down the co-ordinates of the $y$-intercepts.

   (g) Describe the general shape of all the curves you have drawn in questions **1** to **3**. All cubic curves ($x^3$ term is the highest power) have this shape.

**4** (a) Complete the table below then draw $y = \dfrac{1}{x}$

| $x$ | $-5$ | $-4$ | $-3$ | $-2$ | $-1$ | 0 | 1 | 2 | 3 | 4 | 5 |
|---|---|---|---|---|---|---|---|---|---|---|---|
| $y$ | | | | | | no value | | | | | |

   (b) Read off the $y$-value when $x = 2 \cdot 5$

**5** (a) Using $x$-values from $-10$ to $10$, complete a table then draw $y = \dfrac{8}{x}$

   (b) Read off the $x$-value when $y = 6 \cdot 4$

**6** Draw the graph of:

   (a) $y = \dfrac{4}{x - 2}$ using $x$-values from $-3$ to $7$        (b) $y = \dfrac{10}{x + 5}$ using $x$-values from $-10$ to $0$

   (c) $y = \dfrac{5}{x} + 2$ using $x$-values from $-10$ to $10$       (d) $y = \dfrac{10}{x^2}$ using $x$-values from $-5$ to $5$

   (e) $y = \dfrac{5}{(x + 2)^2}$ using $x$-values from $-7$ to $3$

**7** Match each equation to its graph opposite. One of the equations does not have a graph shown.

   (a) $y = x^2 - 4$

   (b) $y = \dfrac{1}{x^2}$

   (c) $y = x^3 - 2x^2 - 3x + 2$

   (d) $y = \dfrac{3}{x}$

   (e) $y = 6 - 2x$

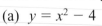
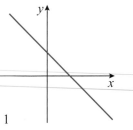
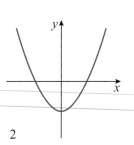
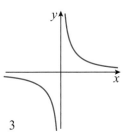
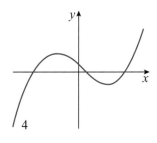

**8** Based on your earlier graphs, *sketch* the graph of any equation of the form $y = \frac{a}{x}$ where $a$ is a positive constant (fixed number).

**9** For each curve below, write down if it is linear, quadratic, cubic or reciprocal.

(a)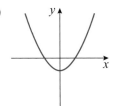

(b)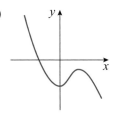

(c)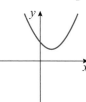

(d)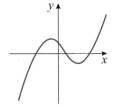

(e)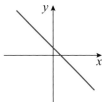

(f)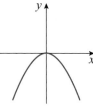

(g)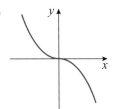

(h)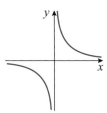

(i)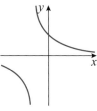

(j)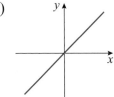

(k)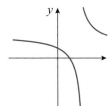

(l)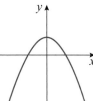

## Rates of change

  **Key Facts**

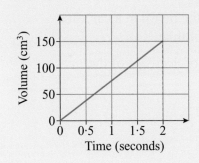

The graph shows the volume of water as it is poured into a glass.

$$\text{gradient} = \frac{\text{vertical distance}}{\text{horizontal distance}}$$

$$= \frac{150}{2} = 75$$

This means the *rate of change* of the volume of water is 75 cm³/second.

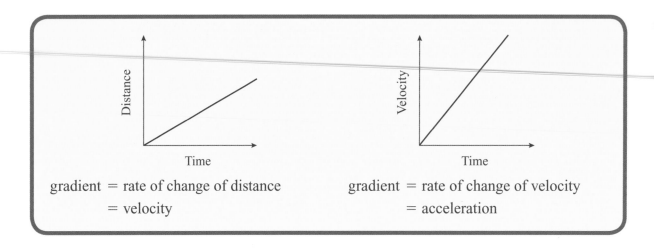

gradient = rate of change of distance
= velocity

gradient = rate of change of velocity
= acceleration

**1**

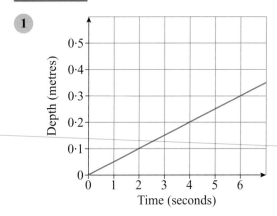

Time (seconds)

A tank is being filled with oil.

The depth of the oil in the tank is shown in the graph opposite.

Work out the rate of change of the depth of oil in metres per second.

**2** (a) The table below shows how far a person has jogged at a steady speed. Draw a graph of the distance travelled against the time taken.

| time (seconds) | 0 | 60 | 120 | 180 | 240 |
|---|---|---|---|---|---|
| distance (metres) | 0 | 150 | 300 | 450 | 600 |

(b) Work out the speed of the person in metres per second.

**3**

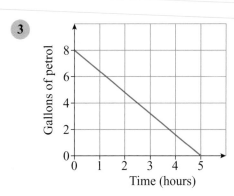

Time (hours)

The graph shows the petrol in a car after a certain amount of time.

Work out the rate of decrease of the petrol.

188

**4**

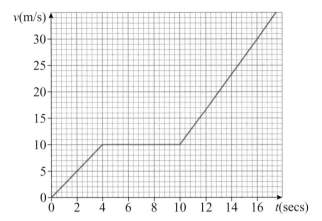

This velocity–time graph shows the motion of a particle. Find:

(a)  the acceleration between $t = 0$ and $t = 4$.

(b)  the acceleration between $t = 10$ and $t = 16$.

(c)  the acceleration between $t = 4$ and $t = 10$.

**5**  $s$ is the distance (in km) from Maria's house. Maria cycles such that $s = 14t$ where $t$ is the time (in hours).

(a)  Draw a graph of $s$ against $t$ for $t$-values from 0 to 4.

(b)  Work out Maria's speed.

**6**

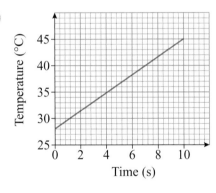

A substance is heated up.
Its change of temperature is shown opposite.

Work out the rate of change in the temperature.

**7**

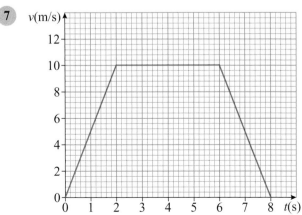

This velocity–time graph shows the motion of a particle. Find:

(a)  the acceleration between $t = 0$ and $t = 2$.

(b)  the deceleration between $t = 6$ and $t = 8$.

# Key Facts

**Reminder:** the equation of a straight line may be written in the form

$$y = mx + c$$

where   $m$ is the gradient of the line

and   $c$ is the $y$-intercept (where the line cuts the $y$-axis)

(a)  Write down the gradient and $y$-intercept of $y = \frac{1}{2}x - 3$

Gradient $= \frac{1}{2}$   $y$-intercept $= -3$

(b)  Write down the gradient of $2x + 3y = 1$ and write down the co-ordinates of the point where the line cuts the $y$-axis.

> rearrange into form $y = mx + c$   $2x + 3y = 1$

$$3y = -2x + 1$$

> write the $x$'s first

$$y = -\frac{2}{3}x + \frac{1}{3}$$

Gradient $= -\frac{2}{3}$ and the line cuts the $y$-axis at $\left(0, \frac{1}{3}\right)$

(c)  Find the equation of the line which passes through $(3, 1)$ and $(6, 13)$.

> Find gradient $m$ first   $m = \dfrac{13 - 1}{6 - 3} = \dfrac{12}{3} = 4$

We know $y = mx + c$   so   $y = 4x + c$

> To find $c$, substitute one pair of $x$ and $y$ values into the equation of the line

$x = 3$ when $y = 1$

so   $1 = 4 \times 3 + c$

$1 = 12 + c$

$c = -11$

equation of line is $y = 4x - 11$

Write down the gradient and $y$-intercept of each line in questions **1** to **12**.

**1** $y = 6x - 3$

**2** $y = \frac{1}{2}x + 4$

**3** $y = 7 + 4x$

**4** $y - 5x = 1$

**5** $y + 4x = 5$

**6** $6x - y = 3$

**7** $2x + 5y = 3$

**8** $3x - 4y = 6$

**9** $5x - 3y = 3$

**10** $4y - 2 = 5x$

**11** $4x + y - 6 = 0$

**12** $5x - 7y - 2 = 0$

**13** Consider $y = 3x + 1$
The line cuts the $y$-axis at $(0, 1)$.
The gradient is 3 so the line goes
up 3 units for every 1 unit across.
Use the above to sketch the line.

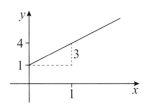

Use your knowledge of
$y = mx + c$ to sketch each
of the following lines:
(a) $y = 2x + 2$
(b) $y = 4x - 3$
(c) $y = -x + 4$
(d) $y = 3 - 2x$
(e) $y - 2x = 1$

**14** Which of the following lines are
parallel?
(a) $y = 4x + 1$
(b) $y = 2 - 4x$
(c) $y = 2x + 4$
(d) $y - 4x = 2$
(e) $4x - y = 2$
(f) $y = 4 - 3x$

**15** Prove that $2x - 6y = 1$ is parallel to $y = \frac{1}{3}x + 2$.

*Can you still?*

**Vectors**

**1** If $\mathbf{m} = \begin{pmatrix} 4 \\ -2 \end{pmatrix}$ and $\mathbf{n} = \begin{pmatrix} 1 \\ 5 \end{pmatrix}$, find as a
column vector:
(a) $3\mathbf{m}$    (b) $2\mathbf{m} + \mathbf{n}$
(c) $3\mathbf{n} - 2\mathbf{m}$

**2**

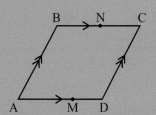

ABCD is a parallelogram. N is the
midpoint of BC.
$AM : MD = 2 : 1$
If $\overrightarrow{AB} = \mathbf{p}$ and $\overrightarrow{BC} = \mathbf{q}$, express each
vector below in terms of $\mathbf{p}$ and $\mathbf{q}$.
(a) $\overrightarrow{BN}$    (b) $\overrightarrow{AN}$    (c) $\overrightarrow{MD}$
(d) $\overrightarrow{MC}$    (e) $\overrightarrow{BM}$    (f) $\overrightarrow{MN}$

**3** Work out the length of vector $\begin{pmatrix} 3 \\ -4 \end{pmatrix}$.

Find the equation of each line in questions **1** to **4**.

**1**   The line passes through (0, 4) with gradient = 5.

**2**   The line passes through (0, 2) with gradient = −4.

**3**   The line passes through (3, 5) with gradient = 3.

**4**   The line passes through (5, −1) with gradient = 1.

Find the equation of the line passing through each pair of points below, giving the answer in the form $y = mx + c$.

**5**   (3, 2) and (5, 8)       **6**   (6, 1) and (8, 9)       **7**   (−3, 4) and (−1, 10)

**8**   (5, −3) and (8, −9)   **9**   (−2, −4) and (−5, −25)   **10**   (1, −7) and (−3, 5)

**11**   Find the equation of the line that is parallel to the line $y = 4x - 3$ and passes through (3, 2).

**12**   Find the equation of each line below:

(a)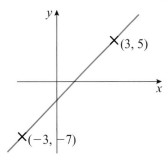

(b)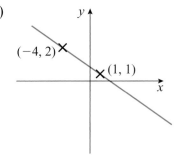

**13**   $y = 0$ for all points which lie on the x-axis. Find the co-ordinates of the point where the line $y = 4x - 8$ crosses the x-axis.

**14**   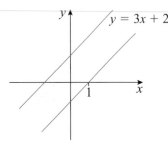   Find the equation of the line which is parallel to $y = 3x + 2$ and crosses the x-axis at (1, 0).

**15**   Find the equation of the line that is parallel to the line $2x + y = 1$ and passes through (1, −4).

192

# USE YOUR MATHS! – The school prom

Most schools now have a prom for students towards the end of year 11. People usually dress up smartly and glamorously.

The prom often takes place at hired places but sometimes at the school. Some students choose to arrive at the prom in style – for example by limousine or horse-drawn carriage.

**Do task A or task B then do task C.**

### Task A

Terry has £80 to spend on the school prom. He has plenty of friends with similar amounts of money. Use all the prices on this page and the next page to decide on what Terry should spend. Show all your calculations clearly.

### Task B

Repeat task A for Annie who has £350 to spend on the school prom.

### Task C

Now price up what you would do for a school prom. Show all your calculations clearly.

| Hire of limos – rate per hour |
|---|
| • White American Stretch Lincoln (8 people) – £138 |
| • White Hummer (16 people) – £360 |
| • Pink Ford Expedition Limo (14 people) – £315 |
| • Black Hummer H2 Leer Jet Door (16 people) – £380 |

Horse-drawn carriage

- 10 seater wagonette – £520 for the whole evening.
- 4 seater landau – £280 for the whole evening.

prom ticket
£21 per person

193

| Hire Cost of dinner suits | Suit | Outfit (includes shirt and bow tie) | Outfit plus shoes or waistcoat | Outfit plus shoes and waistcoat |
|---|---|---|---|---|
| Single Breasted Black | £41 | £46 | £52 | £57 |
| Single Breasted White | £58 | £63 | £69 | £74 |
| Student Deal (Black Only) | £63 for two | £69·50 for two | £79 for two | £86·50 for two |
| Accidental Damage Waiver £4·75 per suit or outfit | | | | |

If you pay the Accidental Damage Waiver, you will not have to pay anything if your suit or outfit is accidently damaged.

| Prom dresses | all shown dress prices reduced by 15% |
|---|---|
| Short Taffeta Dress (red, orange, pink, turquoise) | £71·60 |
| 50s Style Strapless Short Dress (peacock blue) | £122·40 |
| Polka Dot Silver Cocktail Dress | £135·40 |
| Long 2-tone Taffeta Sheath Dress (emerald, lime) | £205 |
| Long Organza Strapless Dress (gold) | £290·20 |
| Long Black Ball Gown with Tulle Skirt and Embroidered Bodice | £332·80 |

**Shoes**

Diamante Stiletto Sandals (silver, gold) – £40

Satin pumps (red, pink, pale blue, black, grey, silver, gold ) – £29·36

Black Stiletto Court Shoes – £55

**Evening Bags**

Red Beaded Evening Bag – £12·67

Gold Leather and Chainmail Bag – £40

Sequinned and Embroidered Black Clutch Bag – £29·95

3 cm height Diamante Tiara £29·35
Viscose Shimmer Shawl £12·50
(grey, blue, red, orange, emerald)
Black Velvet Evening Wrap £40·95

**Hair Salon**

Cut (girls) £28
Cut (boys) £22
Highlighting £80

Home Hair Extensions

23 inch clip in £37·99
10 inch clip in £32·75

| Beauty Treatment (10% off shown prices) | |
|---|---|
| • 40 minute teen facial | £20 |
| • special occasion make-up | £30 |
| • one hour pedicure | £22 |
| • eyebrow shape | £5·40 |
| • spray tan | £27 |
| • manicure-file and polish (French polish £2 extra) | £7·50 |
| • self tanning lotion | £13 |
| • nail art – £1·50 per nail | |

# TEST YOURSELF ON UNIT 7

**1. Consolidating previous algebra work**

Make $n$ the subject of each formula given below:

(a) $m = \dfrac{n}{4}$  (b) $m = 2n - 3$  (c) $y = 6n$  (d) $y = \dfrac{n}{3} - 4$

(e) Complete the table then draw $y = 3x - 2$.

| $x$ | $-2$ | $-1$ | 0 | 1 | 2 |
|---|---|---|---|---|---|
| $y$ | | | | | |

(f) Expand $4n(n + 3)$

(g) Expand $(n + 6)(n - 8)$

(h) Here is a sequence of shapes made from sticks. Let $n$ = shape number and $s$ = number of sticks.

| $n = 1$ | $n = 2$ | $n = 3$ |
|---|---|---|
| $s = 6$ | $s = 11$ | $s = 16$ |

  (i)   Draw the next shape in the sequence.
  (ii)  Find the formula for the number of sticks (s) for the shape number $n$.
  (iii) Use the formula to find out how many sticks are in shape number 100.

(i) 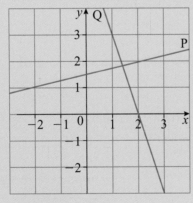  Find the gradients of lines P and Q.

**2. Using and finding $n$th term formulas for sequences**

(a) Write down the first 4 terms of the sequence with $n$th term $= n^2 + 3n$

(b) Find the $n$th term for the sequence 7, 15, 23, 31, …

(c) Find the $n$th term for the sequence 32, 29, 26, 23, …

**3. Recognising more sequences**

Find the next 2 numbers in each sequence below:

(a) 6, 9, 14, 21, ...    (b) 0, 1, 1, 2, 3, ...    (c) 288, 144, 72, 36,...

(d) Which sequence below is geometric?

(i) 19, 13, 7, 1, ...    (ii) 2, −6, 18, −54, ...    (iii) −1, 2, 7, 14, ...

(e) What name is given to each of the other sequences in part (d)?

**4. Changing the subject of a formula**

Make $x$ the subject of each formula given below:

(a) $y = mx + c$    (b) $\dfrac{wx - m}{y} = c$    (c) $2p = m(x - w)$

(d) $x^2 - p = w$    (e) $mx^3 = n$    (f) $m = \sqrt[3]{(x - a)}$

(g) $mx = nx + p$    (h) $ax - n = m - bx$    (i) $y = \dfrac{x + y}{x}$

**5. Dealing with inequalities**

Write down the inequalities shown below:

(a)

4

(b)
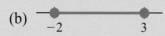

−2        3

(c)

−5        −1

Draw a number line to show the following inequalities:

(d) $x < -2$    (e) $4 < x < 7$    (f) $-6 \leqslant x < 1$

Solve the inequalities below:

(g) $x + 3 \geqslant 7$    (h) $x - 4 > 8$    (i) $5x \leqslant 35$

(j) $\dfrac{x}{9} \geqslant 6$    (k) $3x + 5 < 29$    (l) $2(x - 3) > 14$

(m) Write down all the integer values (whole numbers) of $x$ which satisfy the inequalities

$-4 \leqslant x < 2$  and  $-2 < x < 4$

196

**6.** Solving quadratic equations by factorising

Solve these equations

(a) $x^2 + 7x + 10 = 0$

(b) $x^2 - 3x - 40 = 0$

(c) $(x + 6)(x - 4) = 0$

(d) $x^2 - 6x = 0$

(e) $x^2 - 10x + 25 = 0$

(f) $x^2 - 12 = 4x$

**7.** Using a graph to find roots of quadratic equations

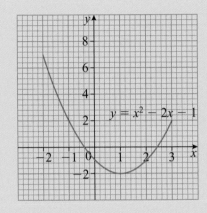

Use the graph opposite to find the roots of $x^2 - 2x - 1 = 0$

**8.** Solving simultaneous equations graphically

(a) Use the graph to solve the simultaneous equations

$$2y - x = 4$$
$$x + y = 5$$

(b) Draw $x$ and $y$ axes from 0 to 6.

Solve graphically the simultaneous equations   $3x + y = 6$
$$x + y = 4$$

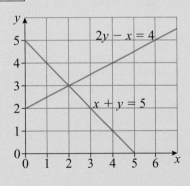

**9.** Solving simultaneous equations algebraically

Solve the simultaneous equations

(a) $3x - 2y = 8$
$x - 2y = 0$

(b) $2a + 3b = 15$
$5a - 2b = -29$

(c) $3m - 4n = 13$
$7m + 2n = 36$

197

**10.** Drawing more curves from equations

    (a)  Complete a table then draw $y = x^3 - 5x + 4$ using $x$-values from $-3$ to $3$.

    (b)  Complete the table below then draw $y = \dfrac{40}{x}$.

| $x$ | $-5$ | $-4$ | $-3$ | $-2$ | $-1$ | 0 | 1 | 2 | 3 | 4 | 5 |
|---|---|---|---|---|---|---|---|---|---|---|---|
| $y$ | | | | | | no value | | | | | |

    (c)  Which of these graphs is  (i) $y = x^3$   (ii) $y = \dfrac{1}{x}$?

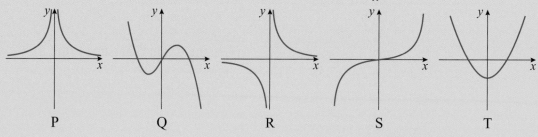

        P            Q            R            S            T

**11.** Finding rates of change

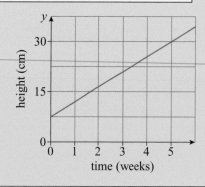

The graph shows the height of a plant over a five week period.

Work out the rate of change of the height of the plant (in cm per week).

**12.** Finding straight line equations

    Write down the gradient and $y$-intercept of each of the following lines:

    (a)  $y = 2x - 6$       (b)  $y = -x - 8$      (c)  $3x + 5y = 8$

    (d)  Write down the equation of this straight line.

    (e)  Find the equation of the straight line which passes through $(2, 4)$ and $(5, 19)$.

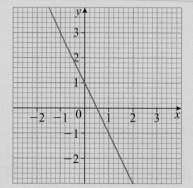

## Mixed examination questions

**1** Make $b$ the subject of the following formula

$$bc = bd + e$$

(WJEC)

**2**

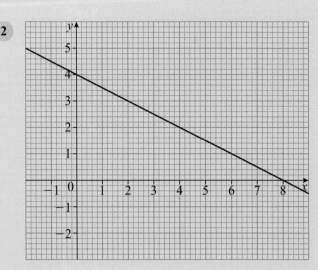

The graph of the straight line $x + 2y = 8$ is shown on the grid.

(a) Copy the grid and draw the graph of $y = \dfrac{x}{2} - 1$

(b) Use the graphs to find estimates for the solution of

$$x + 2y = 8$$
$$y = \frac{x}{2} - 1$$

(EDEXCEL)

**3** Solve the inequality $-2 < 3n \leq 12$ where $n$ is an integer.
List all values of $n$. (CEA)

**4** Solve the following simultaneous equations using an algebraic method.

$$3x + 2y = 27$$
$$2x - 5y = 37$$

(WJEC)

**5** Solve $x^2 - 8x + 12 = 0$

**6** Rearrange $2(a + c) = 5(a - b)$ to make $c$ the subject. (AQA)

**7** Find the equation of the line which passes through $(6, 2)$ and is parallel to the line joining $(1, 4)$ to $(4, -5)$.

**8** The first five terms of a sequence are 9, 13, 17, 21, 25.
Find an expression, in terms of $n$, for the $n$th term of this sequence. (CEA)

**9** The graph of $y = -2x^2 + 5x + 25$ for values of $x$ from $-3$ to 6 is shown below.

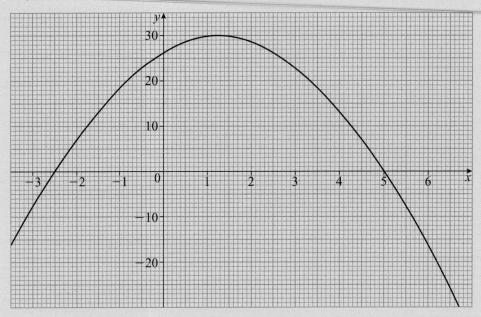

Use the graph to solve $-2x^2 + 5x + 25 = 0$           (WJEC)

**10** (a) Solve the inequality $3x - 5 \geqslant 16$

   (b) The values $-1$, 0, 1, 2 and 3 satisfy **one** of the inequalities below. Write down the correct inequality.

$$-2 < 2y \leqslant 6 \qquad -2 \leqslant 2y \leqslant 6 \qquad -2 \leqslant 2y < 6 \qquad \text{(AQA)}$$

**11** Dan leaves home at 0800. He drives 60 miles from home in the first 90 minutes. He stops for 30 minutes. He then drives home at an average speed of 50 mph.

   (a) Draw a distance–time graph to show Dan's journey.

   (b) A TV programme starts at 1130. Does Dan get home in time for the start? Show how you decide.

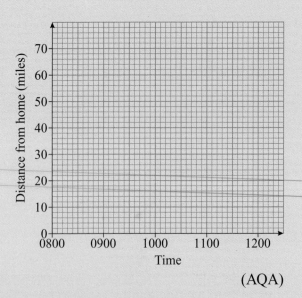

(AQA)

# STATISTICS 1

# 8

**In this unit you will learn how to:**

– consolidate previous probability work

– use Venn diagrams and set notation

– deal with independent events – the 'AND' rule

– use the 'OR' rule

– use probability trees

– USE YOUR MATHS! – buying a house

## Previous probability work

### M8.1

**1** The probability of Hatton Rovers winnng, drawing or losing a football match is shown below.

| Result | win | draw | lose |
|---|---|---|---|
| Probability | 0·65 | 0·15 | |

(a) What is the probability of Hatton Rovers losing a match?

(b) Hatton Rovers play 40 matches during the season. How many matches should they win?

**2** In an Animal Rescue Centre there are 3 Basset hounds, 2 bulldogs and 3 alsatians. Hannah randomly chooses one of these dogs. What is the probability that she chooses

(a) A bulldog?

(b) a bulldog or an alsatian?

**3** There are 6 red socks and 4 blue socks in a bag. There are also some black socks. The probability of randomly taking a black sock is $\frac{2}{3}$.
How many black socks are in the bag?

**4** A bag contains a number of £1 coins, dated 1998 or 2004.
Xanthe takes a coin from the bag at random, notes it then replaces it.
She repeats this 10, 20, 30, 40, 50, 100 and 200 times.
The results are shown in the table below.

| Number of coins | 10 | 20 | 30 | 40 | 50 | 100 | 200 |
|---|---|---|---|---|---|---|---|
| Number of 1998 coins | 5 | 8 | 15 | 22 | 31 | 60 | 122 |

(a) Draw a graph to show the relative frequency of picking out a 1998 coin.

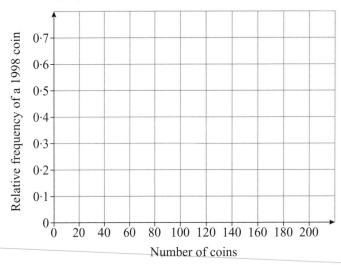

(b) The bag contans 800 coins. Estimate how many 1998 coins are in the bag?

**5** Tom has 3 shirts and 2 pairs of trousers. He must wear a shirt and a pair of trousers. How many ways can he combine a shirt and a pair of trousers? (For example: shirt 2, trousers 1, etc.)

**6** The probability of seeing a panda first at the zoo is $0.2$. The probability of seeing a tiger first is $0.15$. What is the probability of seeing a different animal first (i.e. not a panda or tiger)?

**7** Two spinners are used. The first spinner has numbers from 1 to 4 and the second spinner has numbers from 1 to 6.
The numbers given by each spinner are added together. Work out the probability that the total will be:

(a) 4        (b) greater than 7      (c) a square number.

**1** A bag contains 6 blue beads, 4 green beads and 1 white bead. A bead is taken at random from the bag.

(a) What is the probability that the bead is blue?

(b) What is the probability that the bead is red?

(c) 4 green beads are added to the bag. How many extra blue beads must be added so that the probability of pulling out a blue bead is $\frac{1}{2}$?

**2** 80 people are asked about their hobbies. The information is shown in the Venn diagram below.

$\mathcal{E} = \{$people who were asked$\}$

$A = \{$people who do art$\}$

$M = \{$people who play music$\}$

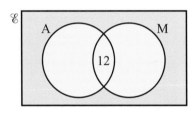

27 people play music.
29 people do not do art or play music.

If one person is chosen at random then find

(a) the probability that the person does art.

(b) the probability that the person does not do art.

**3**

```
├──────────────────────────┼──────────────────────────┤
0                         0·5                          1
```

(a) Draw a probability scale as shown above.

(b) A bag contains 5 balls. Two of the balls are red and the remainder are yellow. Find the probability of removing a red ball if one ball is taken from the bag and mark this on your probability scale.

**4** (a) How many different outcomes are there when three coins are thrown?

(b) Find the probability of obtaining 2 heads and one tail when 3 coins are thrown.

**5** The table shows whether certain people can do a headstand.

|        | Yes | No |
|--------|-----|----|
| Male   | 26  | 14 |
| Female | 33  | 27 |

(a) One person is chosen at random. What is the probability that the person can do a headstand?

(b) One female is chosen at random. What is the probability that she cannot do a headstand?

(c) 'More females can do a headstand than males'. Does the information above suggest this is true. Explain your answer fully.

**6** The hair colour of some children was observed. The probabilities of having some hair colours is shown in the table below.

| Colour      | brown | blond | other |
|-------------|-------|-------|-------|
| Probability |       | 0·35  | 0·2   |

(a) What is the probability of having brown hair?

(b) In a group of 80 children, how many children should have a hair colour other than brown or blond?

**7**

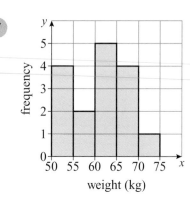

frequency vs weight (kg)

The weights of some people are shown in the chart.
If one person is chosen at random, what is the probability that the person weighs between 60 kg and 70 kg?

Can you still?

**Rearranging formulas**

Make $x$ the subject of each formula below.

① $m(x - p) = y$

② $\dfrac{cx + h}{a} = y$

③ $x^3 - m = a$

④ $v = \dfrac{1}{3}mx^2$

⑤ $ay = mx + nx$

⑥ $wx = py - ax$

⑦ $n(x + p) = m(a - x)$

204

**8** A bag contains 13 beads. $x$ beads are yellow.

(a) How many beads are not yellow?

(b) If one bead is removed, what is the probability that it is yellow?

(c) If one bead is removed, what is the probability that it is not yellow?

**9** During a period of 90 days, Mark travels to work by car one third of the time and cycles to work on the other days.
When Mark travels by car, he is late 10% of the time.
When he cycles, he is late 5% of the time.

(a) Copy and complete the frequency tree.

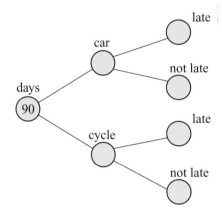

(b) Overall, what is the probability that Mark was late?

(c) Of the times that Mark was late, what proportion was he cycling?

**10** All the kings are removed from a pack of cards.
If one card is now removed at random from
the remaining cards, what is the probability
of getting a:

(a) Queen

(b) black card

(c) an odd number?

**11** One ball is selected from a bag containing $m$ white balls and $n$ green balls.
What is the probability of selecting a white ball?

**12** A bag contains 10 discs. $x$ discs are red and the remaining discs are blue.
$y$ white discs are added to the bag.

(a) How many discs are there in total?

(b) How many discs are blue?

(c) If one disc is removed, what is the probability that it is blue?

# Key Facts

A set is a collection of items, often written inside curly brackets, eg. A = {2, 4, 6, 8}
Each member of a set is called an element.
The number of elements in set A is written as $n(A)$.
If A = {2, 4, 6, 8} then $n\{A\} = 4$

6 'is a member of' A is written as $6 \in A$

The set of all items in a situation is called the Universal set $\mathcal{E}$.

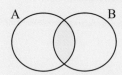
A ∩ B means A 'intersection' B
(elements in both A and B)

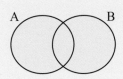
A ∪ B means A 'union' B
(all the elements in both A and B)

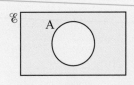
A′ is the 'complement' of A
(everything not in A so A ∪ A′ = $\mathcal{E}$)

∅ or { } is the 'empty set'

A = {$x : x$ is an integer, $-2 \leqslant x < 4$} means A = {$-2, -1, 0, 1, 2, 3$}
ie. A is the set of all elements $x$ such that $x$ is an integer and $-2 \leqslant x < 4$
(: means 'such that')

If all the elements of B are contained in A
then B is a 'subset' of A, written B ⊂ A

A ∩ B = {6, 8}
A ∪ B = {2, 3, 5, 6, 8, 9, 11}
$n(A \cap B) = 2$
B′ = {2, 3, 7, 12, 20}
A′ ∩ B = {5, 9, 11}

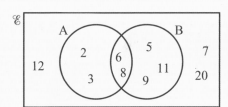

**1**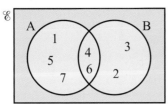

Find

(a) $A \cup B$     (b) $A'$     (c) $A \cap B$

(d) $B'$     (e) $n(A)$     (f) $B' \cap A$

(g) $A \cup B'$     (h) $(A \cap B)'$     (i) $A' \cup B'$

**2** $X = \{1, 2, 3, 4, 5, 6\}$ and $Y = \{1, 3, 5, 7, 9, 11\}$

Find

(a) $X \cap Y$     (b) $n(X \cup Y)$     (c) $Y'$     (d) $n(X \cap Y)$

**3** $P = \{2, 3, 5, 7, 11\}$, $Q = \{3, 5, 7, 9, 11\}$ and $R = \{5, 6, 7, 8, 9\}$

Find

(a) $P \cap R$     (b) $Q \cup R$     (c) $n(P \cap Q)$     (d) $Q \cap R$

(e) $(P \cup Q) \cap R$     (f) $(P \cap Q) \cup R$

**4** $\mathscr{E} = \{$rugby, ice skating, ice hockey, polo, cricket, ice dancing$\}$

$A = \{$sports played on grass$\}$

$B = \{$team sports$\}$

Which of the statements below are true?

(a) $n(B) = 4$     (b) $A \subset B$

(c) rugby $\in A'$     (d) $n(A \cap B) = 3$

**5**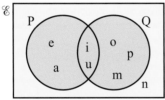

Find

(a) $n(P \cup Q)$     (b) $P'$     (c) $(P \cup Q)'$

(d) $P \cap Q'$     (e) $n(Q \cap P')$     (f) $(P \cap Q)'$

(g) $n(Q)$     (h) $P' \cup Q$     (i) $(P' \cup Q)'$

**6** $A = \{x : x$ is an integer, $10 < x \leqslant 15\}$ and $B = \{10, 12, 14, 16, 18, 20\}$

State which of the statements below are true?

(a) $10 \in A$     (b) $15 \in A \cap B$     (c) $A \cup B = \{11, 12, 13, 14, 15, 16, 18, 20\}$

(d) $n(A \cap B) = 2$     (e) $\{16, 18, 20\} \subset A' \cap B$     (f) $10 \in A \cap B$

**7** Find

(a) $A' \cap B$     (b) $n(A \cap B)$     (c) $B'$

(d) $n(A' \cap B)$     (e) $(A \cap B)'$     (f) $(A \cup B)'$

(g) $A \cup B'$     (h) $(A \cup B')'$     (i) $A' \cup B$

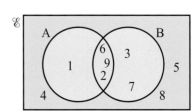

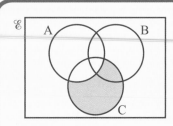

A' ∩ C is shaded pink

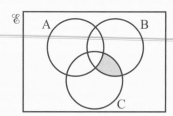

(A' ∩ C) ∩ B is shaded pink

## M8.4

**1** Draw 4 diagrams like the one shown opposite. Shade each of the following sets.

(a) $A \cup B$

(b) $A \cap B'$

(c) $B'$

(d) $(A \cup B)'$

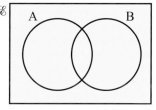

**2** Draw 9 diagrams like the one shown opposite. Shade each of the following sets.

(a) $P \cup Q$

(b) $(P \cup R) \cap Q$

(c) $P \cap R'$

(d) $P \cap (R \cap Q)$

(e) $P \cap (R \cup Q)'$

(f) $R' \cap (P \cup Q)$

(g) $(P \cup Q \cup R)'$

(h) $(P' \cap Q) \cap R$

(i) $(P \cap Q) \cup (R \cap Q)$

**3** Describe each pink region.

(a)

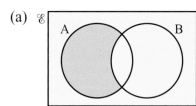

(b)

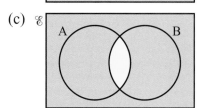

(c)

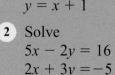

Can you still?

**Simultaneous equations**

**1** Use the graph to solve the simultaneous equations
$x + y = 3$
$y = x + 1$

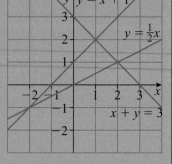

**2** Solve
$5x - 2y = 16$
$2x + 3y = -5$

**3** Solve
$3x + 4y = 14$
$5x + 2y = 21$

59 people play musical instruments. 31 play a string instrument, 24 play percussion and 12 do not play string or percussion. If one person is chosen at random, find the probability that this person plays both string and percussion.

$\mathcal{E}$ = {people who play a musical instrument}

S = {people who play a string instrument}

P = {people who play percussion}

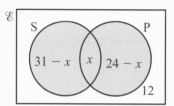

Let $x$ = number of people who play both string and percussion.

We know that $31 - x + x + 24 - x + 12 = 59$  ($n(\mathcal{E}) = 59$)

$$67 - x = 59$$
$$x = 8$$

$p$(person plays both string and percussion) $= \dfrac{8}{59}$

---

**M8.5**

**1** The Venn diagram shows

$\mathcal{E}$ = {people who holiday}

U = {people who holiday in UK}

A = {people who holiday in Australia}

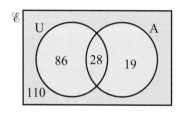

If one person is chosen at random then find

(a)  $p$(holiday in UK)

(b)  $p$(do not holiday in UK or Australia)

(c)  $p$(holiday in UK and Australia)

(d)  $p$(do not holiday in UK)

**2** 155 people visit a Leisure Centre.
97 use the waterslide.
43 use the sauna.
43 do not use the waterslide or the sauna.
If one person is chosen at random, find the probability that this person uses both the waterslide and the sauna.

**3** 46 people attend an Arts day.

18 are writers.

22 are artists.

5 are both writers and artists.

If one of these people is chosen at random, find the probability that this person is not a writer or an artist.

**4**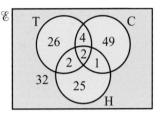

The Venn diagram shows

$\mathscr{E}$ = {people in a coffee shop}

T = {people who drink tea}

C = {people who drink coffee}

H = {people who drink hot chocolate}

If one person is chosen at random then find

(a) $p$(drink tea)

(b) $p$(drink tea and coffee)

(c) $p$(drink hot chocolate but not tea)

(d) $p$(drink no coffee)

(e) $p$(drink tea, coffee and hot chocolate)

(f) $p$(drink coffee and hot chocolate but no tea)

**5** All of 77 Year 11 students in Henton High School study at least one of three languages. 16 study French only, 8 study German only and 19 study Spanish only.

4 students study all 3 languages, $x$ students study French and German only (no Spanish), $x$ students study German and Spanish only (no French) and $3x$ students study French and Spanish only (no German). If one student is chosen at random, find the probability that this student studies French.

**6** 135 people play at least one of the following:

tennis, rounders and athletics. 65 play tennis, 41 play rounders and 68 play athletics. 14 play tennis and rounders, 8 play rounders and athletics, 24 play tennis and athletics. If one person is chosen at random, find the probability that this person plays tennis, rounders and athletics.

**Multiplying probabilities ('AND' rule)**

> If events A and B are independent,
> $p(A \text{ and } B) = p(A) \times p(B)$

The probability that Jack walks to work is $\frac{1}{4}$.

The probability that Jack catches the bus to go home is $\frac{3}{5}$.

What is the probability that one day Jack does *not* walk to work and returns home by bus.

$p(\text{not walk and bus home to work}) = p(\text{not walk to work}) \times p(\text{bus home})$

$$= \frac{3}{4} \times \frac{3}{5}$$

$$= \frac{9}{20}$$

---

### M8.6

**1** A coin and a dice are thrown. Find the probability of getting 'tails' on the coin and a '4' on the dice.

**2** A coin and a dice are thrown. Find the probability of getting 'tails' on the coin and an even number on the dice.

**3**  These two spinners are spun. What is the probability of getting:

    (a) a '1' and an '8'?

    (b) two odd numbers?

**4** A card is taken from a pack of playing cards and a coin is thrown. What is the probability of obtaining:

    (a) the King of Hearts and a 'head' on the coin?

    (b) a picture card (J, Q or K) and 'tails' on the coin?

**5** A bag contains 3 red beads and 5 green beads. If I remove one bead at random, replace it then take another bead, what is the probability that:

    (a) both beads are red?    (b) both beads are green?

**6** If a dice is thrown three times, what is the probability of obtaining three sixes.

Each letter above is written on a card. The cards are shuffled and a card is chosen randomly. The card is replaced then another card is taken. What is the probability that:

(a) both cards are the letter 'C'?

(b) both cards are the letter 'I'?

Can you still?

**Percentage, ratio and proportion**

1 John has new brake pads fitted at the garage, costing £156 including VAT at 20%. The brake pad kit costs £85 before VAT. The remaining cost is for one hour's labour. What is the cost of one hour's labour before VAT?

8 The probability that Sam has toast for breakfast is 0·3. The probability that he has a cup of tea with his breakfast is 0·8.

On Tuesday morning what is the probability that Sam has:

(a) toast and tea?

(b) toast and no tea?

(c) no toast and no tea?

2 A mirror is $\frac{3}{8}$ m long and a painting is 0·4 m long. What is the ratio of their lengths in its simplest whole number form?

3 Sketch a graph to show that $y$ is inversely proportional to $x$.

9 A card is taken from a pack of cards, replaced, then another card is taken. What is the probability that:

(a) both cards are Kings?

(b) both cards are red?

4 P is directly proportional to F. P = 63 when F = 7. Find the value of P when F = 12.

10 If a coin is thrown six times, what is the probability that the coin will land on tails each time?

5 How much interest is made on £8000 invested for 10 years at 5% per annum compound interest?

11

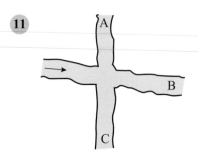

Every day Megan takes her dog for a walk. She always reaches a crossroads and has three choices of route. The probability of taking route A, B or C is equal.

On Monday to Friday, what is the probability that she takes route C every day?

12 A bag contains 7 white beads and 4 green beads. If I remove one bead at random, replace it then take another bead, what is the probability that both beads are green?

# Key Facts

$$p(A \cup B) \quad = \quad p(A) \quad + \quad p(B) \quad - \quad p(A \cap B)$$

p(A or B)     =     p(A)     +     p(B)     −     p(A and B)

If $p(A \cap B) = 0$ then A and B do not overlap.

Events A and B are mutually exclusive
– if one event occurs, the other cannot.

$p(A \text{ or } B) = p(A) + p(B)$ when A and B are mutually exclusive

## M8.7

**1** The table below shows the probability of a team winning, drawing or losing a game of rugby.

| win | draw | lose |
|-----|------|------|
| 0·65 |      | 0·2  |

(a) What is the probability of the team drawing its next game?

(b) The team plays 30 games. How many games would you expect the team to lose?

**2** A car is selected from a garage.
The probability of a red car is 0·5.
The probability of the car being a Fiesta is 0·3.
The probability of the car being a red Fiesta is 0·15.
Work out the probability of choosing a red car or a Fiesta.

213

**3** The probability of choosing a King from a pack of cards is $\frac{1}{4}$.

The probability of choosing a club from a pack of cards is $\frac{1}{13}$.

Work out the probability of choosing a King or a club when a card is removed from a pack.

**4** The probability of Jack eating pizza today is 0·17. What is the probability that Jack will not eat pizza today?

**Sequences**

**1** The $n$th term of a sequence is given by the formula $3^{n-1}$. Find the difference between the 5th term and the 4th term.

**2** Which sequence below is
(i) quadratic     (ii) geometric?
A: 3, 7, 11, 15, …     B: 3, 12, 48, 192, …
C: 8, 11, 16, 23, …     D: 3, 8, 11, 19, …

**3** Find the $n$th term of each sequence below:
(a)  8, 13, 18, 23, …
(b)  60, 53, 46, 39, …

**5** People at Hansen's Kitchens work in the factory or the offices.

If a worker is chosen at random from Hansen's Kitchens, the probability of the person working in the factory is $\frac{5}{18}$.

The probability of the worker being female is $\frac{4}{9}$. The probability of a female factory worker being chosen is $\frac{1}{9}$. Work out the probability of a chosen worker being female or working in the factory.

**6** It is found that in a car park the probability of a blue car is 0·2 and the probability of a car only having 2 doors is 0·15. If a car is chosen at random, which of the statements below are true?

(a)  p(not 2 doors) = 0·85

(b)  p(blue car or 2 doors) = 0·35

(a)  p(not blue) = 0·8

214

A bag contains 4 yellow balls and 3 blue balls. One ball is removed at random then replaced. Another ball is then removed.

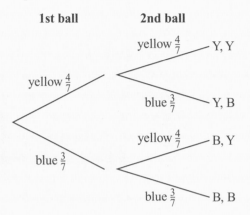

**1st ball**   **2nd ball**

yellow $\frac{4}{7}$ — Y, Y

yellow $\frac{4}{7}$

blue $\frac{3}{7}$ — Y, B

yellow $\frac{4}{7}$ — B, Y

blue $\frac{3}{7}$

blue $\frac{3}{7}$ — B, B

This tree diagram shows all the possible outcomes. If we want the probability of getting one ball of each colour, we can see that there are two ways this can happen, Y, B or B, Y.

The probability of an outcome is found by multiplying together the possibilities on the branches leading to that outcome.

$$p(Y, B) = \frac{4}{7} \times \frac{3}{7} = \frac{12}{49} \qquad\qquad p(B, Y) = \frac{3}{7} \times \frac{4}{7} = \frac{12}{49}$$

The probability of getting one ball of each colour is P(Y, B or B, Y). 'Y, B' and 'B, Y' are mutually exclusive so add the probabilities.

$$p(Y, B \text{ or } B, Y) = p(Y, B) + p(B, Y) = \frac{12}{49} + \frac{12}{49}$$

$$p(\text{one of each colour}) = \frac{24}{49}$$

---

**M8.8**

**1**  A bag contains 8 green beads and 3 blue beads. One bead is removed at random then replaced. Another bead is then removed.

(a) Copy and complete the tree diagram to show all the outcomes.

**1st bead**   **2nd bead**

G ___

G $\frac{8}{11}$

___ $\frac{3}{11}$

B ___

B ___

Find the probability that:

(b) both beads are green.

(c) the first bead is blue and the second bead is green.

**2** A bag contains 15 balls, 7 of which are blue. The remaining balls are white. One ball is removed at random then replaced. Another ball is then removed.

(a) Draw a tree diagram to show all the outcomes.

Find the probability that:

(b) both balls are blue.

(c) there is one ball of each colour.

**3** The probability of Roger eating 'Vital' flakes for breakfast is 0.6 or else he has a 'fry-up'.

(a) Copy and complete the tree diagram showing what he eats for breakfast on Monday and Tuesday mornings (use 'V' for 'Vital flakes' and 'F' for 'fry-up').

Find the probability that:

(b) Roger has a 'fry-up' on both mornings.

(c) He has 'Vital' flakes one morning and a 'fry-up' on the other morning.

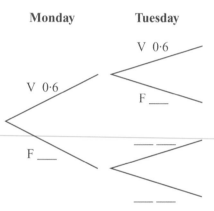

Monday          Tuesday

V 0·6

V 0·6

F ___

F ___

___ ___

___ ___

**4**

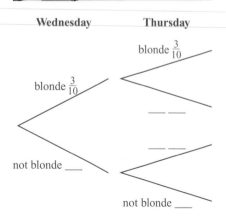

Wednesday          Thursday

blonde $\frac{3}{10}$

blonde $\frac{3}{10}$

___ ___

___ ___

not blonde ___

not blonde ___

3 out of 10 children in a primary school are blonde haired. The tree diagram below shows the hair colour of the first child to get onto the playground on a Wednesday morning and a Thursday morning.

(a) Copy and complete the tree diagram.

Find the probability that:

(b) on both mornings the first child out has blonde hair.

(c) the first child out has blonde hair one morning and not blonde hair on the other morning.

**5** A card is taken at random from a pack of cards then replaced. Another card is then taken. Draw a tree diagram to help you find the probability that:

(a) both cards are Queens.

(b) one card is a Queen and the other is not.

---

A card is taken at random from a pack of cards then replaced. This is done 3 times in total. What is the probability of getting:

(a) no clubs.

(b) *at least* one club.

(a) p(no clubs) = p(no club) $\times$ p(not club) $\times$ p(not club)

$$= \frac{3}{4} \times \frac{3}{4} \times \frac{3}{4} = \frac{27}{64}$$

(b) p(*at least* one club) = $1 - $ p(no clubs) = $1 - \dfrac{27}{64}$

$$= \frac{64}{64} - \frac{27}{64} = \frac{37}{64}$$

---

**6** A coin is thrown three times.

(a) Draw a tree diagram to show all outcomes.

Find the probability that the coin lands showing:

(b) 3 'heads'.

(c) *at least* one 'tail'.

(d) exactly 2 'heads' and one 'tail'.

**7** The probability of a successful heart operation is $0{\cdot}7$. On a particular day 3 patients have the heart operation.

(a) Draw a tree diagram to show all outcomes.

Find the probability that:

(b) all three operations are successful.

(c) *at least* one operation is successful.

(d) exactly two operations are successful.

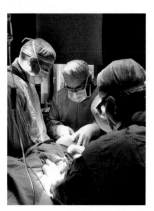

**8** A dice is thrown three times. Find the probability that the dice lands on:

(a) *at least* one 5.

(b) exactly two 5's.

217

**9**    Chloe and Ellie play each other at tennis, badminton and squash. The probability of Chloe winning at tennis is 30%, at badminton is 50% and at squash is 60%.

Draw a tree diagram to help you find the probability that:

(a) Chloe wins all 3 games.

(b) Chloe wins exactly one game.

(c) Chloe wins *at least* one game.

**10**    The probability of Dave passing his driving test is $\frac{2}{3}$.

(a) Copy and complete this tree diagram.

Find the probability that:

(b) Dave passes at the second attempt.

(c) Dave passes at the third attempt.

(d) Dave passes within three tests.

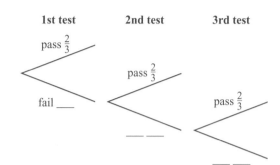

Two cards are taken at random from a pack of cards. Find the probability that:

(a) at least one card is a King.      (b) exactly one card is a King.

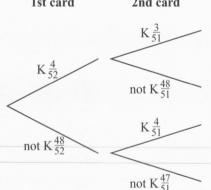

**Note**

Only 51 cards left in the pack when the 2nd card is removed.

The first branch that has been followed determines how many cards of each type are left in the pack before the 2nd card is removed.

(a) p(at least one K) $= 1 - \text{p(no K)} = 1 - \left(\dfrac{48}{52} \times \dfrac{47}{51}\right) = \dfrac{33}{221}$

(b) p(exactly one K) $= \text{p(K, not K) or p(not K, K)} = \left(\dfrac{4}{52} \times \dfrac{48}{51}\right) + \left(\dfrac{48}{52} \times \dfrac{4}{51}\right)$

$$= \dfrac{16}{221} + \dfrac{16}{221} = \dfrac{32}{221}$$

**1** A bag contains 9 red balls and 4 white balls. Two balls are taken out at random, one at a time, without replacement.

(a) Copy and complete the tree diagram

Find the probability that:

(b) both balls are white.

(c) exactly one ball is white.

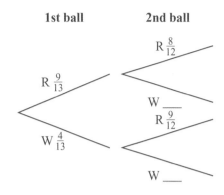

1st ball      2nd ball

R $\frac{9}{13}$

R $\frac{8}{12}$

W ___

W $\frac{4}{13}$

R $\frac{9}{12}$

W ___

**2** A box contains 6 packets of plain crisps and 5 packets of cheese and onion crisps. Two packets of crisps are removed at random, one at a time, without replacement.

(a) Using 'P' for plain crisps and 'C' for cheese and onion crisps, draw a tree diagram to show all outcomes.

Find the probability that:

(b) both packets are plain.

(c) there is one packet of each flavour.

**3** A box contains 10 toffees (T) and 5 mints (M). Two sweets are removed at random.

(a) Draw a tree diagram to show all the outcomes.

Find the probability that:

(b) both sweets are mints.

(c) there is one toffee and one mint.

**4** There are 10 boys and 15 girls in a class. Three children are chosen at random.

(a) Draw a tree diagram to show all outcomes.

Find the probability that:

(b) all three children are girls.

(c) exactly one child is a girl.

(d) *at least* one child is a boy.

**5** Three cards are taken at random from a pack of cards. Find the probability that:

(a) all three cards are red.

(b) *at least* one card is red.

(c) exactly two cards are red.

**6** Joshua buys a box of 12 eggs. Three of the eggs are cracked (C) and nine are good (G). Three eggs are chosen at random.

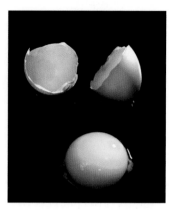

(a) Draw a tree diagram to show all outcomes.

Find the probability that:

(b) all three eggs are good.

(c) exactly two eggs are good.

(d) *at least* one egg is good.

**7** 15 counters are in a bag of which 5 are green, 4 are blue and 6 are red. Two counters are taken out, one after the other, without replacement.

(a) Draw a tree diagram to show all outcomes.

Find the probability that:

(b) *at least* one counter is green.

(c) the two counters are different colours.

**8** A group of 2 women and 4 men are going to travel in two taxis. Each taxi can only take three people. What is the probability that the first taxi will take 2 women and 1 man?

**9** A basket of fruit contains $x$ peaches and $y$ nectarines. Two pieces of fruit are taken at random. What is the probability, in terms of $x$ and $y$, of taking:

(a) two peaches.

(b) one peach and one nectarine.

**10** A bag contains 20 balls. $n$ balls are red and the remainder are green. Two balls are removed at random. What is the probability, in terms of $n$, of removing:

(a) two red balls?

(b) at least one green ball?

**M8.10**

**1** Box A contains 4 blue counters and 3 white counters.
Box B contains 3 blue counters and 5 white counters.

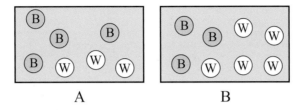

Lauren takes a counter randomly from box A and puts it in box B.
She then takes a counter randomly from box B and puts it in box A. What is the probability that each box then has the original number of counters of each colour?

**2** Helina needs to throw a six with a dice in order to start a game. Work out the probability that she will get a six on her third throw.

**3** 100 members of the Caravan Club are asked where they have been during the year. They have all been to England, Scotland or Wales.

   7 have been to all three countries.
   17 have been to England and Scotland.
   20 have been to Scotland and Wales.
   30 have been to England and Wales.
   35 have been to Scotland.

The same number of members have been to England only as have been to Wales only.

(a) Draw a Venn diagram for this information.

(b) One of the 100 members is selected at random. Find the probability that this person went to Wales but not Scotland.

**4** A box of crayons contains 6 red crayons, 8 blue crayons and 5 green crayons. Find the probability that if three crayons are randomly taken, they will all be of the same colour.

**5**  One evening 80 people go to the cinema or the theatre. Some of the people then go to a restaurant for a curry. The number of people is shown in the frequency tree below.

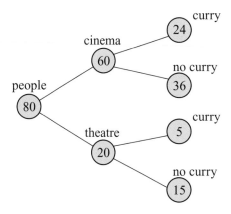

(a) Draw a probability tree to show the above information.

(b) If one person is chosen at random, what is the probability that the person goes for a curry?

(c) If the person went to the theatre, what is the probability that the person then went for a curry?

**6**  The Venn diagram shows a group of people who watch TV.

B = {people who watch BBC2}

C = {people who watch Channel 5}

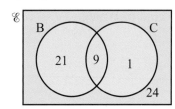

Work out

(a) p(B ∪ C)

(b) p(B ∩ C)

(c) p(B′)

(d) p(B ∩ C′)

*Can you still?*   **Number Work**

*Do not use a calculator*

**1**  Express 1925 as a product of its prime factors.

**2**  Work out $(-5)^2 - (-5)$

**3**  Work out $\frac{1}{3} + \frac{2}{5} \times \frac{1}{6}$

**4**  Find the difference between $4 \times 10^{-2}$ and $3 \times 10^{-3}$.

**5**  An adult ticket for the theatre is £32·50. A child's ticket is half this price. How much change from £150 will I get if I buy 3 adult tickets and 3 child tickets?

222

**7** There are goldfish in two bowls $P$ and $Q$. During one minute the probability of one goldfish jumping from bowl $P$ to $Q$ is $\frac{2}{5}$.

During one minute the probability of one goldfish jumping from bowl $Q$ to $P$ is $\frac{1}{3}$.

Calculate the probability that:

(a) the number of goldfish in each bowl at the end of 1 minute is equal to the number of goldfish in each bowl at the start of the minute.

(b) the number of goldfish in each bowl at the end of 2 minutes is equal to the number of goldfish in each bowl at the start of this two minute period.

## USE YOUR MATHS! – Buying a house

Although house prices may seem very expensive at the moment you may one day in the future wish to buy a house.

### Mortgages

Most people need to take out a mortgage which they usually pay back over 25 years. Interest has to be paid on the mortgage so it is important to shop around for the best deal.

### Repayment mortgage

An amount is paid each month to pay the interest and some of the borrowed money. The monthly amount is worked out so that all the money is usually paid back after 25 years.

### Interest-only mortgage

This costs less than a repayment mortgage because only the interest is paid back each month. This means that after 25 years you will still owe the same amount of money as you borrowed at the start.

You would have to save money to pay back the mortgage at the end or have another plan. If not, you would have to sell your home to pay back the mortgage at the end.

### Deposit

If you save some money towards your new home before you buy it, your mortgage payments will be smaller. Often if you have at least a 5% deposit you will get a better deal on the mortgage interest rate.

### Hidden costs

Solicitor – to make sure there are no legal problems.

Surveyor – to check that your new property is safe.

Stamp duty – money paid to the government when a property is bought.

---

Stamp duty works like income tax, charging different rates on separate chunks of the cost of the house.

| At the time of writing | stamp duty |
|---|---|
| property worth up to £125,000 | – no stamp duty |
| the amount of property value from £125,001 up to £250,000 | – 2% |
| the amount of property value from £250,001 up to £925,000 | – 5% |
| the amount of property value from £925,001 up to £1·5 million | – 10% |
| more than £1·5 million | – 12% |

For example, stamp duty on a £275,000 house is £3750
(2% of (£250,000 − £125,000) + 5% of (£275,000 − £250,000))

---

### Task

1. Dan wants to buy a house for £140,000. He earns £35,000 each year. A building society will give him a mortgage of 3·5 times his annual (yearly) salary.

   (a) How much mortgage can Dan get?

   (b) How much more money does he need to buy the house?

   (c) Stamp duty is 2% of the £140,000 cost of the house less the £125,000 threshold. The solicitor and surveyor bills amount to £2000. How much money will he really need to have saved to buy this house if he takes the full mortgage?

2  Jim and Hannah have saved £40,000. They earn £30,000 between them each year. A bank will give them a mortgage of 4 times their joint annual salary.

   (a) How much mortgage can they get?

   (b) They want to buy a house for £155,000. They must pay stamp duty. The solicitor and surveyor bills amount to £2800. Can they afford this house? How much money will be left over if they take out the full mortgage?

3  Donna sells her flat and makes £173,000 profit. She earns £27,000 each year. A bank will give her a mortgage of 3·5 times her annual salary.

   (a) What is the most money she will have available to buy a new property?

   (b) If she bought a house for this amount of money, how much stamp duty would she have to pay?

4  4 friends want to buy a house together. They can jointly raise a mortgage of £240,000 and have a total deposit of £41,000.

   They buy a house costing £268,000. The solicitor and surveyor bills amount to £3420. They must pay stamp duty.

   How much money will they have left over if they take out the full mortgage?

5  Laura earns £26,000 each year and Bruce earns £19,000. They can both get a mortgage of 3·5 times their salary.

   (a) How much mortgage can Laura get?

   (b) How much mortgage can Bruce get?

   (c) They have a joint deposit of £33,000. They buy a property costing £182,000. They have to pay stamp duty. The solicitor and surveyor bills amount to £2950. What is the lowest joint mortgage they would need to take out?

6  Peter and Sonia can *rent* a flat for £560 each month. They could *buy* a similar flat and the monthly mortgage payments would be £560. *Discuss with your teacher* the advantages and disadvantages of buying the flat compared to renting the flat.

1. Consolidating previous probability work

(a) A box contains 6 silver discs and 5 gold discs. One gold disc is removed. Another disc is now removed. What is the probability that this is a silver disc?

(b) The frequency tree shows a group of 40 people and how many went on holiday abroad and how many went by car.

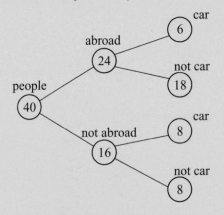

(i) What is the probability that a person chosen at random goes on holiday by car?

(ii) A person who goes on holiday abroad is chosen at random. What is the probability that this person goes by car?

(c) Ravi keeps throwing a button in the air to see which way up it will land the most.
The table below shows the total number of times the button landed with its most curved surface showing after every 50 throws.

| Number of throws | 50 | 100 | 150 | 200 | 250 | 300 | 350 | 400 | 450 | 500 | 550 | 600 | 650 | 700 |
|---|---|---|---|---|---|---|---|---|---|---|---|---|---|---|
| Number of times the curved surface is showing | 23 | 58 | 93 | 136 | 170 | 186 | 210 | 252 | 288 | 310 | 352 | 378 | 416 | 448 |

(i) Work out the relative frequency of the button landing with its most curved surface showing after every 50 throws.

(ii) Plot a graph of the relative frequency of 'curved surface showing' against the total number of throws.

(iii) Write down the number around which the relative frequency of 'curved surface showing' is settling.

(iv) If the button was thrown 2000 times, estimate how many times the button would land with its most curved surface showing.

**2.** Using Venn diagrams, including set notation

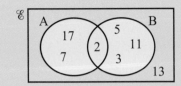

Find:
(a) A ∪ B
(b) A ∩ B′
(c) (A ∪ B)′
(d) (A ∩ B)′
(e) A′ ∪ B
(f) $n$(A′ ∩ B)

(g) Copy the diagram below and shade A′ ∪ B′

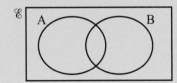

(h) Copy the diagram below and shade A′ ∩ B

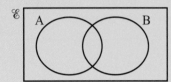

**3.** Dealing with independent events – the 'AND' rule

(a) A dice is thrown and a card is taken from a pack of playing cards. What is the probability of obtaining:

(i) a '3' on the dice and a black card?

(ii) an even number on the dice and a Queen?

(b) A coin is thrown five times. What is the probability that the coin will land on 'heads' each time?

**4.** Using the 'OR' rule

(a) Gwen likes a wide range of music. The table below shows the probability of Gwen listening to a particular type of music.

| Rock | Opera | Jazz | Classical |
|------|-------|------|-----------|
| 0·5 | 0·15 | $x$ | 0·05 |

(i) What is the probability of Gwen listening to opera *or* classical music?

(ii) What is the probability of Gwen listening to jazz?

(iii) For the next 50 times that Gwen listens to music, how many times would you expect her to listen to rock music?

(b) Some people are on a weekend break.

If one person is chosen at random, the probability of this person going to the cinema is 0·3

The probability of going to the restaurant is 0·5

The probability of going to the cinema and the restaurant is 0·1

Work out the probability of the chosen person going to the cinema or going to the restaurant.

## 5. Using probability trees

(a) A bag contains 8 strawberry chews (S) and 3 blackcurrant chews (B). One chew is taken at random then replaced. Another chew is then removed.

1st chew      2nd chew

$S \frac{8}{11}$

$S \frac{8}{11}$

B ___

S ___

B ___

B ___

   (i) Copy and complete the tree diagram to show all the outcomes.

Find the probability that:

  (ii) both chews are blackcurrant.

 (iii) one chew is strawberry and one chew is blackcurrant.

(b) Five yellow balls and three red balls are placed in a bag and two balls are removed, one at a time, without replacement.

   (i) Draw a tree diagram to represent the above information.

Find the probability that:

  (ii) both balls are red.

 (iii) both balls are the same colour.

 (iv) *at least* one ball is red.

---

## Mixed examination questions

**1** Rhiana plays a game.

The probability that she will lose the game is 0·32
The probability that she will draw the game is 0·05

Rhiana is going to play the game 200 times.

Work out an estimate for the number of times Rhiana will win the game.      (EDEXCEL)

**2** There are 480 boys and 560 girls in Digby High School.
The probability that a boy has brown hair is 0·6
The probability that a girl has brown hair is 0·45
How many pupils in the school have brown hair?      (CEA)

**3** A bag contains 4 blue, 4 red and 4 white counters.
Two counters are chosen at random without replacement.

What is the probability that the counters are different colours?      (AQA)

**4**   Amir sells laptops.
Before selling each laptop, he checks the hard drive and the screen.

The probability that the hard drive is faulty is $\frac{1}{10}$.

The probability that the screen is faulty is $\frac{1}{5}$.

These probabilities are independent.

(a) Complete the tree diagram to represent this information.

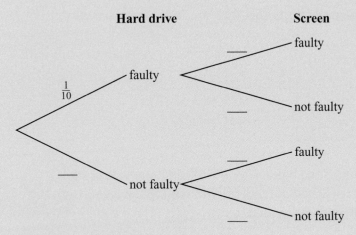

**Hard drive**   **Screen**

(b) Amir tests a laptop at random.

Find the probability that both the hard drive and the screen are
*not* faulty.

(OCR)

**5**   In a supermarket, the probability that John buys fruit is 0·7

In the same supermarket, the probability that John independently buys
vegetables is 0·4

Work out the probability that John buys fruit or buys vegetables or
buys both.

(EDEXCEL)

**6**

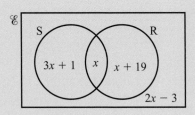

$\mathscr{E} = \{$group of children doing sports$\}$
$S = \{$children who swim$\}$
$R = \{$children who run$\}$
The total number of children who run is equal to the total number of
children who swim. One child is chosen at random.
Find the probability that this child did not swim or run.

**7** (a) A school has 400 boys and 500 girls.

The probability that a boy is vegetarian is 0·1
The probability that a girl is vegetarian is 0·2

Estimate the total number of vegetarians in the school.

(b) There are ten prefects in the school.
Four of the prefects are vegetarian.
Two of the prefects are chosen at random to have lunch with a visitor.

Show that the probability that they are *both* vegetarian is $\frac{2}{15}$    (AQA)

**8**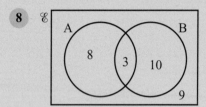

Use the Venn diagram to work out:

(a)  p(A′ ∩ B)

(b)  p(A ∪ B′)

(c)  p(B′)

**9** (a) A bag contains 5 red balls, 4 blue balls and one yellow ball.
Two balls are selected at random, without replacement, from the bag.
Calculate the probability that the two balls selected are *not* the same colour.

(b) A bag contains a very large number of ball bearings.
65% of the ball bearings are made of steel. The other ball bearings are made of cast iron.
Two ball bearings are selected at random from the bag.
Calculate the probability that they are both made of cast iron.
Give your answer as a percentage.    (WJEC)

**10** The table shows the probabilities that I am on time or late for work each day.
It also shows the amount of pay deducted for being late each day.

|  | On time | Up to 30 minutes late | 30 minutes to 1 hour late |
|---|---|---|---|
| Probability | 0·6 | 0·3 | 0·1 |
| Amount deducted | — | £8 | £16 |

Work out the probability that I have exactly £16 deducted **over two days**.

    (AQA)

**10** A bag contains 21 raffle tickets, 16 of which are white, 4 are yellow and 1 is purple.

Two raffle tickets are drawn at random without replacement from the bag.

Calculate the probability that at least one white raffle ticket is drawn.

You *must* give your answer as a fraction in its simplest form.    (WJEC)

# GEOMETRY 2

**9**

## Previous geometry work

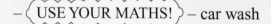

### M9.1

**1** Ella leaves home at 07:55 and takes 38 minutes to get to school.
Aryan leaves his house at 07:48 and takes 43 minutes to get to school
Who arrives at school first and by how many minutes?

**2** Some climbers travel 2·3 km on day 1.
They travel 1·85 km on day 2 then 840 m
on day 3. How far do the climbers travel
in total during the 3 days?

**3** Copy and complete the table:

|     | speed  | distance  | time              |
|-----|--------|-----------|-------------------|
| (a) |        | 120 miles | 3 hours           |
| (b) | 52 mph |           | 2 hours 30 minutes |
| (c) | 60 mph | 20 miles  |                   |
| (d) |        | 9 miles   | 15 minutes        |

**3** 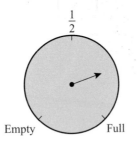 A car has 45 litres of petrol in its petrol tank.
Its petrol gauge is shown opposite
How much more petrol is needed to fill up the tank completely?

**5** Simon is ill and thinks that he has to take a 5 litre dose of medicine.
He is confused when he looks at the medicine bottle.
Explain why?

**6** A young child falls asleep at 3:25 pm.
The child wakes up at 4:19 pm.
How long does the child sleep for?

**7** Ben can run 16 km in one hour.
Hamish can run at a speed of 4·2 m/s for one hour.
Who is the faster runner?
Show all your working out.

**8** Addison cycles $3\frac{1}{2}$ miles in quarter of an hour then 4 miles in the next 15 minutes.
Find Addison's average speed over the 30 minutes

**9** The alarm clock opposite is 20 minutes fast.
What will the real time be one hour 5 minutes later than this?

**Remember**

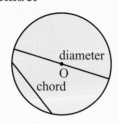

circumference = $\pi d$

radius = $\pi r^2$

(O is the centre of the circle)

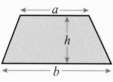

area of trapezium
$= \frac{1}{2}h(a + b)$

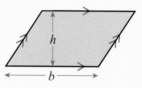

area of parallelogram
$= bh$

---

**M9.2**

*Give answers to 1 decimal place when necessary.*

**1** Work out the area of each shape.

(a)

(b)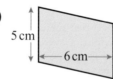

(c)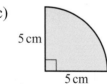

(d)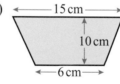

(e)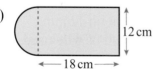

(f)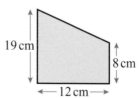

**2** The diameter of a wheel on a kart
is 14 cm.
How many times does the wheel turn
a complete circle during a 2 km race?

233

**3** A circle is shown opposite inside a square.
Calculate the red area.

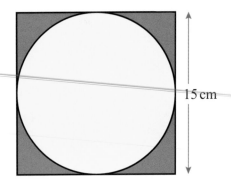

15 cm

**4**

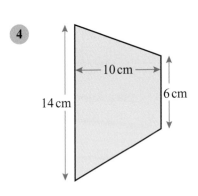

14 cm

10 cm

6 cm

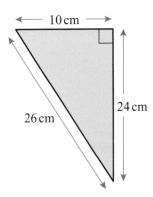

10 cm

26 cm

24 cm

Find the ratio of the area of the trapezium to the area of the triangle.
Give the answer in its simplest form.

**5** Brandon sprays a circular area on the
table top in his kitchen. This area has
diameter 45 cm.
The table top is rectangular with
dimensions 1·2 m by 0·6 m.
Calculate the area on the table top which
is not sprayed.

**6**

A piece of jewellery is made from wire in the
shape of a semi-circle with diameter 30 mm
and 2 chords each of length 12 mm.
Calculate the total length of wire used.

**7**

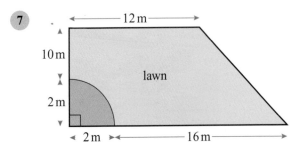

12 m

10 m

lawn

2 m

2 m

16 m

Olivia's garden is shown opposite.
A quarter circle is not grass as
shown.
A box of fertiliser covers 21 m² and
costs £4.98.
How much will it cost Olivia to put
fertiliser on all her grass?

**Remember**

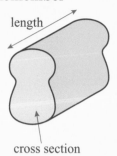

length

cross section

A prism has the same cross-section throughout its length.

Volume of prism = (Area of cross-section) × length

$$V = Al$$

**surface area** – find the area of each face of the prism.

---

**M9.3**

*Give answers to 1 decimal place when necessary.*

Find the volume of each prism.

**1**
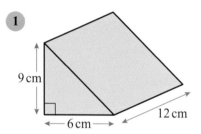
9 cm

6 cm

12 cm

**2**
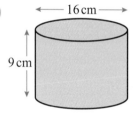
16 cm

9 cm

**3**
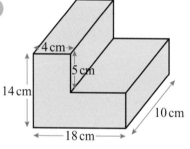
4 cm

5 cm

14 cm

18 cm

10 cm

**4** The ratio of the volume of cuboid A to the volume of cuboid B is 2:3.
Work out the value of x.

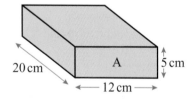
20 cm

A

5 cm

12 cm

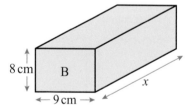
8 cm

B

9 cm

x

**5**
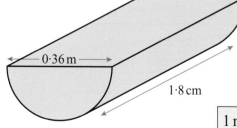
0·36 m

1·8 cm

The trough opposite has a
semi-circular cross-section.
It is filled from empty at a rate of
25 litres per minute.
How long does it take to fill up
the tank?

$1\,m^3 = 1000$ litres

**6**

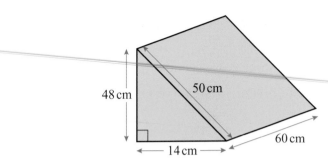

The entire surface area of this triangular prism is to be sprayed with a special paint.
It costs £3.95 to spray each 1000 cm².
How much does it cost to spray the whole prism?
Give your answer to the nearest pence.

**7** A person fetches water to his caravan in a barrel of height 75 cm and
diameter 40 cm. He then uses a pump to get the water from the barrel
into the water system in his caravan. How long does it take to empty a
completely full barrel of water if the pump works at 0·4 litres per second?
Give your answer to the nearest second.

## Measuring – upper and lower bounds

When you measure something, the measurement is never exact.
Suppose the width of a book is measured at 16 cm to the nearest cm.

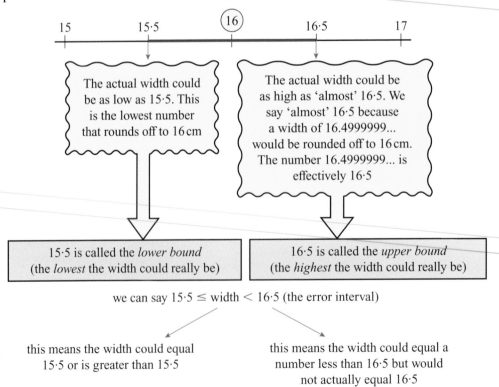

The length of a nail is measured at 3·4 cm to the nearest 0·1 cm.

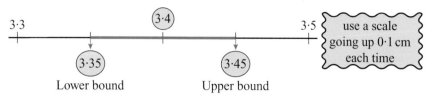

we can say $3·35 \leqslant$ length $< 3·45$ (the error interval)

(a) temperature of a room is 23·5°C to one decimal place.

$23·45 \leqslant t < 23·55$

(b) length of a table is 1430 mm to the nearest 10 mm

$1425 \leqslant l < 1435$

(c) weight of a lorry is 21 000 kg to 2 significant figures

$20\,500 \leqslant w < 21\,500$

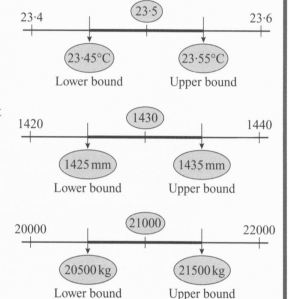

---

**M9.4**

**1** The length of a pen is measured at 14 cm to the nearest cm.

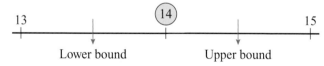

Write down  (a) the lower bound  (b) the upper bound

**2** The height of a church tower is 42 m, measured to the nearest metre.

Write down  (a) the lower bound  (b) the upper bound

**3** A man weighs 83 kg, measured to the nearest kg.

Write down  (a) the lower bound

(b) the upper bound

237

**4** The diameter of a one pound coin is 21·5 mm, measured to the nearest 0·1 mm.

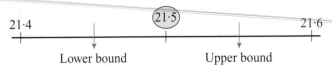

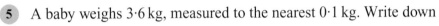

21·4      (21·5)      21·6

Lower bound      Upper bound

Write down   (a) the lower bound

(b) the upper bound

**5** A baby weighs 3·6 kg, measured to the nearest 0·1 kg. Write down

(a) the lower bound      (b) the upper bound

**6** Copy and complete the table.

| | | Lower bound | Upper bound |
|---|---|---|---|
| (a) | length = 79 cm, to nearest cm | | |
| (b) | mass = 32 kg, to nearest kg | | |
| (c) | length = 6·3 m, to nearest 0·1 m | | |
| (d) | volume = 15·7 m³, to nearest 0·1 m³ | | |
| (e) | width = 9·1 cm, to nearest 0·1 cm | | |

**7** A coin weighs 10·3 g, correct to one decimal place. What is the least possible weight of the coin?

**8** A famous rock singer has a fortune of £24 712 000, correct to the nearest £1000. What is the least amount of money the rock singer might have?

**9** The width of a field is 530 m, correct to the nearest 10 m. What is the least possible width of the field?

**10** In a 100 m race a sprinter is timed at 10·12 seconds to the nearest 0·01 seconds. Write down the least possible time.

*Can you still?*

**Mixed algebra**

**1** Expand and simplify
$$4(2x + 3) - 2(3x - 1)$$

**2** Factorise $6a^2 - 4ab$

**3** Solve $5(3x - 4) = 70 - 5x$

**4** Simplify $\dfrac{m^2 \times m^7}{(m^2)^3 \times m^2}$

**5** Expand $(x + 6)(x - 2)$

**6** Find the value of $3m^2$ when $m = 2$

**7** Factorise $x^2 - 6x + 8$

**8** Solve   $4x - 3y = 13$
            $3x + 5y = -12$

**11** Copy and complete each statement. Part (a) is done as an example.

    (a) A mass $m$ is 48 g, to the nearest g, so $47 \cdot 5 \leqslant m < 48 \cdot 5$.

    (b) A length $l$ is 92·6 mm, to the nearest 0·1 mm, so $92 \cdot 55 \leqslant l < \boxed{\phantom{xxx}}$.

    (c) A diameter $d$ is 16·2 cm, to the nearest 0·1 cm, so $\boxed{\phantom{xxx}} \leqslant d < \boxed{\phantom{xxx}}$.

    (d) A capacity $C$ is 1200 litres, to the nearest 100 litres, so $\boxed{\phantom{xxx}} \leqslant C < 1250$.

    (e) A height $h$ is 3·86 m, to the nearest 0·01 m, so $\boxed{\phantom{xxx}} \leqslant h < \boxed{\phantom{xxx}}$.

 **Key Facts**

**Truncation**

Sometimes a number has to be shortened to become more manageable. A computer might cut off all the digits of a number after the decimal point and display the number as an integer (whole number).

A number is *truncated* when it is 'cut off' after a certain number of decimal places.

2·1377641 becomes 2·13 when it is truncated after the 2nd decimal place. The last digit is not rounded up. If $x = 2 \cdot 13$ (truncated to 3 decimal places) then we know that $2 \cdot 13 \leqslant x < 2 \cdot 14$.

**M9.5**

**1** Truncate the numbers below to 3 decimal places:

    (a) 6·31765      (b) 14·719248      (c) 2·0169468

**2** Write down an inequality for the possible values of $x$ if $x = 16 \cdot 83$ when truncated to 2 decimal places.

**3** Jack rounds the number 7·48912 to 2 decimal places. Rachel truncates the same number to 2 decimal places. Who has the greater answer and by how much?

**4** The length and width of a field are measured to the nearest 0·1 m.

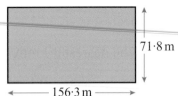

71·8 m

156·3 m

(a) Write down the lower bound for the length of the field.

(b) Write down the upper bound for the width of the field.

(c) The area of the field is length × width. Use a calculator to find the *lowest* possible value of the area of the field.

**5** Write down an inequality for the possible values of $m$ if $m = 7·612$ when truncated to 3 decimal places.

**6** 133 people turn up for a tug of war competition.
There must be 8 teams with the same number of people.
The organiser divides the number of people by the number of teams then truncates the answer to the nearest whole number.
How many people miss out on the competition?

**7** A card has length 14·5 cm (to nearest mm). Will the card definitely fit inside an envelope of length 15 cm (to nearest cm)? Justify your answer fully.

**8**

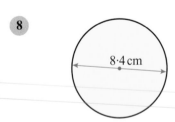

8·4 cm

The diameter of the circle is measured to the nearest 0·1 cm.

Circumference = $\pi$ × diameter

Use a calculator to find the *greatest* possible value of the circumference of the circle. (Give the answer to 1 decimal place).

**9** The volume of a liquid is measured at 1·4 litres, correct to the nearest 0·2 litres. Write down the upper and lower bounds as an inequality.

**10** The number 8·6 is obtained either from rounding off to
1 decimal place or truncating to 1 decimal place.
Copy and complete:

(a) the true value before rounding could be in error by as much as ____.

(b) The greatest error from truncation could be ____ the maximum error after rounding.

**11** The length of a park is measured at 2·2 km,
correct to the nearest 50 m.
Write down the upper and lower bounds
as an inequality.

## Density, pressure and other compound measures

 **Key Facts**

If the density of a substance is 30 g/cm³, it means that 1 cm³ of the substance has a mass of 30 g.

$$\text{Density} = \frac{\text{Mass}}{\text{Volume}}$$

We can use a triangle again to remember the formulas.

To find M: cover M and you have $D \times V$

To find D: cover D and you have $\frac{M}{V}$

To find V: cover V and you have $\frac{M}{D}$

Pressure is the force on an object that is spread over a surface area.

$$\text{Pressure} = \frac{\text{Force}}{\text{Area}}$$

The SI unit for pressure is the Pascal (Pa). $1\ \text{Pa} = 1\ \text{N/m}^2$.

To find F: cover F and you have $P \times A$

To find P: cover P and you have $\frac{F}{A}$

To find A: cover A and you have $\frac{F}{P}$

(a)  The density of copper is $8 \cdot 9 \, \text{g/cm}^3$. The mass of a copper bar is $106 \cdot 8 \, \text{g}$.
Find the volume of the copper bar.

$$V = \frac{M}{D} = \frac{106 \cdot 8}{8 \cdot 9} = 12 \, \text{cm}^3$$

(b)  The pressure over an area of $28 \, \text{m}^2$ is $3 \cdot 8 \, \text{Pa}$.
Work out the force.

$$F = P \times A = 3 \cdot 8 \times 28 = 106 \cdot 4 \, \text{N}$$

Force is measured in Newtons (N).

**M9.6**

Note – there is a difference between 'mass' and 'weight' but in this book you may assume they have the same meaning.

1  Copy and complete the table below:

| Density (g/cm³) | Mass (g) | Volume (cm³) |
|---|---|---|
| 10 | 150 | |
| 60 | | 0·5 |
| | 36 | 9 |
| 16 | 320 | |
| 0·1 | 19 | |

2  The density of brass is $8 \cdot 2 \, \text{g/cm}^3$. The volume of a brass ring is $20 \, \text{cm}^3$.
Find the mass of the brass ring.

3  A gold bar has a volume of $80 \, \text{cm}^3$ and a mass of $1544 \, \text{g}$.
Find the density of the gold.

4  A pile of money has a base area of $144 \, \text{cm}^2$.
The money weighs $1 \cdot 296 \, \text{Newtons}$
(i.e. force = $1 \cdot 296 \, \text{Newtons}$)
and is placed on a table.
What pressure does the pile of money
exert on the table?

**5** A piece of cotton has a volume of 250 cm³ and a mass of 385 g. Find the density of the cotton.

**6** A liquid weighs 500 g and has a density of 2·5 g/cm³. Find the volume of the liquid.

**7** A force of 101·5 Newtons is applied across an area of 3·5 m². Find the pressure.

**8** Find the volume of some lead weighing 3 kg. The density of lead is 11·4 g/cm³. Give your answer to the nearest whole number.

**9** A cup and saucer of weight 8 N exert a pressure of 0·11 N/cm² on the circular area of contact with a table. Calculate the diameter of this circular underside part of the saucer.

**10** A box exerts a pressure of 1·5 N/cm² on its area of contact with the floor.

Its area of contact is a rectangle 12 cm by 8 cm. Find the force creating this pressure.

**11** A curtain material costs £38 per metre. How much will 4·5 m cost?

**12** 40 m² of carpet costs £878. What is the cost per m² of the carpet?

**13** The population of a country is 35 million and the area of the country is 160 000 km². What is the population density of the country (number of people per km²)?

**14** A car travels 80 km at an average speed of 50 km/h then travels 64 km at an average speed of 80 km/h. Find the average speed for the whole journey.

*Can you still?*

**Fractions**

*Do not use a calculator.*

**1** Convert $\frac{4}{11}$ into a recurring decimal.

**2** Express $\frac{2}{3} : \frac{4}{5}$ as a ratio in its simplest form.

**3** Tom takes $\frac{2}{3}$ kg from a bag of potatoes weighing $3\frac{1}{4}$ kg. How much does the bag of potatoes weigh now?

**4** Express $\frac{7}{32}$ as a percentage of $\frac{5}{8}$.

**5** Work out $-\frac{9}{20} \div \frac{2}{5}$

**6** Work out the area of this trapezium.

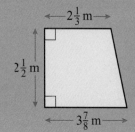

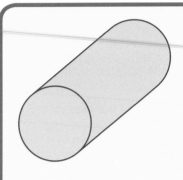

This metal cylinder weighs $x$ kg.

The metal has density = 8 g/cm$^3$.

Volume = $\dfrac{\text{Mass}}{\text{Density}}$

Mass = $1000x$ grams (match up units)

Volume = $\dfrac{1000x}{8}$ = $125x$ cm$^3$

**1** Jordan travels at a speed of $x$ m/s for 30 minutes. Write down an expression for how far he travels during this time.

**2** The density of zinc is 7·14 g/cm$^3$ and the density of copper is 8·96 g/cm$^3$. 1·428 kg of zinc is mixed with 2·688 kg of copper to make a brass alloy. Calculate the density of this brass alloy.

**3** Two cyclists, Nerys and Ben, complete a race. Nerys has an average speed of 14·5 km/h and Ben has an average speed of 4 m/s. Who wins the race?

**4** A plane travels 920 km at an average speed of 800 km/h. It then increases its speed by 50% and travels another 1020 km. Find the average speed for the whole journey.

**5** A force of $A$ Newtons provides a pressure of $B$ Pa across a square area. Write down an expression for the length of one side of the square.

**6** Write down an expression for $x$ km/h in m/s.

**7** 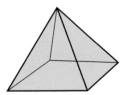 A pyramid has a volume of $y$ m$^3$. It is made from a substance with a density of $n$ g/m$^3$. Write down an expression, in kg, for the mass of the pyramid.

**8** Write down an expression for $p$ m/s in km/h.

**9** In a marathon race, Candice is 40 m behind Jess. Candice is running at 0·7 m/s but Jess is only running at 0.5 m/s. How long will it take Candice to catch up Jess?

**10**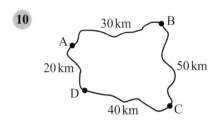

Brooke travels from A to B at a steady speed of $x$ km/h, from B to C at $y$ km/h, from C to D at $z$ km/h and from D to A at 60 km/h. Find an expression for Brooke's average speed for the whole journey.

## Arcs of circles

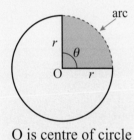

O is centre of circle

### Key Facts

An arc is part of the circumference

circumference = $\pi d$ where $d$ = diameter

360° in a whole circle

so, arc length = $\frac{\theta}{360}$ of the circumference

$$\text{arc length} = \frac{\theta}{360} \times \pi d$$

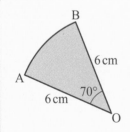

Find the perimeter of this shape, leaving the answer in terms of $\pi$.

Arc AB = $\frac{70}{360} \times \pi \times 12$   (diameter = 12 cm)

$$= \frac{70}{_{3}360} \times \frac{\pi}{1} \times \frac{12^{1}}{1}$$

$$= \frac{7\pi}{3} \text{ cm}$$

Perimeter = arc AB + AO + OB

$$= \frac{7\pi}{3} + 6 + 6$$

$$= \left(\frac{7\pi}{3} + 12\right) \text{ cm}$$

This is an 'exact' answer in terms of $\pi$. If a calculator is used, the answer is 19.3 cm (to one decimal place).

In questions ① to ③ , use a calculator to work out the length of arc MN to one decimal place.

**1**

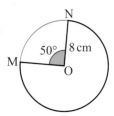

**2**

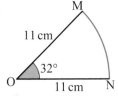

**3**

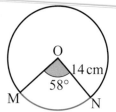

In questions ④ to ⑥ , use a calculator to work out the perimeter of each shape to one decimal place.

**4**

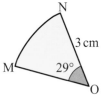

**5**

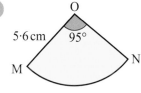

**6**

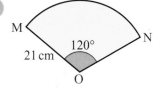

**7** Find the perimeter of the shaded area below.

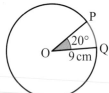

**8** Show that arc PQ below is equal to $\pi$ cm.

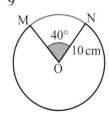

**9** Show that arc MN below is equal to $\dfrac{20\pi}{9}$ cm.

Can you still?

**Equations of lines**

**1** Which 2 lines below are parallel?

$$y = 4x + 3 \qquad y - 4x = 1 \qquad y = 2 - 4x$$

**2** Find the gradient of the line which passes through (1, 2) and (4, 17).

(4, 17)

(1, 2)

**3** Write down the gradient of the line $2x + y - 5 = 0$.

**4** Write down the equation of any line parallel to $y = -5x + 3$.

**5** Find the equation of the line which passes through (2, 6) and (4, 14).

(4, 14)

(2, 6)

**6** Find the equation of the line that is parallel to the line $y - 6x + 1 = 0$ and passes through (1, 3).

**10**

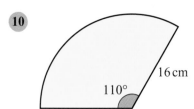

16 cm

110°

Find the perimeter of this shape, leaving the answer in terms of $\pi$.

**11**

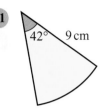

42°  9 cm

Find the perimeter of this shape, leaving the answer in terms of $\pi$.

**12**

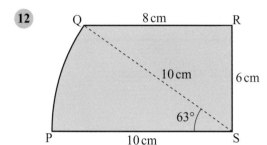

Q    8 cm    R

10 cm

6 cm

63°

P    10 cm    S

PQ is the arc of a circle with centre at S. Calculate the perimeter of PQRS.

**13** The diagram opposite shows a steel structure. The two curved corners are both quarter circles with the same radius. Calculate the total length of the steel.

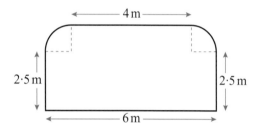

4 m

2·5 m                    2·5 m

6 m

---

## Areas of sectors

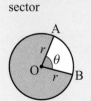

# Key Facts

minor sector

O

major sector

A

$r$

$\theta$

O    $r$    B

minor segment

tangent

major segment

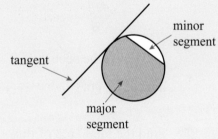

Area of circle $= \pi r^2$

area of sector AOB $= \dfrac{\theta}{360} \times \pi r^2$

Note: A tangent is a line which touches a circle at one point only.

247

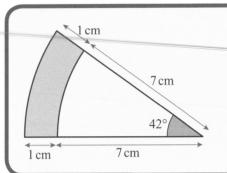

Calculate the pink area.

$$\text{area of large sector} = \frac{42}{360} \times \pi 8^2 = 23 \cdot 46\,\text{cm}^2$$

$$\text{area of small sector} = \frac{42}{360} \times \pi 7^2 = 17 \cdot 96\,\text{cm}^2$$

$$\text{pink area} = 23 \cdot 46 - 17 \cdot 96 = 5 \cdot 5\,\text{cm}^2$$

## M9.8

In this Exercise, give the answer to one decimal place when necessary.

In questions **1** to **3**, find the area of each sector.

**1**
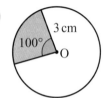

**2**
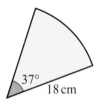

**3**

**4** Find the shaded area.
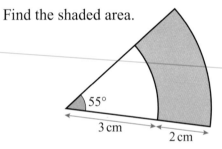

**5**

Show that the sector area is $\frac{4\pi}{9}$ cm².

**6**
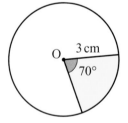

Show that the sector area is $\frac{7\pi}{4}$ cm².

**7** Find the total area of this shape, leaving your answer in terms of $\pi$.

**8** A circle has radius 6 cm with centre O. A and B are points on the circumference such that the angle AOB is 30°. Show that the area of the sector AOB is exactly $3\pi$.

**9** Part of a drain cover is in the shape of a sector as shown opposite. The 3 holes shown are also sectors, each with an angle of 10° and a radius of 20 cm. Find the area of this part of the drain cover.

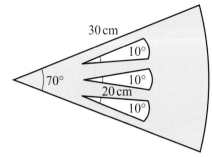

**10** Find the area of the shaded segment below.

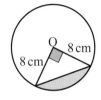

**11** Find the value of $\theta$ if the sector area is 10·7 cm².

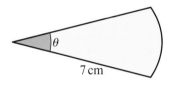

**12** Find the area of the shaded major segment below.

**13** Work out the pink area shown below. The three circles shown each have a diameter of 8 cm.

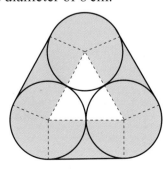

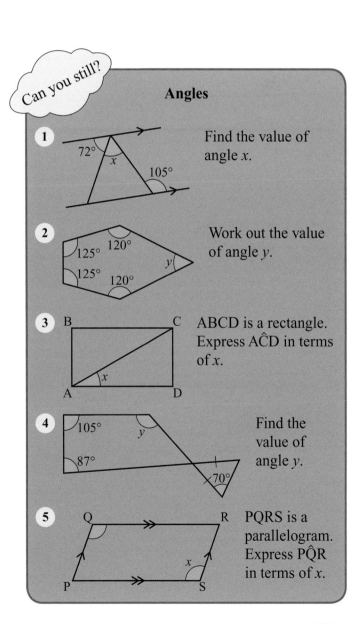

Can you still?

**Angles**

**1** Find the value of angle $x$.

**2** Work out the value of angle $y$.

**3** ABCD is a rectangle. Express AĈD in terms of $x$.

**4** Find the value of angle $y$.

**5** PQRS is a parallelogram. Express PQ̂R in terms of $x$.

## Converting units of area and volume

*Length*:    $1\,m = 100\,cm$

*Area*:   $1\,m \times 1\,m = 100\,cm \times 100\,cm$

    $1\,m^2 = 10\,000\,cm^2$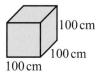

*Volume*:   $1\,m \times 1\,m \times 1\,m = 100\,cm \times 100\,cm \times 100\,cm$

   $1\,m^3 = 1000\,000\,cm^3$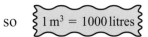

*Capacity*:

$1\,litre = 1000\,ml$   1 ml is the same as $1\,cm^3$

From above, $1\,m^3 = 1\,000\,000\,cm^3$   so   $1\,m^3 = 1000\,litres$

---

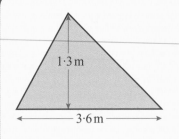

Find the area *in cm²*.

**either**

Area $= \dfrac{1}{2}\,bh = \dfrac{1}{2} \times 3\cdot6 \times 1\cdot3$

$= 2\cdot34\,m^2$

$= 2\cdot34 \times 10\,000\,cm^2$

$= 23\,400\,cm^2$

**or change lengths first**

Area $= \dfrac{1}{2}\,bh = \dfrac{1}{2} \times 360\,cm \times 130\,cm$

$= 23\,400\,cm^2$

---

### M9.9

**1** Find the area of each shape below *in cm²*.

(a)

1·7 m

8·2 m

(b)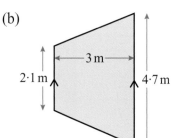

2·1 m   —3 m—   4·7 m

(c)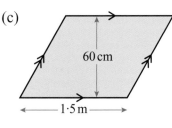

60 cm

1·5 m

250

**2** (a) Work out the volume of this solid in m³.

(b) What is the volume of this solid in cm³?

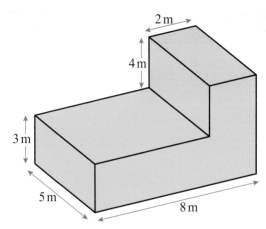

**3** Copy and complete:

(a)  $1\,\text{m}^3 = \boxed{\phantom{00}}\,\text{cm}^3$
(b)  $2\,\text{m}^3 = \boxed{\phantom{00}}\,\text{cm}^3$
(c)  $4{\cdot}7\,\text{m}^3 = \boxed{\phantom{00}}\,\text{cm}^3$

(d)  $1\,\text{m}^2 = \boxed{\phantom{00}}\,\text{cm}^2$
(e)  $3\,\text{m}^2 = \boxed{\phantom{00}}\,\text{cm}^2$
(f)  $80\,000\,\text{cm}^2 = \boxed{\phantom{00}}\,\text{m}^2$

(g)  $35\,000\,\text{cm}^2 = \boxed{\phantom{00}}\,\text{m}^2$
(h)  $9{\cdot}25\,\text{m}^2 = \boxed{\phantom{00}}\,\text{cm}^2$
(i)  $1\,\text{m}^3 = \boxed{\phantom{00}}\,\text{litres}$

(j)  $7\,\text{m}^3 = \boxed{\phantom{00}}\,\text{litres}$
(k)  $5600\,\text{litres} = \boxed{\phantom{00}}\,\text{m}^3$
(l)  $3{\cdot}9\,\text{m}^3 = \boxed{\phantom{00}}\,\text{cm}^3$

**4** The capacity of the rectangular tank below is 72 000 litres. Find the missing value $x$.

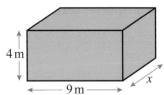

**5** How many litres of water will fill the trough below?

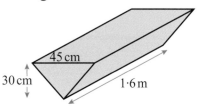

**6** A pyramid has a surface area of 3·4m². The triangular prism below has a greater surface area. By how much is it greater?

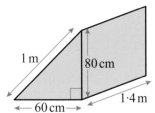

Can you still?

**Probability**

**1** Find the probability of getting one head and two tails when 3 coins are thrown.

**2** P = {1, 3, 5, 7} and Q = {2, 3, 4, 5}
Find (a) P ∪ Q    (b) P ∩ Q′

**3** The probability of a child going to Henton High School is 0·7 and the probability of a child having blond hair is 0·3. If a child is chosen at random, what is the probability that the child goes to Henton High School or has blond hair?

**4** Emily has 9 christmas tree decorations, 4 of which are stars. If she randomly picks out two decorations, what is the probability that *only* one of the decorations will be a star?

# Key Facts

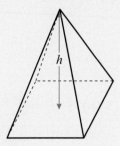 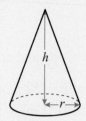

Sphere

Volume $= \frac{4}{3}\pi r^3$

Pyramid

Volume $= \frac{1}{3} \times$ (base area) $\times h$

Cone

Volume $= \frac{1}{3}\pi r^2 h$

---

Find the volume of this hemisphere, leaving the answer in terms of $\pi$.

Volume $= \frac{1}{2} \times \frac{4}{3}\pi r^3 = \frac{2}{3}\pi r^3$

$= \frac{2}{3_1} \times \pi \times 6^2 \times 6 \times 6$

$= 144\,\pi\,\text{cm}^3$

---

### M9.10

*In this Exercise give answers to 3 significant figures where necessary.*

**1** Find the volume of each solid.

(a)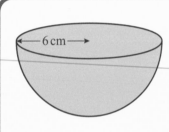

(b)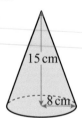

(c)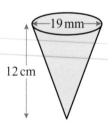

**2** Work out the volume of a hemisphere of diameter 18 cm.

**3** A square-based pyramid is made from gold. The density of gold is 19.3 g/cm³. What does the pyramid weigh if the base length is 5 cm and the pyramid height is 11 cm?

**4** Find the volume of each solid.

(a)
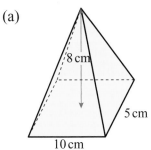

(b)
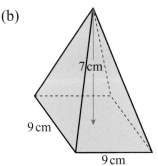

(c)
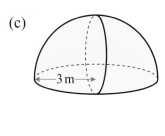

**5** A sphere of radius 2·1 cm is made from a zinc alloy of density 6 g/cm³. Find the mass of the sphere.

**6** A golf ball is covered in a coating of width 3 mm. If it has a radius of 2 cm before it is covered then find the volume of the coating.

**7** Find the 'exact' volume of each solid, *leaving your answers in terms of π*.

(a)
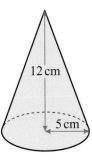

(b)
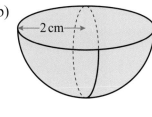

(c)
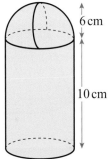

**8** Find the height of a cone of radius 3 cm and volume 170 cm³.

**9** Find the base area of a pyramid of height 12 cm and volume 192 cm³.

**10** Find the volume of each solid, *leaving your answer in terms of π when necessary.*

(a)
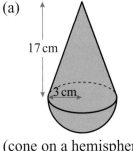
(cone on a hemisphere)

(b)
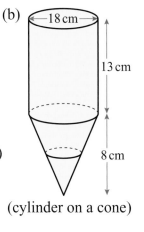
(cylinder on a cone)

(c)
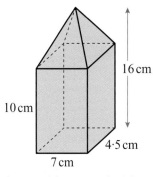
(pyramid on a cuboid)

253

**11** A cake has diameter 35 cm and height 8 cm. A slice of cake is cut so that the angle of the slice is 40°. Calculate the volume of this piece of cake.

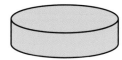

**12** The shaded frustum is made by cutting off a small cone from the large cone. Find the volume of the frustum.

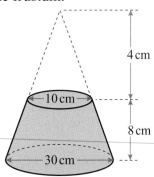

Can you still?

**Percentage, ratio, proportion**

**1** Evelyn invests £30 000 at 4% per annum simple interest for 2 years. She shares the interest between herself and her daughter in the ratio 7 : 5. She spends 40% of her money on a laptop. She spends the rest on a holiday. How much does the holiday cost?

**2** Adam buys a cooker for £702 including VAT at 20%. How much of the cost of the cooker was VAT?

**3** Gina has enough food for 4 dogs for 4 weeks. How many days would this food last for 7 dogs of the same size?

**4** Write the ratio $0.4 : \dfrac{3}{8}$ in its simplest whole number form.

**5** P is directly proportional to Q. P = 30 when Q = 4. Work out the value of P when Q = 9.

---

## Surface areas of cylinders, spheres and cones

## Key Facts

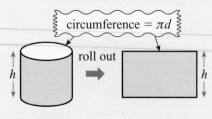

cylinder

sphere
surface area $= 4\pi r^2$

Curved surface area $= \pi dh$ or $2\pi rh$
Total surface area $= \pi dh + 2\pi r^2$
(including two ends)

or $2\pi rh + 2\pi r^2$

# Key Facts

$l$ is called the 'slant' height.

cone

Curved surface area $= \pi r l$

**Note**

The perpendicular height $h$, the radius $r$ and the slant height $l$ are connected by Pythagoras' theorem (see Unit 11).

$$h^2 + r^2 = l^2$$

---

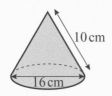

Find the total surface area of this cone.

radius = 8 cm          slant height = 10 cm

Total surface area = curved surface area + base

$$= \pi r l + \pi r^2$$

$$= (\pi \times 8 \times 10) + (\pi \times 8^2)$$

$$= 452{\cdot}4 = 452 \text{ cm}^2 \text{ (3 sig. figs.)}$$

---

**M9.11**

*In this Exercise give answers to 3 significant figures where necessary.*

**1** Find the *curved* surface area of each solid.

(a)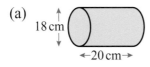

(b)

(c)

**2** An apple (assume that it is spherical) of radius 4 cm is cut in half. What area of cling film will be needed to cover completely one half of the apple?

**3** The planet Jupiter has diameter 142 984 km. Taking Jupiter to be a sphere, work out the surface area of the planet. Give your answer in standard form to 3 significant figures.

4 Find the 'exact' *total* surface area of each solid, leaving answers in terms of $\pi$.

(a)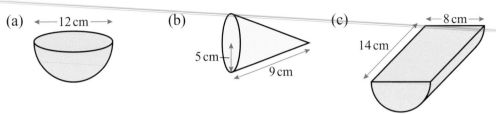

←12 cm→

(b)

5 cm

9 cm

(c)

←8 cm→

14 cm

5 Which of these two cylinders has the larger total surface area and by how much?

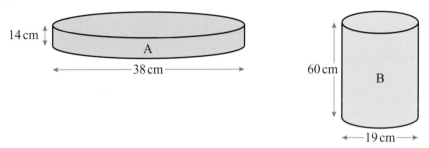

14 cm

A

←38 cm→

60 cm

B

←19 cm→

6 A cone has curved surface area $6\ cm^2$ and radius 1 cm. What is the slant height of the cone?

7 Find the 'exact' total surface area of each solid, leaving answers in terms of $\pi$.

(a)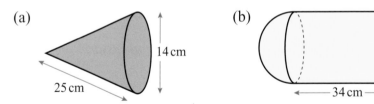

14 cm

25 cm

(b)

16 cm

←34 cm→

8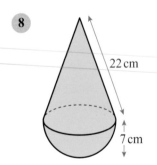

22 cm

7 cm

A cone is joined to a hemisphere as shown.
The solid is to be protected by using a spray which costs 29p per $cm^2$.

How much will it cost to spray the whole solid?

256

**9** The surface area of a closed cylinder is 175 cm²
and its radius is 4 cm.

Find the height of this cylinder.

**10** Use Pythagoras (see Unit 11) to find the slant height of
the cone opposite then calculate the total surface area
of the cone.

**11** Find the 'exact' total surface area of the cone
opposite, leaving your answer in terms of $\pi$.

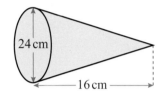

## Similar shapes

Two triangles are *similar* if they have the same angles.

Any two shapes are *similar* if one shape is an enlargement of the other. Corresponding
sides must be in the same proportion.

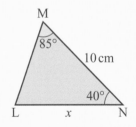

Find *x*.

The triangles are similar because all
3 angles are the same.

Redraw the triangles so that the angles
correspond more clearly.

Sides AC and MN correspond.

MN is $\frac{10}{4}$ times longer, i.e. 2·5 times longer.

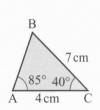
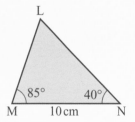

Each side in the larger triangle is 2·5 times longer than the corresponding side in the
smaller triangle. Sides LN and BC correspond so $x = 2·5 \times 7 = 17·5$ cm.

**1**

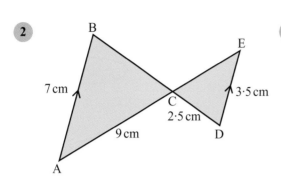

Explain exactly why these two rectangles are similar.

**2**

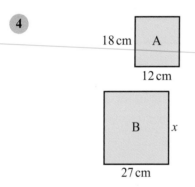

(a) Prove that triangles ABC and CDE are similar.

(b) Find BC.     (c) Find CE.

**3**

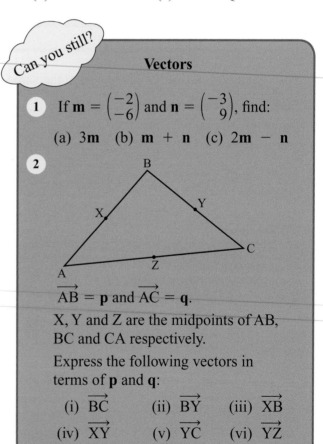

(a) Prove that triangles PQT and PRS are similar.

(b) Find PS.     (c) Find PQ.

**4**

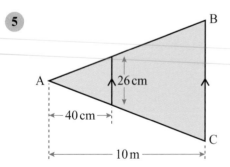

Picture A above is enlarged to make picture B. Find x.

**5**

Work out the value of BC above.

*Can you still?*

**Vectors**

**1** If $\mathbf{m} = \begin{pmatrix} -2 \\ -6 \end{pmatrix}$ and $\mathbf{n} = \begin{pmatrix} -3 \\ 9 \end{pmatrix}$, find:

(a) $3\mathbf{m}$   (b) $\mathbf{m} + \mathbf{n}$   (c) $2\mathbf{m} - \mathbf{n}$

**2**

$\overrightarrow{AB} = \mathbf{p}$ and $\overrightarrow{AC} = \mathbf{q}$.

X, Y and Z are the midpoints of AB, BC and CA respectively.

Express the following vectors in terms of $\mathbf{p}$ and $\mathbf{q}$:

(i) $\overrightarrow{BC}$    (ii) $\overrightarrow{BY}$    (iii) $\overrightarrow{XB}$

(iv) $\overrightarrow{XY}$    (v) $\overrightarrow{YC}$    (vi) $\overrightarrow{YZ}$

(vii) $\overrightarrow{AZ}$    (viii) $\overrightarrow{XZ}$

**6** Find $x$ in each diagram below.

(a)
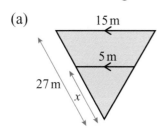

(b)
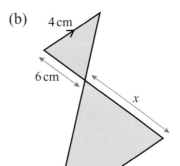

(c)
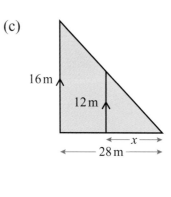

(a)
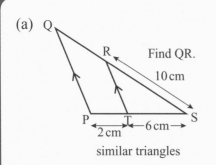

Find QR.

similar triangles

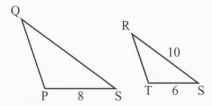

$\dfrac{PS}{TS} = \dfrac{8}{6} = \dfrac{4}{3}$

$QS = \dfrac{4}{3} \times 10 = \dfrac{40}{3} = 13\dfrac{1}{3}$

$QR = QS - RS = 13\dfrac{1}{3} - 10 = 3\dfrac{1}{3}\,\text{cm}$

(b)
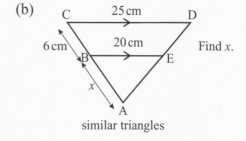

Find $x$.

similar triangles

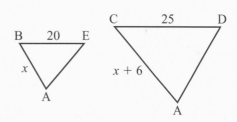

$\dfrac{CD}{BE} = \dfrac{25}{20} = \dfrac{5}{4}$

$x + 6 = \dfrac{5}{4}x$

$4x + 24 = 5x$

$x = 24\,\text{cm}$

**E9.2**

**1** A man of height 2 m casts a shadow of 3·75 m. At the same moment a tower of height 47 m casts a shadow. How long is the shadow?

In questions ② to ⑦, find $x$.

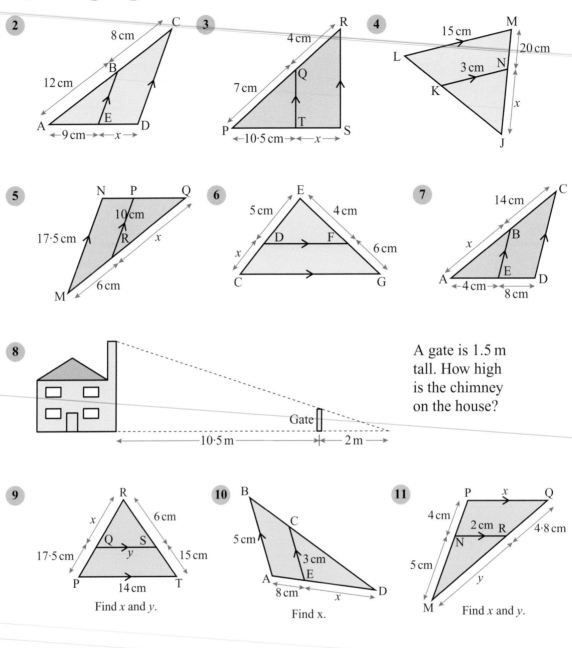

**②**

8 cm, 12 cm, B, E, A, 9 cm, $x$, D, C

**③**

4 cm, R, Q, 7 cm, P, T, 10·5 cm, $x$, S

**④**

15 cm, M, 20 cm, L, 3 cm, N, K, $x$, J

**⑤**

N, P, Q, 10 cm, 17·5 cm, R, $x$, 6 cm, M

**⑥**

E, 5 cm, 4 cm, D, F, $x$, 6 cm, C, G

**⑦**

14 cm, C, $x$, B, A, E, 4 cm, 8 cm, D

**⑧**

A gate is 1.5 m tall. How high is the chimney on the house?

Gate, 10·5 m, 2 m

**⑨**

R, $x$, 6 cm, Q, S, 17·5 cm, $y$, 15 cm, P, 14 cm, T

Find $x$ and $y$.

**⑩**

B, C, 5 cm, 3 cm, A, E, 8 cm, $x$, D

Find x.

**⑪**

P, $x$, Q, 4 cm, 2 cm, R, 4·8 cm, N, 5 cm, $y$, M

Find $x$ and $y$.

**⑫**

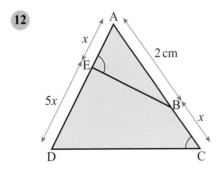

A, $x$, E, 2 cm, 5$x$, B, $x$, D, C

$\hat{AEB} = \hat{ACD}$.

Find $x$.

All units are in cm.

260

**13**

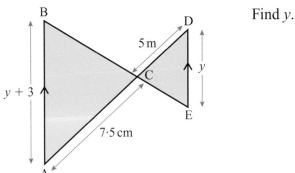

Find $y$.

**14** Find PQ and PT.

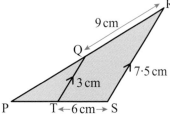

**15** PQSU is a parallelogram.

$P\hat{Q}V = R\hat{T}S$.

Find PV.

All units are in cm.

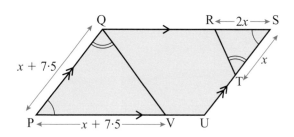

**16**

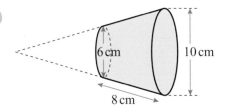

Calculate the total surface area of this frustum.

Ross, Alice, Phil and Vicky are raising money for a World Challenge expedition. One day they decide to wash cars.

> A bucket of warm water holds 7·5 litres

> A bucket of cold water holds 12 litres

5 litre bottle of carwash £8·99.

Use 2 capfuls of carwash for every 5 litres of water.

1 capful contains 40 ml of carwash.

Ross and his friends identify each car as being small, medium or large. They charge the following rates.

| type of car | small | medium | large |
|---|---|---|---|
| cost | £4·20 | £4·70 | £5·50 |

Firstly they wash the cars with buckets of warm water (which require carwash) then rinse by throwing buckets of cold water (no carwash needed) over the car.

The table below shows how many buckets of water are needed for each type of car.

| type of car | number of buckets of warm water | number of buckets of cold water |
|---|---|---|
| small | 2 | 4 |
| medium | 3 | 5 |
| large | 4 | 7 |

One day Ross, Alice, Phil and Vicky wash the number of cars shown below:

| type of car | Ross | Alice | Phil | Vicky |
|---|---|---|---|---|
| small | 4 | 5 | 6 | $x$ |
| medium | 7 | 5 | 5 | $y$ |
| large | 3 | 2 | 4 | $n$ |

The time taken to wash each type of car is shown below:

Ross, Alice, Phil and Vicky buy four 5-litre bottles of car wash in total. They borrow everything else.

| type of car | small | medium | large |
|---|---|---|---|
| Ross | 25 mins | 35 mins | 40 mins |
| Alice | 22 mins | $\frac{1}{2}$ hour | 35 mins |
| Phil | 25 mins | 36 mins | 40 mins |
| Vicky | $\frac{1}{2}$ hour | 40 mins | $\frac{3}{4}$ hour |

**Task A**

Phil and Vicky spend 11 hours in total washing small and medium cars during this day. Vicky uses 72 capfuls of carwash for her small and medium cars. How many small cars does Vicky wash and how many medium cars does she wash?

**Task B**

During the day 5 capfuls of carwash are lost when one of the bottles is knocked over. If all the carwash is used during the day, how many large cars does Vicky wash?

**Task C**

How much profit is made during the day?

## TEST YOURSELF ON UNIT 9

> **1.** Consolidating previous geometry work

(a)

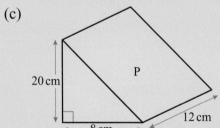

The perimeter of the square is equal to the perimeter of the triangle.
Work out the sum of the areas of the triangle and the square.

(b) Karli joins the motorway at 08 : 53 and leaves it at 09 : 41. She travels at 70 mph on the motorway. How far did she travel on the motorway?

(c)

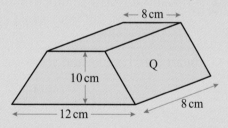

Work out the ratio of the volume of prism P to the volume of prism Q.
Give the ratio in its simplest form.

(d) Three friends are on a trek. They only have 12 litres of water remaining for 5 days. How many millilitres of water is each friend allowed to drink each day if the water is to last the full 5 days?

(e) The cylindrical tank shown opposite is filled with oil at a rate of 50 litres per minute.
How long does it take to completely fill the tank?
Give your answer to the nearest minute.

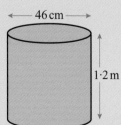

263

**2.** Finding upper/lower bounds

Copy and complete the table.

|  |  | Lower bound | Upper bound |
|---|---|---|---|
| (a) | mass = 58 kg, to nearest kg | | |
| (b) | width = 3·7 m, to nearest 0·1 m | | |
| (c) | height = 72·6 cm, to nearest 0·1 cm | | |
| (d) | capacity = 8·12 *l*, to nearest 0·01 *l* | | |

(e) Write the answer to part (c) as an inequality.

(f) Write out an inequality to show the possible values of $x$ if $x = 8·573$ (truncated to 3 decimal places).

**3.** Calculating with density, pressure and other compound measures

(a) Ben cycles 72 km at a speed of 16 km/h. How long does the journey take him?

(b) Wendy is cycling at 12 km/h. How many minutes does it take her to travel 300 m?

(c) A steel bar has a volume of 600 cm³. If the density of steel is 8·3 g/cm³, find the mass of the steel bar.

(d) 12 cm³ of gold weighs 231·6 g. Find the density of gold.

(e) Calculate the force which exerts a pressure of 7·2 Pa on a triangular area with base 6 m and height 9 m.

(f) Kabir travels $x$ kilometres in 4 hours. Find an expression for his speed in metres per second.

**4.** Finding arc lengths and sector areas

(a) Find the 'exact' perimeter of the shape opposite, leaving the answer in terms of $\pi$.

(b)

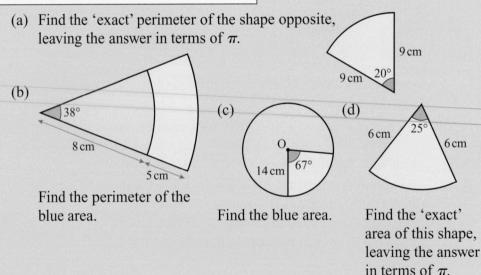

Find the perimeter of the blue area.

(c) Find the blue area.

(d) Find the 'exact' area of this shape, leaving the answer in terms of $\pi$.

**5.** Converting units of area and volume

Copy and complete

(a)  $1 \, \text{m}^2 = \boxed{\phantom{00}} \, \text{cm}^2$     (b)  $5 \, \text{m}^3 = \boxed{\phantom{00}} \, \text{cm}^3$     (c)  $9 \cdot 4 \, \text{m}^3 = \boxed{\phantom{00}} \, \text{cm}^3$

(d)  $5 \cdot 6 \, \text{m}^2 = \boxed{\phantom{00}} \, \text{cm}^2$     (e)  $2 \, \text{m}^3 = \boxed{\phantom{00}} \, \text{litres}$     (f)  $3 \cdot 72 \, \text{m}^3 = \boxed{\phantom{00}} \, \text{litres}$

(g)  How many litres of water will this tank contain when full?

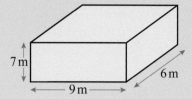

(h)  Find the area of the shape below in cm².

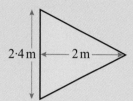

---

**6.** Finding volumes of spheres, cones and pyramids

(a)

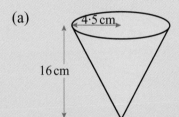

Find the volume.

(b)

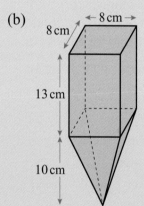

Find the volume to one decimal place.

---

**7.** Finding surface areas of spheres, cones and cylinders

(a)

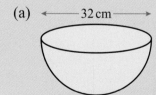

Find the curved surface area of this hemisphere.

(b)

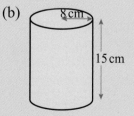

Find the 'exact' total surface area of this cylinder, leaving the answer in terms of $\pi$.

**8.** Finding unknown lengths in similar shapes

(a)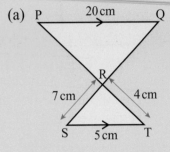

Find QR

(b)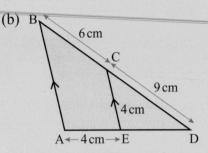

Find AB and DE

## Mixed examination questions

**1** A solid hexagonal prism of mass 8600 g has a cross-sectional area of 60 cm² and length 23 cm.

Calculate the density of the prism in g/cm³.

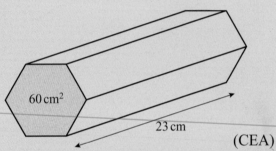

(CEA)

**2** You are given that

$$1 \text{ kilometre} = 1000 \text{ metres}$$

and

$$1 \text{ hour} = 3600 \text{ seconds}$$

A lorry is travelling at 13·6 m/s.
The speed limit is 50 km/h.

Show that the lorry is travelling below the speed limit.

(AQA)

**3** A rectangle has a semicircle of radius 6 cm removed.

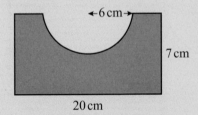

Find an expression, in terms of $\pi$, for the shaded area.
Give your answer in the form $a - b\pi$.

(OCR)

**4** The diagram shows a triangle cut into a smaller triangle and a trapezium.

Work out the area of the trapezium ABDE.

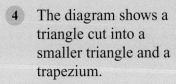

12 cm

E

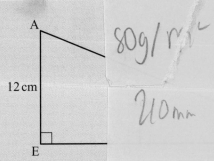

80g/m²

210mm

0·06280 m²

41.

**5** Teresa is moving packets of A4 paper usin[...]
Each packet contains 500 sheets and each [...]
The paper has a density of 80 g per m².

Her trolley has a maximum safe load of 6[...]

How many packets can the trolley hold sa[...]

**6** A solid object is made out of two identica[...]
The three shapes are joined together as sh[...]
touching the centres of the circular bases of both cones.

<u>Side View</u>

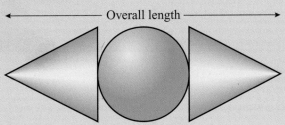

Overall length

*Diagram NOT drawn to scale*

The radius of the sphere and the radius of the circular base of each cone is 3 cm.
The volume of the whole object is 245 cm³.

Calculate the overall length of the object. (WJEC)

**7** A jug has a capacity of 600 ml measured correct to the nearest 10 ml.
Write down the least and greatest possible values of the capacity
of the jug. (WJEC)

**8**

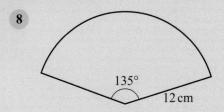

135°

12 cm

The diagram shows a sector of a circle,
radius 12 cm.

Show that the perimeter of the sector is
greater than 52 cm. (AQA)

**9** Two cars each travel 120 miles.
One of the cars travels the whole distance at an average speed of 50 mph.
The second car travels half the distance at an average speed of 40 mph and
half the distance at an average speed of 60 mph.

What is the difference in the times taken by the two cars, in minutes, to
complete the journey? (WJEC)

**10** 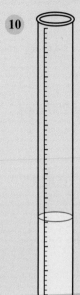 A hollow circular cylinder with internal radius of 0·9 cm is joined
to a hollow hemisphere of the same internal radius to make a test
tube 12 cm long.

Will the test tube be large enough to hold 32 cm³?
Explain your answer.

**Show all your working.**

(CEA)

**11** Which statement below is true if $n = 1·87$ when truncated to 2 decimal places?

(a)  $1·865 \leqslant n < 1·875$    (b)  $1·87 \leqslant n < 1·88$    (c)  $1·87 \leqslant n < 1·875$

**12** A frustum is the shape remaining when the top of a cone has been removed.

(a)  Find the volume of the solid metal frustum shown below.

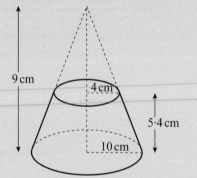

(b)  The metal frustum shown opposite
is melted down and is re-shaped
into a sphere. Assuming there is
no waste, what is the radius of this
sphere in centimetres?

Give your answer correct to two
decimal places. (WJEC)

**13** The cylinder opposite has a capacity
of 3 litres. It is 25 cm high.

Find the radius of the cylinder.

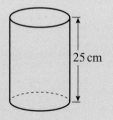

(CEA)

# STATISTICS 2

**In this unit you will learn how to:**

– consolidate previous statistics work

– examine trends

– draw a line of best fit and use it to estimate values

– take samples

– USE YOUR MATHS! – the real cost

## Previous statistics work

**M10.1**

**1** The chart below shows the percentage of smokers for different age groups in 2011.

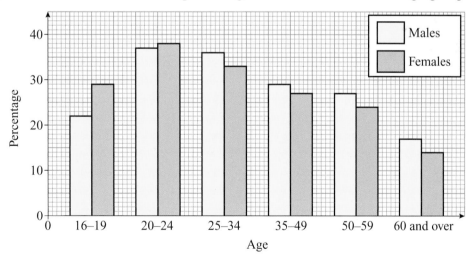

(a) In which age group were the percentage of female smokers greater than the percentage of male smokers?

(b) What percentage of 25–34 year-old males are smokers?

(c) What percentage of 16–19 year-old females are smokers?

(d) What is the *difference* in the percentage of 16–19 year-old female smokers compared to 16–19 year-old male smokers?

(e) As people get older, what happens to the percentage of people who smoke?

**2** 400 students in years 10 and 11 were asked if they smoked or drank alcohol on a regular basis. The information is shown in the two-way table below.

| | Smoke | Drink alcohol | Neither | Smoke and drink alcohol | Total |
|---|---|---|---|---|---|
| Year 10 | 21 | 40 | | | |
| Year 11 | 23 | | | 38 | 227 |
| Total | | | 198 | 62 | 400 |

(a) Copy and complete the two-way table.

(b) One of these students is picked at random. Write down the *probability* that the student will not smoke or drink alcohol.

**3** Henry rather likes eating biscuits.

The list of numbers below shows how many biscuits he ate on each day of one week.

6, 8, 6, 9, 5, 7, 8

Melanie also likes biscuits.
During the same week she ate a mean average of 6·5 biscuits each day.

Who ate the most biscuits?
Justify your answer.

**4** Draw an ordered stem and leaf diagram for the ages of a group of people shown below.

| 32 | 29 | 41 | 38 | 52 | 53 | 41 | 28 | 36 | 52 |
|---|---|---|---|---|---|---|---|---|---|
| 44 | 26 | 47 | 43 | 38 | 27 | 36 | 63 | 62 | 28 |

| Stem | Leaf |
|---|---|
| 2 | |
| 3 | |
| 4 | |
| 5 | |
| 6 | |

**5** Some people were asked what their favourite kind of television programme was. The data is recorded below:

| Type of programme | Frequency (number of people) |
|---|---|
| soap | 25 |
| drama | 11 |
| news | 5 |
| comedy | 15 |
| other | 4 |

(a) Find the total frequency.

(b) Work out the angle for each person to help draw a pie chart (i.e. 360° ÷ 'total frequency').

(c) Work out the angle for each type of programme and draw a pie chart.

**6** Eight friends take a maths test.

The marks for seven of them are shown below.

| 59 | 60 | 86 | 71 | 42 | 59 | 74 |

The mean mark for all eight friends is 66.

What position did the 8th friend come in the test?


**7** During one week Anna spends £215 making 480 cakes.

She sells them from Tuesday to Saturday.

The pictogram below shows how many cakes she sold on each day.

| Tuesday | ⊕ ⊕ ⊕ |
| Wednesday | ⊕ ⊕ ⊕ ⊕ |
| Thursday | ⊕ ⊕ ⊕ ◿ |
| Friday | ⊕ ⊕ ⊕ ⊕ ⊕ ◖ |
| Saturday | ⊕ ⊕ ⊕ ⊕ ⊕ ⊕ ◔ |

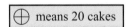 means 20 cakes

She sells each cake for £1·20.

(a) How much profit does she make for the whole week?

(b) How many cakes does she have left over at the end of the week?

**8** An expedition company assist people who want to climb to the top of Mount Everest.

260 people tried in 2013 and 336 people tried in 2014. The pie charts below show what proportion of the people successfully made it to the top.

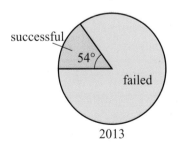

2013

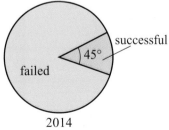

2014

In which year did more people make it to the top of the mountain?

How many more people made it during this year?

**1** A number of 16/17 year-olds were asked how much money they earned in pounds each week from part-time jobs.
The data is recorded below:

| | | | | | | | | | | |
|---|---|---|---|---|---|---|---|---|---|---|
| 32 | 40 | 36 | 51 | 82 | 69 | 38 | 43 | 28 | 51 | 65 |
| 74 | 63 | 42 | 70 | 65 | 71 | 30 | 25 | 38 | 26 | 70 |
| 68 | 70 | 32 | 37 | 24 | 42 | 32 | 65 | 48 | 42 | 36 |

(a) Draw a stem and leaf diagram to show this data.

(b) How many people were asked?

(c) What is the median amount of money earned?

(d) Find the range for this data.

**2** Some people were asked which football team they support.
Draw a pie chart to display this information from the table below.

| Team | Frequency |
|---|---|
| Arsenal | 15 |
| Liverpool | 15 |
| Chelsea | 20 |
| Manchester Utd. | 25 |
| Everton | 6 |
| Aston Villa | 9 |

**3** At the end of Year 11, all the 220 students either stay at school, go to college or do an apprenticeship.

34 out of 115 females do an apprenticeship.

Half of the 58 students who go to college are male.

51 males stay at school.

If one student is chosen at random, find the probability that this student does an apprenticeship.

*Can you still?*

**Mixed Number Work**

*Do not use a calculator*

**1** $280 = 2^3 \times 5 \times 7$
Find the Highest Common Factor and Lowest Common Multiple of 280 and 60.

**2** Find the value of $5^{-1} - 5^{-2}$

**3** Find the approximate value of
$\sqrt{150} + \sqrt[3]{(3^2 + 4^2)}$

**4** If $V = IR$, find the value of $V$ if $I = 4 \times 10^{12}$ and $R = 3 \times 10^7$.
Give the answer in standard form.

**5** What fraction of this shape is red?

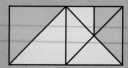

**6** Kate invests £5000 for 2 years at 5% per annum compound interest. She then shares the interest between herself and her daughter in the ratio 3 : 2. How much money does her daughter receive?

**4** The chart below shows the amount of money spent on different items by the average household in Wales during one year.

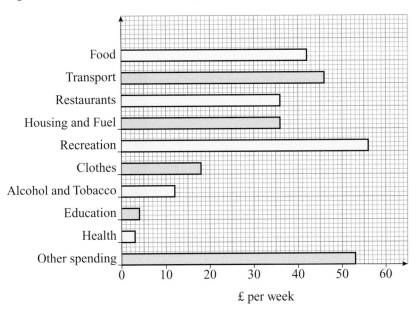

£ per week

How much money was spent on:

(a) transport          (b) education          (c) clothes?

(d) How much *more* money was spent on recreation than on health?

(e) What was the total amount of money spent on food and restaurants?

(f) What was the total amount spent on everything each week?

**5** The vertical line graph below shows the number of hours of exercise done each week by 19 men.

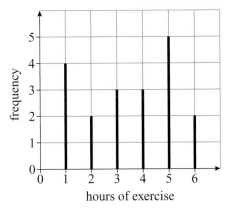

hours of exercise

The hours of exercise done by a group of 14 women is shown opposite.

| 0 | 0 | 1 | 1 | 2 | 2 | 2 |
|---|---|---|---|---|---|---|
| 3 | 3 | 5 | 6 | 8 | 9 | 9 |

Compare the time spent on exercise by the group of men and the group of women. (Remember to mention the average and the spread of data).

**6** The mean average height of 30 women is 1·7 m. The mean average height of 20 men is 1·75 m.

Calculate the mean average height of all the 50 people.

**7** 125 children study French, German or Spanish. 22 girls study French. There are 70 girls in total.

25 boys study German. There are 42 children who study Spanish, of which 12 are boys.

If one child is chosen at random, what is the probability that this child studies German?

**8**

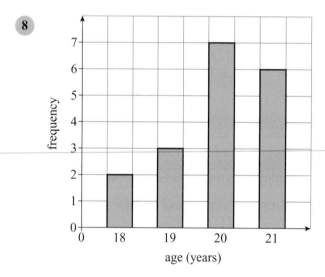

The bar chart opposite shows the ages of members of a women's rugby squad.

Display this information on a pie chart.

---

**Reminder:** means from tables.

The number of pets owned by 50 families is shown in the table below.

| number of pets | 0 | 1 | 2 | 3 | 4 | 5 |
|---|---|---|---|---|---|---|
| frequency (number of families) | 8 | 14 | 11 | 5 | 9 | 3 |

$$\text{mean} = \frac{(0 \times 8) + (1 \times 14) + (2 \times 11) + (3 \times 5) + (4 \times 9) + (5 \times 3)}{50}$$

$$= \frac{102}{50} = 2 \cdot 04$$

**Note:** if the data is given as intervals, eg. $10 < p \leqslant 20$, then use the mid-value, eg. 15, to estimate the mean.

**1** 100 families are asked how many children they have. The information is recorded in this table.

| Number of children | Frequency |
|---|---|
| 0 | 12 |
| 1 | 38 |
| 2 | 30 |
| 3 | 14 |
| 4 | 6 |

(a) Find the total number of children.

(b) Find the mean average

**2** Some teenagers were asked how often they had been to the cinema in the last month. The information is shown in the table below.

| Cinema trips | 0 | 1 | 2 | 3 | 4 | 5 |
|---|---|---|---|---|---|---|
| Frequency | 98 | 42 | 34 | 15 | 8 | 3 |

Find the mean average number of cinema trips.

**3** The table below shows the shoe sizes of some people.

| Shoe size | Frequency |
|---|---|
| 6 | 11 |
| 7 | 7 |
| 8 | 15 |
| 9 | 24 |

Find  (a)  the modal shoe size

(b)  the median shoe size

**4** The table below shows the heights of some children in Year 11.

| Height (cm) | Frequency |
|---|---|
| 171 | 9 |
| 172 | 27 |
| 173 | 15 |
| 174 | 21 |
| 175 | 17 |

Some children in Year 10 have a median height of 172 cm and a range of 7 cm. Compare the data for Year 10 with that of Year 11.

*Can you still?*

**Mixed Algebra**

**1** Expand and simplify
$$4(3n + 2) - 5(n - 3)$$

**2** Write down a formula for the total cost, $C$, of $n$ grapefruits at 55p each and $m$ lemons at 35p each.

**3** Expand $(x + 4)^2$

**4** Solve $4(2x - 1) = 5(x + 4)$

**5** Solve the simultaneous equations
$$5x - 3y = 21$$
$$2x + 4y = -2$$

**6** The masses of a pound coin and a 50p coin differ by 1·5 g. Two pound coins and three 50p coins have a total mass of 43 g. Find the mass of a 50p coin.

**5** 1000 people were asked how many hours of exercise they do during an average week. The information is shown in the table.

| Number of hours of exercise ($n$) | Frequency |
|---|---|
| $0 \leqslant n < 1$ | 225 |
| $1 \leqslant n < 3$ | 301 |
| $3 \leqslant n < 5$ | 260 |
| $5 \leqslant n < 7$ | 134 |
| $7 \leqslant n < 9$ | 56 |
| $9 \leqslant n < 12$ | 24 |

(a) Estimate the total number of hours of exercise.

(b) Estimate the mean average.

**6** The table below shows how many days absence from school for some Year 10 pupils during the last term.

| Number of days | 0 to 2 | 3 to 5 | 6 to 8 | over 8 |
|---|---|---|---|---|
| Frequency | 103 | 44 | 16 | 6 |

Find (a) the modal interval

(b) the interval which contains the median

**7** 18 people who work for Applied Interior Design were asked how many cups of tea they drank last week. The information is shown in the stem and leaf diagram below.

Another 100 people who work for Merchant Kitchens were also asked the same question. Their information is shown in the table below.

| Stem | Leaf |
|---|---|
| 0 | 7 7 |
| 1 | 2 8 |
| 2 | 6 |
| 3 | 4 |
| 4 | 2 2 6 8 |
| 5 | 1 3 6 |
| 6 | 2 |

Key
4|6 = 46 cups

**Applied Interior Design**

| Number of cups of tea ($n$) | Frequency |
|---|---|
| $0 \leqslant n < 10$ | 23 |
| $10 \leqslant n < 20$ | 29 |
| $20 \leqslant n < 30$ | 38 |
| $30 \leqslant n < 40$ | 7 |
| $40 \leqslant n < 50$ | 3 |

**Merchant Kitchens**

Which set of workers had the greater mean average and by how much?

The table below shows how many DVDs were sold in each month of a year by a large store.

| month | Apr | May | Jun | Jul | Aug | Sep | Oct | Nov | Dec | Jan | Feb | Mar |
|---|---|---|---|---|---|---|---|---|---|---|---|---|
| number of DVD's | 860 | 700 | 640 | 680 | 920 | 640 | 780 | 1000 | 1060 | 840 | 640 | 540 |

This information is shown in the graph below.

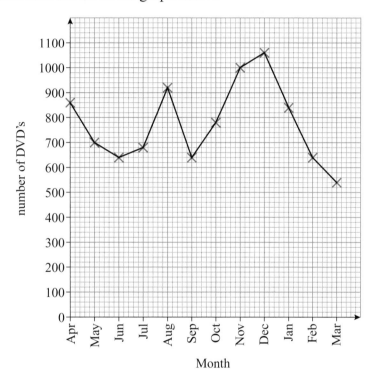

The line graph shows the monthly figures. The general *trend* can be shown more clearly by *using mean averages*.

Choose at least the first 3 months. We will in fact choose the first 4 months. Find the mean average for these 4 months.

Apr, May, Jun, Jul: mean = (860 + 700 + 640 + 680) ÷ 4

= 720

Plot this on the same graph at the midpoint of the 4 months: (see point A on next graph)

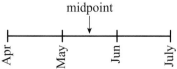

Now **move** on one month and find the mean average for these 4 months.

May, Jun, Jul, Aug: mean = (700 + 640 + 680 + 920) ÷ 4 = 735

Plot this on the graph at the mid point of the 4 months.

Now **move** on one month and find the mean average for the 4 months Jun, Jul, Aug, Sep (i.e. 720). Plot the point then keep **moving** on one month and repeating the process (i.e. 755, 835, 870, 920, 885 and 770). We call these averages the **moving average**.

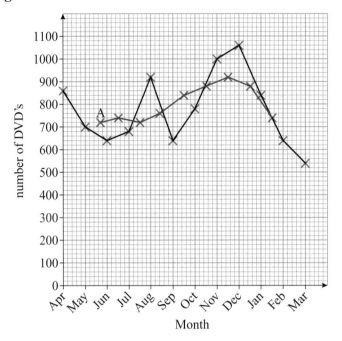

The **moving average** ( joined by the blue line) gives a better idea of the trend. We can see that there is a steady rise in the number of DVD's sold towards December then a steady fall after December.

**Note**

The moving average gives a clearer idea of the trend for a set of data. It deals with short-term differences.

Groups of 4 months were used in the example but 3, 5, 6 or more months could also have been used. We say a group of 4 months gives a '4-*point moving average*'.

**M10.4**

1   The table below shows how many cars a garage sells during one year.

| month | Jan | Feb | Mar | Apr | May | Jun | Jul | Aug | Sep | Oct | Nov | Dec |
|---|---|---|---|---|---|---|---|---|---|---|---|---|
| number of cars | 8 | 9 | 7 | 20 | 8 | 29 | 27 | 28 | 12 | 29 | 27 | 28 |

(a)  Draw a line graph for the information in this table.

(b)  Find the 4-point moving average (ie. use groups of 4 months). Plot the new moving average on the graph each time.

(c)  Join up the moving average points with a dotted line. Comment on the trend of car sales.

**2** The table below shows the weekly wage bill for a centre forward at a football team during the years shown.

| year | 2004 | 2005 | 2006 | 2007 | 2008 | 2009 | 2010 | 2011 | 2012 | 2013 | 2014 | 2015 |
|------|------|------|------|------|------|------|------|------|------|------|------|------|
| wage (£1000's) | 50 | 52 | 55 | 31 | 34 | 60 | 63 | 67 | 30 | 52 | 59 | 67 |

(a) Draw a line graph for the information in this table.

(b) Find the 4-point moving average.

(c) Plot the moving average points on the graph and join them up with a dotted line.

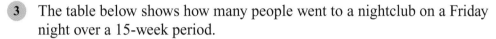

(d) Comment on the trend shown. Can you suggest any reasons for the lower wage bill in 2007, 2008 and 2012?

**3** The table below shows how many people went to a nightclub on a Friday night over a 15-week period.

| week | number of people |
|------|------------------|
| 1 | 800 |
| 2 | 680 |
| 3 | 1720 |
| 4 | 760 |
| 5 | 840 |
| 6 | 720 |
| 7 | 1640 |
| 8 | 800 |
| 9 | 1720 |
| 10 | 880 |
| 11 | 1080 |
| 12 | 1920 |
| 13 | 1520 |
| 14 | 1400 |
| 15 | 1720 |

(a) Draw a line graph for the information in this table.

(b) Find the 6-point moving average (ie. use groups of 6 weeks).

(c) Plot the moving average points on the graph and join them up with a dotted line.

(d) Comment on the trend shown.

4 A company announces its profits every quarter (ie. every 3 months).
Profits (in £ million's) over a 4-year period are shown in the table below.

| | First quarter | Second quarter | Third quarter | Fourth quarter |
|---|---|---|---|---|
| 2012 | 4·5 | 4·6 | 1·4 | 4·7 |
| 2013 | 4·3 | 4·5 | 4·1 | 0·9 |
| 2014 | 4·2 | 2·3 | 1·5 | 1·6 |
| 2015 | 1·4 | 3·2 | 4·3 | 4·5 |

(a) Draw a line graph for the information in this table.

(b) Find the 5-point moving average (ie. use groups of 5 quarters). Plot the new moving average on the graph each time.

(c) Join up the moving average points with a dotted line. Comment on the profits trend for this company.

## Pressure, area and volume

1 A cone and a cylinder each have a base radius of 4 cm. The perpendicular height of the cone is 27 cm and the length of the cylinder is 9 cm. Which solid has the greater volume?

2 Find the force which provides a pressure of 4·5 Pa over a square area with side length 2·5 m.

3 Convert $5·6\,m^3$ into $cm^3$.

## Line of Best Fit – scatter graphs

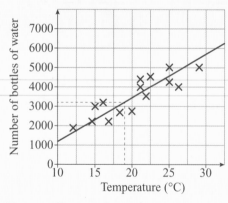

This scatter diagram shows the number of bottles of water sold by a supermarket each week and the average weekly temperature.

(a) A line of best fit is drawn (try to get the same number of points above the line as below).

(b) How many bottles of water are likely to be sold if the average weekly temperature is 19°C?

Draw a line up from the temperature axis to the line of best fit and then across the vertical axis (as shown). We can estimate that 3200 bottles of water will be sold if the average weekly temperature is 19°C.

The 100 m race times of a top athlete are recorded against the months of training completed. The information is shown on the scatter graph.

The line of best fit can be used to estimate the race time within the 24 month period shown.

We can only predict a time within the range of values plotted. It would be dangerous to extend the line of best fit and to read off values. For example, a 100 m race time of 9 seconds would be considered impossible.

## M10.5

**1** 16 people were given a short term memory test where they could achieve a maximum score of 20. The table below shows their ages and marks.

| Age | 55 | 65 | 75 | 50 | 45 | 64 | 70 | 59 | 67 | 80 | 50 | 72 | 48 | 80 | 57 | 60 |
|-------|----|----|----|----|----|----|----|----|----|----|----|----|----|----|----|----|
| Score | 17 | 12 | 10 | 16 | 18 | 13 | 15 | 15 | 15 | 20 | 17 | 12 | 19 | 10 | 15 | 12 |

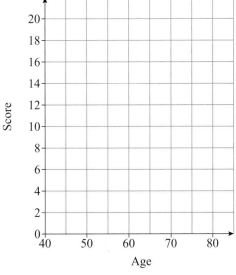

(a) Copy and complete the scatter diagram to show the data in the table

(b) Draw the line of best fit.

(c) What score would you expect a 63 year-old to get?

(d) One of the points does not follow the trend. Write down the values of this point (called an *outlier*).

(e) Why can the line of best fit not be used to estimate the test score of a 20 year-old?

(2) In a certain area, 15 people are asked what their yearly household salary is and how much their house is worth. The information is shown in the table below.

| Salary (£1000's) | 47 | 70 | 23 | 40 | 32 | 55 | 15 | 49 |
|---|---|---|---|---|---|---|---|---|
| Value of house (£1000's) | 275 | 340 | 180 | 240 | 205 | 310 | 125 | 250 |

| Salary (£1000's) | 35 | 25 | 60 | 15 | 62 | 52 | 28 |
|---|---|---|---|---|---|---|---|
| Value of house (£1000's) | 250 | 210 | 130 | 300 | 290 | 275 | 190 |

(a) Draw a scatter diagram to show this data. Use the x-axis for salaries from 10 to 70. Use the y-axis for the values of the houses from 100 to 350.

(b) Draw the line of best fit.

(c) What would you expect the salary to be for the people living in a house worth £230,000?

(d) 2 points on the scatter diagram seem 'odd'. Give reasons why these points might have occurred.

(3) A golfer records his weekly average score and how many hours he practises each week (in golf a score of 70 is *better* than a score of 80!). The information is shown in the table below.

| Weekly average score | 79 | 75 | 87 | 81 | 84 | 73 | 77 | 88 | 72 | 78 | 84 | 76 |
|---|---|---|---|---|---|---|---|---|---|---|---|---|
| Weekly hours practising | 22 | 24 | 19 | 21 | 22 | 23 | 24 | 17 | 26 | 22 | 19 | 21 |

(a) Draw a scatter diagram to show this data. Use the x-axis for the weekly average score from 70 to 90. Use the y-axis for the weekly hours practising from 0 to 30.

(b) Describe the correlation in this scatter graph.

(c) Draw the line of best fit.

(d) If the golfer practised for 25 hours one week, what average score would you expect the golfer to get that week?

**4** Information was recorded about 13 smokers. The table shows how many cigarettes they smoked each day and their age when they died.

| Age | 65 | 51 | 58 | 80 | 46 | 72 | 45 | 61 | 80 | 75 | 48 | 52 | 68 |
|---|---|---|---|---|---|---|---|---|---|---|---|---|---|
| Number of cigarettes per day | 37 | 42 | 40 | 10 | 44 | 23 | 12 | 35 | 20 | 26 | 49 | 44 | 32 |

(a) Draw a scatter graph to show this data. Use the $x$-axis for ages from 40 to 90. Use the $y$-axis for the number of cigarettes per day from 0 to 50.

(b) Describe the correlation in this scatter graph.

(c) Write down the values of the point which does not follow the trend.

(d) If a person smoked 38 cigarettes each day, what age would you expect that person to live to?

(e) Can the line of best fit be used to estimate the expected age for a person who smokes 100 cigarettes in a day. Justify your answer.

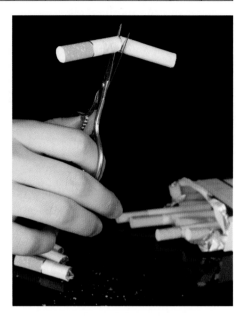

Can you still?

**Mixed Shape**

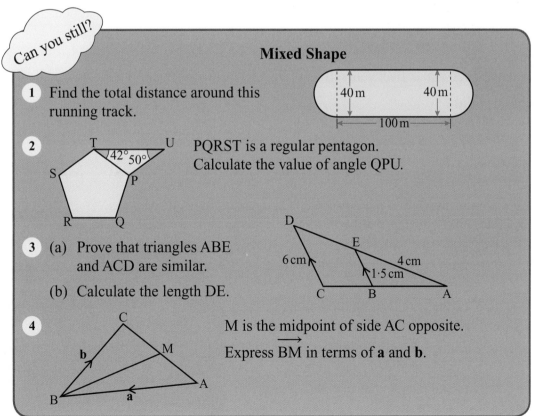

**1** Find the total distance around this running track.

40 m      40 m

100 m

**2** PQRST is a regular pentagon. Calculate the value of angle QPU.

T  42° 50°  U
S
P
R  Q

**3** (a) Prove that triangles ABE and ACD are similar.

(b) Calculate the length DE.

D
E
6 cm    4 cm
1·5 cm
C   B   A

**4** M is the midpoint of side AC opposite.

Express $\overrightarrow{BM}$ in terms of **a** and **b**.

C
b    M
B   a   A

Surveys often have to be undertaken to gather information.
For example:

- a supermarket wants to improve the service it offers
- a person wants to start a business and needs to find out the likely sales
- the Government wants to discover the eating habits of people so that it can advise.

## 🗝 Key Facts

The whole group of whatever is under investigation is called the *population*.

The whole population is often very large so not every member of the population can always be surveyed. A *sample* of the population is surveyed (a small part of the population). This sample must be *representative* of the whole population.

The *sample size* is affected by the cost of collecting the data and the precision of the findings required. If a larger sample size is taken, the precision of the findings should be greater.

Every effort should be made to avoid *bias*. It is not likely to be very reliable to survey people entering Old Trafford (Manchester United's ground) to find out what percentage of people like each football club in the whole country!

**Primary data**
Raw data which you collect yourself, e.g. pulse rates of students in your class.

**Secondary data**
Data which is already in place, e.g. trading figures on a spreadsheet or on the internet.

### M10.6

1. Tom wants to find out how much each person in his town earns.
   He selects a sample of people. Which methods below are likely to give representative samples?

   (a) asking every 5th adult at the local swimming pool.

   (b) asking people at random on the High Street.

   (c) asking each person in the 'Dog and Duck' pub on a Friday night.

   (d) asking people in every 10th house on every street.

**2** Write down which samples below are likely to be representative. For any sample which is not representative, give a reason why it is not.

(a) To test the contents of tins of baked beans made in a factory. The sample is chosen by selecting the first 30 tins made each day and the last 30 tins.

(b) To investigate the level of pollution on Britain's beaches. The sample is chosen by selecting at random 5% of the beaches from a complete list of Britain's beaches.

(c) To find out the average amount of time people spend gardening each week.
The sample is chosen by asking people as they enter a local garden centre.

(d) To check the contents in boxes of 'Quality Street' chocolates in a supermarket. The sample is chosen by selecting every 15th box of 'Quality Street'.

(e) To find out the average amount of homework given in a secondary school. The sample is chosen by selecting at random 20 pupils from each year group.

(f) To survey people about the local train services. The sample is chosen by selecting at random 8% of the town's population from the town's telephone directory.

(g) To survey the nation's favourite food. The sample is chosen by sending questionnaires to randomly selected Indian restaurants throughout the country.

**3** Describe how you would select a representative sample for each of the following:

(a) To investigate the most popular colour of sock owned by people in Cheltenham town.

(b) To find out the most popular cars owned by people in Wales.

(c) To investigate the smoking habits of students in a secondary school.

(d) To survey people about their favourite pastimes.

(e) To survey opinion about a new TV comedy programme.

 **Key Facts**

## Sampling methods

> *Simple random sampling* – every member of the population has the same chance of being chosen.

For example, we could assign each member of the population a number, write each number on an identical disc then put all the discs in a container. We could then take out a disc from the container to select a member of the population at random.

We could also use a *random number table* (your teacher may wish to illustrate this).

A *random number generator* such as a *computer* or a *calculator* may be used.

On some calculators $\boxed{\text{SHIFT}}$ $\boxed{\text{RAN \#}}$ will generate random three-digit numbers between 0·001 and 0·999. The decimal point can then be ignored.

> *Systematic sampling* – every *n*th item is chosen (for example, every 5th item or every 100th item).

> *Stratified random sampling* – the population is divided into groups where the groups have something in common. Every member of the population should belong to one and only one group. Simple random samples are then taken from each group. The numbers in each sample must be proportional to the numbers in each group making up the population.

---

800 people attend an athletics match. 210 people are Scottish, 328 are English, 149 are Irish and 113 are Welsh.

Sabby wants to survey 50 people on the sports provision in their home towns. She decides to take a stratified sample of 50 people.

What should be the sample size for each of the Scottish, English, Irish and Welsh people?

There are 800 people in total.

Fraction of Scottish people to be chosen $= \dfrac{210}{800}$

So Scottish sample size $= \dfrac{210}{800} \times 50 = 13$ (rounded off)    English sample size $= \dfrac{328}{800} \times 50 = 21$

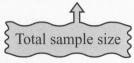
Total sample size

Irish sample size $= \dfrac{149}{800} \times 50 = 9$          Welsh sample size $= \dfrac{113}{800} \times 50 = 7$

An appropriate method would then be used to take each random sample. The total sample chosen should then be representative of all the people attending the athletics match.

1. 347 people work for a finance company called 'Loothold'. 138 people are male. A survey is to be undertaken to find out about the working conditions at 'Loothold'. A stratified sample of 40 people is to be taken from the male and female workers. How many females will be chosen in the sample?

2. The list below shows the numbers of students in each year group in a certain school. It is wanted to take a sample of 50 students from the school to question them about their attitudes to exams.

| Year | Number of students |
|------|--------------------|
| 9 | 137 |
| 10 | 121 |
| 11 | 118 |
| 12 | 95 |
| 13 | 89 |

   (a) Explain why you would want to use a stratified sample.

   (b) Work out how many students you would want from each year group.

3. A restaurant wants detailed feedback from its customers. The owner decides to ask every 10th customer.

   (a) Name this type of sampling.

   (b) Will the owner's sample provide a representative view?

4. Marcus needs to survey people who go to the local cinema. Explain how Marcus could take a simple random sample.

5. Students in a certain school were asked to list their favourite sports. Their choices are shown below. A sample of 100 students is to be taken from the school to question them about their attitudes to sport.

| Sport | Number of students |
|------|--------------------|
| Football | 302 |
| Rugby | 128 |
| Hockey | 95 |
| Basketball | 45 |
| Cricket | 140 |
| Netball | 62 |
| None | 59 |

   (a) Explain why you would want to use a stratified sample.

   (b) Work out how many students you would want in your sample from each category.

6   A breakdown of the people attending a rock concert is shown below.
Mel wants to find out about the musical backgrounds of the people at the
rock concert.

| Age group | Male | Female | Total |
|-----------|------|--------|-------|
| 12–18     | 32   | 18     | 50    |
| 19–25     | 71   | 70     | 141   |
| 26–45     | 93   | 112    | 205   |
| 46–55     | 62   | 93     | 155   |
| Over 55   | 24   | 27     | 51    |
|           |      |        | 602   |

She takes a sample of 60 people.

(a) How many people should she have sampled in the 19–25 age group?

(b) Explain whether Mel should sample the same number of males and
females in the 26–45 age group.

(c) How many people in the over 55 age group should she have sampled?

7   The height of one hundred trees is shown below (in cm) in the position in
which they were planted.

| 55 | 84 | 91 | 86 | 76 | 67 | 88 | 89 | 97 | 47 | 43 | 58 | 57 | 49 | 57 | 45 | 51 | 28 | 65 | 90 | 82 | 91 | 83 | 74 | 82 |
|----|----|----|----|----|----|----|----|----|----|----|----|----|----|----|----|----|----|----|----|----|----|----|----|----|
| 81 | 80 | 70 | 81 | 75 | 39 | 91 | 57 | 80 | 78 | 96 | 88 | 92 | 87 | 79 | 62 | 69 | 72 | 60 | 50 | 41 | 50 | 35 | 26 | 36 |
| 71 | 82 | 45 | 37 | 41 | 45 | 56 | 47 | 38 | 37 | 80 | 63 | 77 | 70 | 63 | 75 | 79 | 68 | 95 | 60 | 54 | 83 | 77 | 82 | 55 |
| 47 | 42 | 42 | 95 | 87 | 92 | 91 | 80 | 91 | 76 | 91 | 80 | 71 | 66 | 87 | 83 | 40 | 92 | 87 | 85 | 82 | 95 | 92 | 89 | 86 |

(a) Use a systematic sample to find an estimate for the mean height of the
trees (use the 1st, 6th, 11th etc. value), writing down the 20 values that
you use.

(b) Now use only the 1st, 11th, 21st etc. to find another estimate for the
mean height of the tree.

(c) Which estimate is more reliable?

(d) What other method of sampling might be more reliable?

8   Mehm investigates the health history of common pets in his town. He takes a
total stratified sample of 10% of all the pets.

(a) What is the greatest possible number of dogs in his town if his sample
contains 33 dogs?

(b) What is the least possible number of cats in his town if his sample
contains 21 cats?

(c) Describe how he might have taken a simple random sample for each
category of pet.

# USE YOUR MATHS! – The real cost

### Task A

Choose any regular activity that you like to do, eg. swim, play football, climb, play computer games, watch TV, play in a band and so on.

Your task is to calculate the real weekly cost of your chosen activity. All your calculations must be shown very clearly.

## RESEARCH EVERY ASPECT!

- if you travel to do your activity, what is the real cost of this?
- what are the initial costs like buying a television or a pair of football boots?
- have you considered the cost of electricity when you are using a computer, etc. at home? The real cost must be worked out even if adults pay for it!

### Task B

Could your chosen activity be done more cheaply?

Research the options using the internet or other sources of information.

### Task C

Look at a partner's calculations for a different activity. Does the information seem sensible? Are the calculations correct? Has anything been missed out in your opinion?

**1. Consolidating previous statistics work**

(a) Seven women have a mean weight of 63 kg and eleven men have a mean weight of 74 kg. Find the mean weight (to one decimal place) of all 18 men and women.

(b) Some people are asked what their favourite snack is. The information is shown in the table opposite. Display this information in an accurate pie chart.

| Snack | Frequency |
|---|---|
| crisps | 60 |
| fruit | 35 |
| nuts | 10 |
| biscuits | 18 |
| chocolate | 34 |
| other | 23 |

(c) The table opposite shows the number of bicycles owned by families who live in Camden Terrace. The families who live in Penn Street own a mean average of 1·9 bicycles. The number of bicycles owned by families in Penn Street range from 0 to 9. Compare the number of bicycles owned by families in Camden Terrace to those in Penn Street.

| Number of bicycles | Frequency |
|---|---|
| 0 | 8 |
| 1 | 4 |
| 2 | 17 |
| 3 | 24 |
| 4 | 16 |
| 5 | 6 |

**2. Examining trends**

The table below shows how many umbrellas are sold by a store during one year.

| month | Jan | Feb | Mar | Apr | May | Jun | Jul | Aug | Sep | Oct | Nov | Dec |
|---|---|---|---|---|---|---|---|---|---|---|---|---|
| number of umbrellas sold | 420 | 440 | 400 | 380 | 200 | 360 | 100 | 120 | 300 | 420 | 460 | 480 |

(a) Draw a line graph for the information in this table.

(b) Find the 4-point moving average.

(c) Plot the moving average points on the graph and join them up with a dotted line.

(d) Comment on the trend shown. Suggest reasons for this trend.

**3.** Using lines of best fit

The table below shows the engine sizes of 12 cars and how many miles per gallon they operate at.

| Engine size (litres) | 1·8 | 1·1 | 2 | 1·6 | 1 | 1·8 | 2·6 | 2·8 | 1·2 | 2 | 1·6 | 1·4 | 2·4 | 2·1 |
|---|---|---|---|---|---|---|---|---|---|---|---|---|---|---|
| Miles per gallon | 35 | 53 | 24 | 33 | 47 | 31 | 49 | 16 | 46 | 30 | 40 | 42 | 20 | 22 |

(a) Copy and complete the scatter diagram to show the data in the table.

(b) One of the points does not follow the trend. Circle this point on your graph.

(c) Estimate how many miles per gallon a 1·3 litre car would do.

(d) Roughly with what engine size would you expect the car to do 23 miles per gallon?

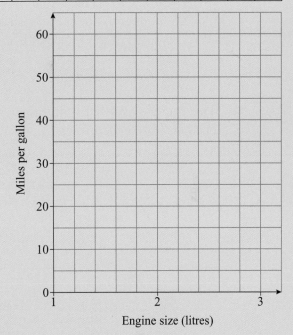

**4.** Taking samples

(a) Calli wants to find out what leisure facilities the people in her town would like. She stands outside the main supermarket in the town one Thursday morning and asks the first 100 people she sees. Criticise this method of taking a sample of the people who live in her town.

(b) People who work for a certain firm were asked to list their favourite holiday destinations. Their choices are shown opposite. A sample of 80 people is to be taken from the firm to question them about their requirements for a satisfying holiday.
   (i) Explain why you would want to use a stratified sample.
   (ii) How many people would you want in your sample from each category?

| Holiday destination | Number of people |
|---|---|
| Spain | 61 |
| Greece | 49 |
| USA | 82 |
| Australia | 37 |
| Thailand | 28 |
| France | 79 |
| India | 21 |
| China | 17 |

(c) A local council wishes to survey the students in three different secondary schools about their attitudes to education.
Suggest how the council should obtain a representative sample.

**1** (a) The mean of 5 numbers in a list is 24.
When two extra numbers are added to the list, the mean increases by
four. What does this tell you about the values of the two extra numbers?

(b) Four numbers are listed in ascending order.
The mode of the four numbers is 3.
No number in the list is greater than 3.
The range of the four numbers is 5.
The median of the four numbers is 2.
Find the four numbers. (WJEC)

**2** The scatter graph shows information about the height and the arm length of
each of 8 students in Year 11.

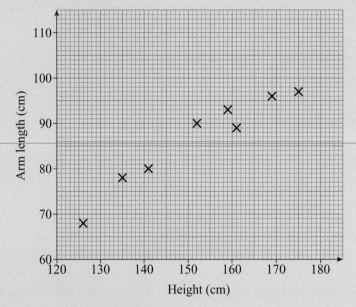

(a) What type of correlation does this scatter graph show?

A different student in Year 11 has a height of 148 cm.

(b) Estimate the arm length of this student. (EDEXCEL)

**3** The manager of a company wants to survey his employees.
He decides to sample 20% of them, stratified by the type of job they do.
This table shows the number of employees.

| Office staff | Drivers | Mechanics | **Total** |
|---|---|---|---|
| 12 | 24 | 4 | 40 |

Copy and fill in the table
opposite to show how many of
each group he should survey.

| Office staff | Drivers | Mechanics |
|---|---|---|
|  |  |  |

(AQA)

**4** The total number of people living in a street is 30.
The table shows the number of people living in each house.

| Number of people living in each house | Number of houses |
|---|---|
| 2 | 4 |
| 3 | 3 |
| 4 | $a$ |
| 5 | 1 |

Work out the value of $a$.
You **must** show your working. (AQA)

**5** There are 130 adults at a language school.
Each adult studies one of either French or Spanish or German.

96 of the adults are women.
12 of the women study French.
73 of the adults study Spanish.
55 of the women study Spanish.
9 of the men study German.

How many of the adults study French? (EDEXCEL)

**6** (a) Explain what is meant by simple random sampling.

(b) Explain how a simple random sample can be taken from some people at a theatre.

(c) There are 800 people at a theatre.
The table shows the ages of these people.
A stratified sample of 80 of these people is taken.

| Age | Male | Female |
|---|---|---|
| Under 21 years | ? | ? |
| 21–45 years | 146 | 116 |
| Over 45 years | 138 | 164 |

There are ten males under 21 years old in the sample.

Work out the greatest number of the 800 people who might be females under 21 years old.

**7** Hertford Junior is a basketball team.

At the end of 10 games, their mean score is 35 points per game.
At the end of 11 games, their mean score has gone down to 33 points per game.

How many points did the team score in the 11th game? (EDEXCEL)

**8** These expressions represent three numbers.

$$x \qquad x + 3 \qquad 4x$$

Work out the mean in terms of $x$.
Give your answer in its simplest form. (AQA)

**9** There are 900 students in the school.
This table shows the number of students in each year group.

| Year | 7 | 8 | 9 | 10 | 11 |
|---|---|---|---|---|---|
| Number of students | 210 | 190 | 175 | 175 | 150 |

Lewis decides to interview a representative stratified sample of 120 students.
How many students should he interview from Year 11? (OCR)

**10** Decide whether each of these sets of data is discrete or continuous.

(a) The heights of people. (b) The number of coins in a bag.

(c) The weights of bicycles. (d) The shoe sizes of women. (AQA)

**11** The two graphs below show similar information but look different.

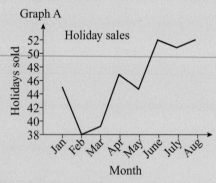
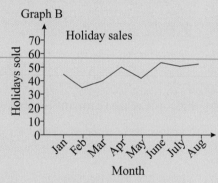

(a) Which graph appears to show the biggest increase in sales?

(b) What causes this graph to be misleading? (CEA)

**12** (a) In Kingstone, the mean daily snowfall for a week was 5·6 cm.
What would the mean daily snowfall have been if it had snowed 2 cm more on each day?

(b) In Greyfield, the snowfall for each of 10 days was measured. The results are summarised in the table opposite.

| Daily snowfall, $s$, in cm | Number of days |
|---|---|
| $4{\cdot}5 \leqslant s < 5{\cdot}5$ | 4 |
| $5{\cdot}5 \leqslant s < 6{\cdot}5$ | 2 |
| $6{\cdot}5 \leqslant s < 7{\cdot}5$ | 1 |
| $7{\cdot}5 \leqslant s < 8{\cdot}5$ | 1 |
| $8{\cdot}5 \leqslant s < 9{\cdot}5$ | 2 |

(i) Calculate an estimate for the mean daily snowfall for the 10 days.

(ii) State the modal class.

(iii) Write down the class in which the median lies. (WJEC)

# GEOMETRY 3

# 11

**In this unit you will learn how to:**

– consolidate previous geometry work

– construct with compasses

– draw loci

– use plans and elevations

– use Pythagoras' theorem

– use trigonometry

– ( USE YOUR MATHS! ) – Spruce it up

## Previous geometry work

**M11.1**

**1** Use a ruler and protractor to draw:

(a)

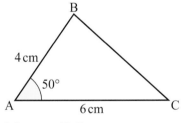

Measure BC.

(b)

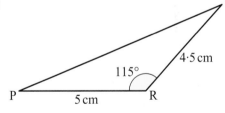

Measure PQ.

**2** Use a ruler and compasses only to draw:

(a)

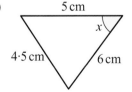

Measure angle *x*.

(b)

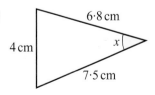

Measure angle *x*.

**3** An isosceles triangle has a 7 cm side and a 5·5 cm side.
Use a ruler and compasses only to construct the two possible triangles.
Measure and write down the angles in both triangles.

**4** Make an accurate scale drawing of the diagram below, using a scale of 1 cm for every 8 m. Write down the real length of CD.

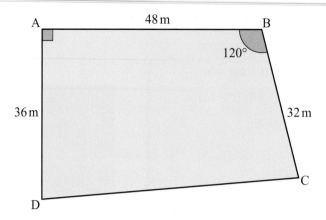

**5** The distance between two towns on a map is 3·5 cm. What is the real distance between the towns if the map scale is 1: 500 000?

**6** A map has scale 1 : 25 000. A rectangular field has length 600 m and width 350 m. What is its length and width on the map?

Remember:

Bearings are measured from the North line in a *clockwise* direction. A bearing is always given as a *three-figure number*.

B is on a bearing of 215° from A.

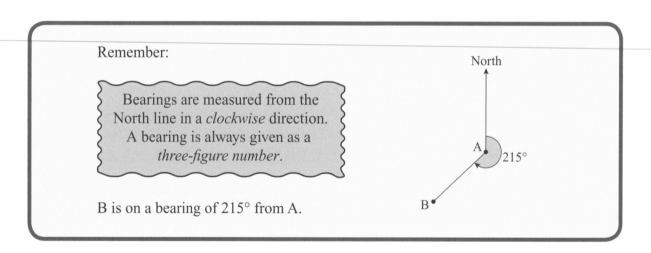

**M11.2**

**1** 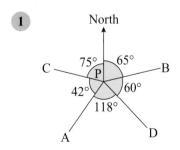 Write down the bearing of:

(a) A from P

(b) B from P

(c) C from P

(d) D from P

**2**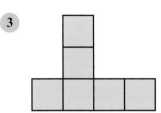

North

Oscar

Mark Oscar's position on a diagram. Louise is on a bearing of 300° from Oscar and a distance of 250 m away.

(a) Draw the position of Louise using a scale of 1 cm for every 50 m.

(b) What is the bearing of Oscar from Louise?

**3**

Can this net be folded to make a cube?

**4** Look at the prism opposite. How many more edges does it have than vertices?

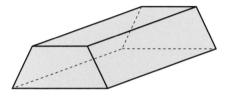

**5** A cargo ship leaves a port and travels 40 km on a bearing of 040°.

It then changes direction and travels 25 km on a bearing of 115°.

(a) Use a scale of 1 cm for 5 km to draw this journey.

(b) At the end of this journey, how far is the ship from the port?

(c) What is the bearing of the ship from the port?

**6**

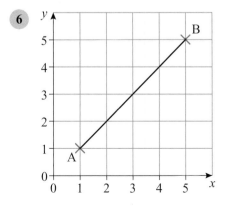

(a) AB is the diagonal of a square. Write down the co-ordinates of the point of intersection of the two diagonals of this square.

(b) Triangle BCD has vertices at (5, 5), (5, 3) and (3, 3). A point E has co-ordinates (5, 1). Find the ratio of the area of the triangle BCD to the area of triangle ABE. Give the answer in its simplest form.

**7** Draw an accurate net of the triangular prism shown below.

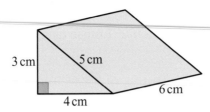

**8** The plan and elevations of a cuboid are shown below.
Each square has area 1 cm². Work out the volume of the cuboid.

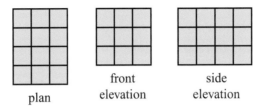

plan          front          side
              elevation      elevation

**9** Riley is making a model of her car.
The car is 4 m long and she uses a scale of 1 : 25.
Sam makes a model of his car which is 3·5 m long.
He uses a scale of 1 : 20.
Who has the longer model car and by how much?

**10**

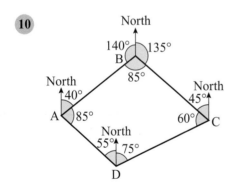

Arnav walks from A to B to C to D
and back to A. Work out the bearing he
walked on from

(a) A to B

(b) B to C

(c) C to D

(d) D to A

**11** (a) Copy the diagram opposite and
complete the parallelogram PQRS.
Write down the co-ordinates of S.

(b) Mark on a point T with a *y*-value
greater than 1 such that the area
of triangle PQT is half the area of
parallelogram PQRS.
Write down the co-ordinates of T.

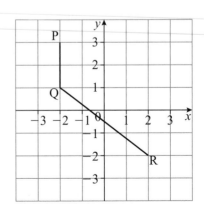

## Constructions with compasses

**Perpendicular bisector**

Draw a line AB 8 cm long.

Set the pair of compasses to more than 4 cm (half the line AB). Put the compass point on A and draw an arc as shown.

Put the compass point on B **(Do not let the compasses slip).** Draw another arc as shown.

This broken line cuts line AB in half (*bisects*) and is at right angles to line AB (*perpendicular*).

The broken line is called the *perpendicular* bisector of line AB.

**Bisector of an angle**

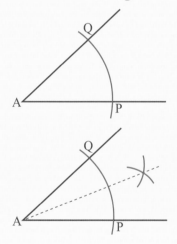

Put the compass point on A and draw an arc as shown.

Put the compass point on P and draw an arc as shown.
Put the compass point on Q and draw an arc as shown.
This broken line cuts the angle in half (*bisects*).
This broken line is called the *angle bisector*.

### M11.3

1. Draw a horizontal line AB of length 9 cm. Construct the perpendicular bisector of AB. Check that each half of the line measures 4·5 cm exactly.

2. Draw a horiontal line CD of length 6 cm. Construct the perpendicular bisector of CD. Check that each half of the line measures 3 cm exactly.

3. Draw a *vertical* line EF of length 10 cm. Construct the perpendicular bisector of EF.

4. Draw an angle of 80°. Construct the bisector of the angle.
   Use a protractor to check that each half of the angle now measures 40°.

**5** Draw an angle of 110°. Construct the bisector of the angle.

**6** (a) Use a pencil, ruler and a pair of compasses *only* to *construct* the triangle ABC shown opposite.

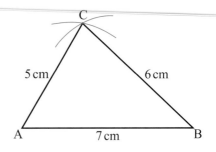

(b) Construct the perpendicular bisector of line AB.

(c) Construct the perpendicular bisector of line BC.

(d) Construct the perpendicular bisector of line AC. The 3 perpendicular bisectors should cross at the same point.

**7** Draw any triangle XYZ and construct:

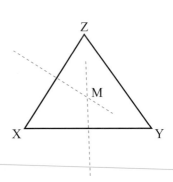

(a) the perpendicular bisector of XY.

(b) the perpendicular bisector of XZ. Mark the point of intersection M.

(c) Take a pair of compasses and, with centre at M and radius MX, draw a circle through the points X, Y and Z. This is the *circumcircle of triangle XYZ*.

(d) Repeat this construction for another triangle with different sides.

**8** Draw any triangle ABC and then construct the bisectors of angles A, B and C. If done accurately the three bisectors should all pass through one point.

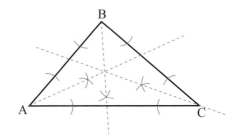

**9** Draw any triangle XYZ and construct the bisectors of angles X and Y to meet at point M.

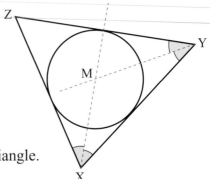

With centre at M draw a circle which just touches the sides of the triangle. This is the *inscribed circle of the triangle*.

Repeat the construction for a different triangle.

## Constructing a 60° angle

Draw a line 6 cm long.

Set the pair of compasses to less than 6 cm. Put the compass point on A and draw an arc as shown.

Put the compass point on B (**Do not let the compasses slip**). Draw another arc as shown.

Join C to the end of the line. The two lines make an angle of 60°. BÂC = 60°

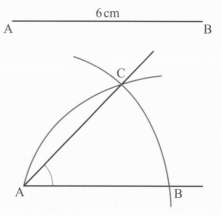

## Constructing a 90° angle at a point on a line

Draw any line and mark a point on that line.

Set the pair of compasses to around 3 cm. Put the compass point on A and draw 2 small arcs which cross the line on each side of A. (If necessary, make the line longer)

Put the compass point on B and set the compasses longer than BA. Draw an arc above the line.

Put the compass point on C (**Do not let the compasses slip**). Draw another arc as shown.

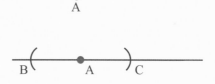

Join D and A with a straight line.

The two lines make an angle of 90°.
CÂD = 90°

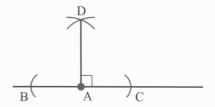

---

**E11.1**

**1**  (a)  Draw a line 9 cm long and mark the point A on the line as shown.

<pre>
      _____•_____
          4 cm           A          5 cm
</pre>

(b)  Construct an angle of 90° at A.

**2**  Construct an angle of 60°.

**3** (a) Draw a line 7 cm long and mark the point B on the line as shown.

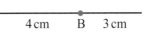

4 cm    B    3 cm

    (b) Construct an angle of 45° at B.

**4** Construct an angle of 30°.

**5** Construct an equilateral triangle with each side equal to 5 cm.

**6** Construct these triangles (only use a protractor to *check* at the end).

(a)

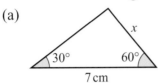

30°      60°

7 cm

Measure *x*.

(b)

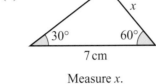

6 cm

8 cm

Measure *x*.

**7** Construct each shape below with ruler and compasses only. Measure *x* on each diagram.

(a)

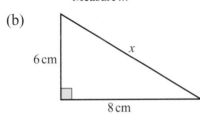

45°

5 cm

*x*

30°

(b)

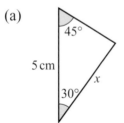

*x*

4 cm

60°      45°

10 cm

(c)

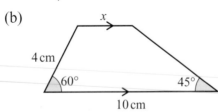

4 cm

8 cm    *x*

4 cm

**1**

−3      4

Write down the inequalities for *x* shown on the number line.

**2** Solve $x^2 - 6x + 8 = 0$

**3** Describe the type of sequence:

$5, -10, 20, -40, \ldots$

**4**

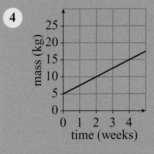

mass (kg)

25
20
15
10
5
0

0 1 2 3 4
time (weeks)

The graph shows the mass of a creature during a four week period. Work out the rate of change of the mass of the creature (in kg per week).

**5** Factorise   (i) $n^2 - ny$   (ii) $n^2 - 25$

**6** Solve $3(4x - 3) = 8x + 11$

**7** Find the *n*th term of the sequence

$3, 7, 11, 15, \ldots$

**8** Solve $5x - 2y = 18$

$3x - 5y = 26$

**8** (a) Draw any line and any point as shown opposite.

(b) Put the compass point on A and set the compasses so that an arc can be drawn as shown.

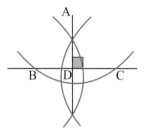

(c) Now draw the perpendicular bisector of the line BC.

The line AD is described as the *perpendicular from the point A to the line*. AD is the shortest distance from the point to the line.

**9** Construct an angle of 15°.

**10** Construct a right-angled triangle ABC, where AB = 7 cm, AB̂C = 90° and BÂC = 45°. Measure the length of BC.

**11** Construct an angle of 22·5°.

**12** Draw any vertical line and any point as shown opposite.

*Construct* the perpendicular from the point to the line.

**13** Explain clearly why the construction of the 60° angle works.

**14** Construct any triangle with an area of 15 cm².

## Locus

Sarah walks so that she is always 2 km from a point A.

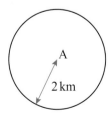

She ends up walking in a circle. She walks in a circle because she is following the rule that she is always 2 km from point A. The circle is called a '*locus*'. These are all the points which are *equidistant* from A.

A *locus* is the *set of points* which fit a given rule

The plural of locus is '*loci*'.

For Sarah walking above, the circle is the *locus* of points 2 km from point A.

(a) Draw the locus of all points which are 2 cm from the line AB.

2 cm

A ——— B

2 cm

each point is 2 cm from line AB

(b) A garden has a tree at the corner B. A lawn is made so that it is greater than or equal to 1 m from the edge of the garden and *at least* 2 m from the tree. Draw the lawn in the garden.

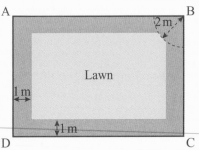

A      12 m      B

8 m

D      C

The lawn is a 'locus' even though the word 'locus' was *not* used in the question.

---

**M11.4**

You will need a ruler and a pair of compasses.

1. Draw the locus of all points which are 4 cm from a point A.

2. Draw the locus of all points which are 3 cm from the line AB.

A      6 cm      B

3. A goat is tied by a 5 m rope to a peg in the middle of a large field. Using a scale of 1 cm for 1 m, shade the area that the goat can graze in.

4. Draw the locus of all points which are less than or equal to 1·5 cm from the line PQ.

P      5 cm      Q

5. A wild headteacher is placed in a cage. The pupils are not allowed to be within one metre of the cage. Using a scale of 1 cm for 1 m, sketch the cage and show the locus of points where the pupils are *not* allowed.

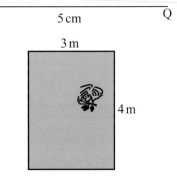

3 m

4 m

**6**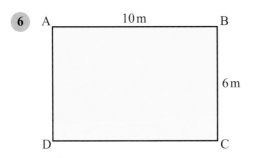

A garden has a tree at the corners C and D. The whole garden is made into a lawn except for anywhere less than or equal to 4 m from any tree. Using a scale of 1 cm for 2 m, draw the garden and shade in the lawn.

**7** Another garden has a tree at the corner A. A lawn is made so that it is greater than or equal to 2 m from the edge of the garden and *at least* 5 m from the tree.

Using a scale of 1 cm for 2 m, draw the garden and shade in the lawn.

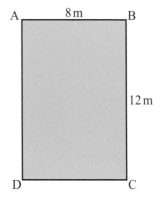

**8**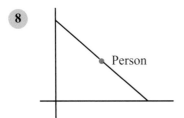

A ladder leans against a wall. A person is standing at the centre of the ladder. The ladder starts to slip! Draw the locus of the person as the ladder falls (make sure in your drawing, the ladder stays the same length!).

**9**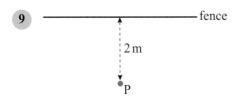

A goat is tied by a 3 m rope to a peg P as shown. Using a scale of 1 cm for 1 m, copy the diagram then shade the area that the goat can graze in.

**10**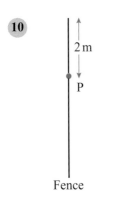

The goat is moved so that it is tied by a 3 m rope to a peg P as shown. Using a scale of 1 cm for 1 m, copy the diagram then shade the area that the goat can graze in.

305

You will need a ruler and a pair of compasses.

**1** Draw the locus of points which are the same distance from P and Q below.

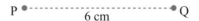

P •- - - - - - - - - - - - - - - - - - - - - - - - -• Q

6 cm

**2**

Draw the locus of points which are the same distance from the lines PQ and QR.

**3**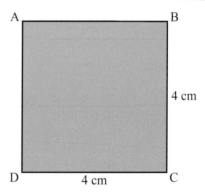

A ship sails so that it is *equidistant* from ports P and Q. Using a scale of 1 cm for 1 km, draw a rough copy of this diagram with P and Q 4 km apart.

Construct the path taken by the ship.

**4** Draw this square.

Show the locus of points inside the square which are nearer to A than to C *and* are more than 3 cm from B.

A ▢ B

4 cm

D  4 cm  C

**5**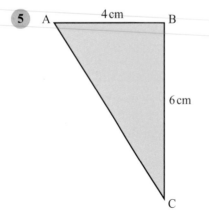

A — 4 cm — B

6 cm

C

Draw one copy of triangle ABC and show on it:

(a) the locus of points equidistant from A and B

(b) the locus of points equidistant from lines AB and AC.

(c) the locus of points nearer to AC than to AB

**6** A transmitter at Redford has a range of 80 km and another transmitter at Hatton has a range of 60 km. The 2 transmitters are 120 km apart.

Using a scale of 1 cm for 20 km, draw the 2 transmitters then shade the area where a signal can be received from both transmitters.

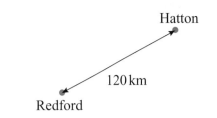

**7** A child's block is rolled along the floor by rotating about its corners.

Draw the locus of B.

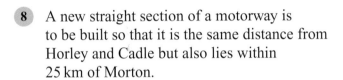

**8** A new straight section of a motorway is to be built so that it is the same distance from Horley and Cadle but also lies within 25 km of Morton.

Using a scale of 1 cm for 5 km, draw the diagram opposite then draw the new section of motorway.

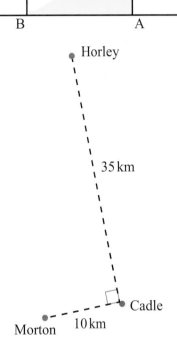

---

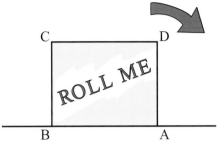 **Can you still?**

### Percentages and proportion

**1** Emma invests £6000 for 3 years at 4% per annum compound interest. Liam invests the same amount of money for 4 years at 3·5% per annum compound interest. Who now has more money and by how much?

**2** If 9 people take 4 hours to dig a trench, how long will it take 3 people?

**3** Myfi runs a business. Last year she paid herself 35% of the profit and this year pays herself 40% of the profit. This year the profit is £92160 which is a 4% drop on last year's profit. How much more money does Myfi pay herself this year compared to last year?

## Key Facts

Remember:

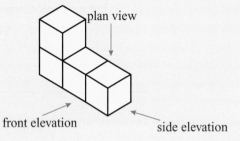

---

**M11.6**

In questions **1** to **6** draw (a) the plan view, (b) the front view and (c) the side view of the object.

**1**

**2**

**3**

**4**  **5**  **6**

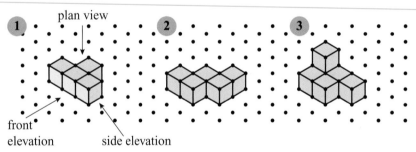

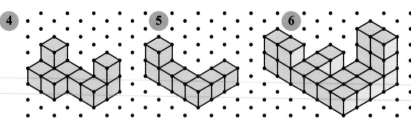

**7** The plan and elevations of a solid are shown opposite.
All lengths are in cm.
Work out the total surface area of the solid.

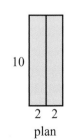

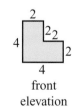

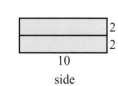

In questions ⑧ to ⑪ you are given the plan and two elevations of an object.
Use the information to make the shape using centimetre cubes.
Draw the object on isometric paper if you can.

⑧
front elevation
plan view
side elevation

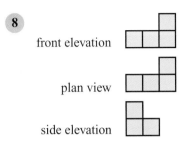

⑨
front elevation
plan view
side elevation

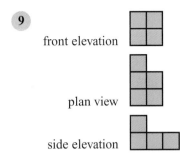

⑩ front elevation
plan view
side elevation

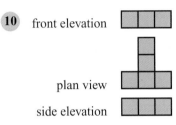

⑪
front elevation
plan view
side elevation

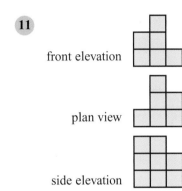

⑫ Each square in the plan
and elevations opposite
is 1 cm². Work out the
volume of the solid.

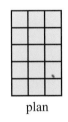
plan

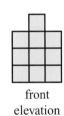
front
elevation

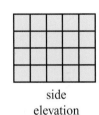
side
elevation

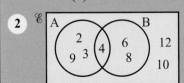
Can you still?

**Averages, Venn diagrams and set notation**

① 500 people were asked how much their houses were worth.
The table below shows the information.

| Value of house (£1000's) ($v$) | $50 \leqslant v < 100$ | $100 \leqslant v < 200$ | $200 \leqslant v < 300$ | $300 \leqslant v < 400$ | $400 \leqslant v < 500$ | $500 \leqslant v < 700$ |
|---|---|---|---|---|---|---|
| Frequency | 75 | 184 | 112 | 72 | 41 | 16 |

Find (a) the modal interval. (b) the interval which contains the median.
(c) estimate the mean average value of a house.

② 𝒠 A ⬭ B
2
9 3  4  6
8
12
10

$A' = \{6, 8, 10, 12\}$     $A \cap B = \{4\}$

Find (a) $(A \cap B)'$        (b) $A \cup B$
(c) $A \cup B'$        (d) $n(B')$

Here is a dissection which demonstrates a result called Pythagoras' theorem. Pythagoras was a famous Greek mathematician who proved the result in about 550 B.C. The dissection works only for isosceles right angled triangles.

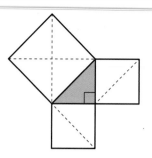

## Key Facts

**Pythagoras' theorem**

In a *right angled* triangle, the square on the hypotenuse is equal to the sum of the squares on the other two sides.

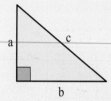

$$a^2 + b^2 = c^2$$

The 'hypotenuse' is the *longest* side in a right angled triangle.

To find the *hypotenuse*, square the known sides, *add* then square root. To find one of the *shorter sides*, square the known sides, *subtract* then square root.

(a)  Find the length $x$.

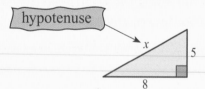

$x^2 = 5^2 + 8^2$

$x^2 = 25 + 64$

$x^2 = 89$

$x = \sqrt{89}$

$x = 9{\cdot}43$ (to 2 decimal places)

(b)  Find the length $y$.

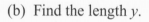
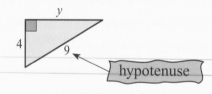

$y^2 + 4^2 = 9^2$

$y^2 + 16 = 81$

$y^2 = 81 - 16$

$y^2 = 65$

$y = \sqrt{65}$

$y = 8{\cdot}06$ (to 2 decimal places)

*You will need a calculator.*
*Give your answers correct to 2 decimal places where necessary.*
*The units are cm.*

**1** Find the length $x$.

(a)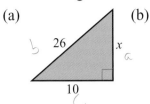

(b)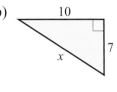

(c)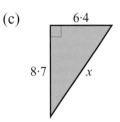

(d)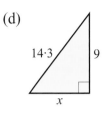

(e)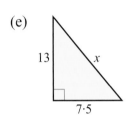

(f)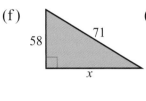

(g)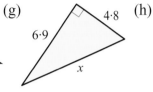

(h)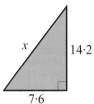

**2** Find the length AB.

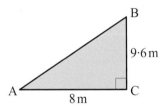

**3** Find the length PQ.

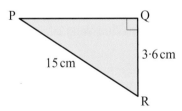

**4** Work out the perimeter of triangle MLN.

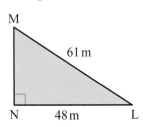

*Can you still?*

**Mixed geometry**

**1** 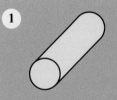 This cylinder has diameter 10 cm and length 16 cm. Find its mass if it is made from a metal with density $7.3$ g/cm$^3$.

**2** Write down the possible values of P as an inequality if P is measured as 8·2 cm, correct to one decimal place.

**3** Write down an algebraic expression for the size of an exterior angle of an $n$-sided regular polygon.

**4** ABCD is a square. Calculate CÊE, giving reasons for your answer.

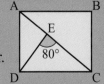

**5** A cube measures $x$ cm by $x$ cm by $y$ m. It is made of a material with density $n$ g/cm$^3$. Find an expression for its mass in grams.

**5**  Work out the area of triangle XYZ opposite.

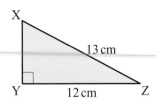

**6**  A ladder of length 6 m rests against a vertical wall, with its foot 2·4 m from the wall. How far up the wall does the ladder reach?

**7**
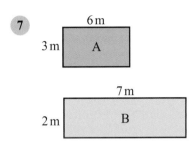

Which rectangle has the longer diagonal and by how much?

**8**
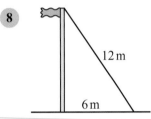

A rope attached to a flagpole is 12 m long. The rope is fixed to the ground 6 m from the foot of the flagpole. How tall is the flagpole?

**9**  Towley is 8 km due east of Hapton.
Castleton is 12 km due south of Hapton.
How far is Towley from Castleton?

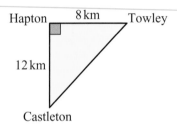

**10**  Redford is 9 km due north of Hagshed. Peltsham is 7 km due west of Hagshed. How far is Redford from Peltsham?

**11**  A ship sails 50 km due north and then a further 62 km due east.
How far is the ship from its starting point?

**12**
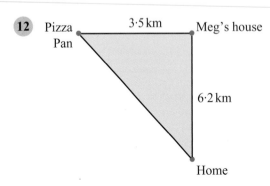

Kat and Holly are sisters. They are meeting friends at Pizza Pan. Kat drives *directly* to Pizza Pan. Holly has to pick up Meg on the way to Pizza Pan. How much further does Holly drive than Kat?

An *isosceles* triangle has a line of symmetry which divides the triangle into two right-angled triangles as shown.

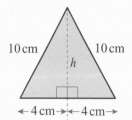

Pythagoras' theorem can then be used to find the height $h$ of the triangle.

## E11.2

**1** Find the height of each isosceles triangle below.

(a)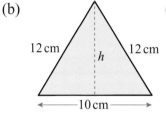

(b)

(c)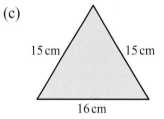

**2** A clothes line is attached to 2 vertical walls as shown. How long is the clothes line?

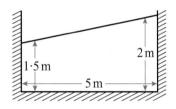

**3** Area of triangle $= \frac{1}{2}bh$
Find the area of this isosceles triangle.

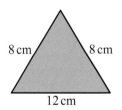

**4** Work out the area of the trapezium opposite.

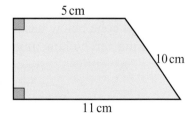

**5** Calculate the vertical height and hence the area of an equilateral triangle of side 16 cm.

313

**6**

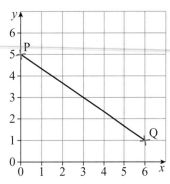

*Calculate* the length PQ.

**7** Calculate the length of the line joining (2, 1) to (8, 9).

**8**

Reminder:

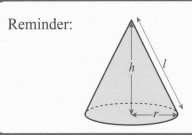

volume of cone $= \dfrac{1}{3}\pi r^2 h$

curved surface area $= \pi rl$

where $h$ = perpendicular height

and $l$ = slant height

(a) Find the curved surface area of the cone below.

24 cm

7 cm

(b) Work out the volume of the cone below.

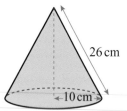

26 cm

10 cm

(c) Which cone below has the greater volume and by how much?

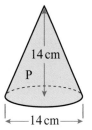

14 cm

P

14 cm

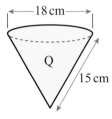

18 cm

Q

15 cm

---

**Can you still?**

**Mixed algebra**

**1** Expand $(x + 3)(x - 7)$

**2** Expand $(x + 5)^2$

**3** ABC is an isosceles triangle. Work out the actual area of a square with side length $(n + 2)$ cm.

A

5n − 1

B

2n + 11

C

**4** Factorise $x^2 + 7x + 12$

**5** Solve $\dfrac{5n + 1}{3} - 2 = 5$

**6** Factorise $x^2 - 3x - 10$

**7** Simplify $\dfrac{(x^4)^2 \times x^5}{x^7}$

314

**9** Find the exact total surface area of the cone opposite, leaving the answer in terms of $\pi$.

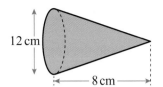

**10**

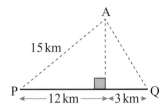

Tom walks from P to Q.
What will be his shortest distance from A at any point on his walk?

**11** Calculate the length of the line joining $(-3, 2)$ to $(3, -4)$.

**12** Find the length $x$. The units are cm.

(a)
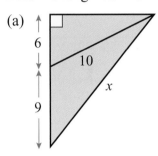

(b)
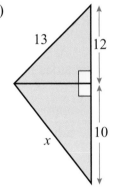

(c)
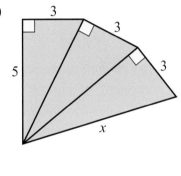

---

## Trigonometry

# Key Facts

Trigonometry is used to find angles and sides in triangles. All work in this section refers to right angled triangles.

**Naming the sides**

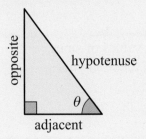

The longest side is the '**hypotenuse**'.

The side opposite an angle being used ($\theta$) is the '**opposite**'.

The other side (touching both $\theta$ and the right angle) is the '**adjacent**'.

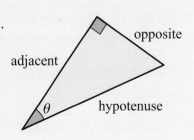

315

In each triangle below, note the angle given and state whether side $x$ is the opposite, adjacent or hypotenuse.

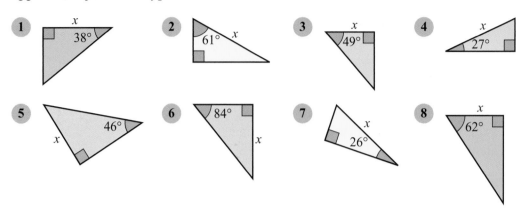

## Ratios of sides

The ratio of the opposite and adjacent sides for an angle $\theta$ is known as the 'tangent' of angle $\theta$. We say that

$$\tan \theta = \frac{\text{opp}}{\text{adj}}$$

There are two more important ratios:

$$\sin \theta = \frac{\text{opp}}{\text{hyp}} \qquad\qquad \cos \theta = \frac{\text{adj}}{\text{hyp}}$$

(sin $\theta$ means the '**sine**' of angle $\theta$)　　　(cos $\theta$ means the '**cosine**' of angle $\theta$)

You **must** learn these three formulas. Some people memorise the word

```
      S O H        C A H        T O A
        ↓            ↓            ↓
or     /O\          /A\          /O\
      /S|H\        /C|H\        /T|A\
```

Some people learn a sentence:

eg. **S**ome **O**fficers **H**ave **C**oaches **A**nd **H**orses **T**o **O**rder **A**bout

Make up your own?

tan 45° is simply a number, ie. 1. For example, sin 30° = 0·5. The values of sines, cosines and tangents are stored on calculators. Check you can find them on your calculator.

**Warning!** Most calculators have 3 trigonometry modes:
'Deg', 'Rad' and 'Gra'. Make sure you work in 'Deg' mode.

# Key Facts

**Finding a side in a right-angled triangle.**

1. Draw a diagram.
2. Label the sides opp, hyp, adj, according to the angle being used.
3. Decide whether to use the formula for sin, cos or tan.
4. Write down the formula from ,  or

then cover up the quantity you wish to find and substitute the numbers (alternatively write down the formula, substitute the numbers then rearrange the formula).

5. Use a calculator to evaluate the answer.

---

(a) Find $x$

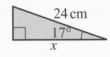

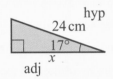

Adj = cos $\theta$ × Hyp

$x = \cos 17° × 24$

$x = 23 \cdot 0$ cm (3 sig. figs)

(b) Find $y$

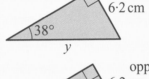

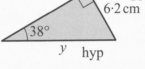

Hyp = $\dfrac{\text{Opp}}{\sin \theta}$

$y = \dfrac{6 \cdot 2}{\sin 38°}$

$y = 10 \cdot 1$ cm (3 sig. figs)

---

**M11.9**

For each triangle below, find the sides marked with letters, correct to 3 significant figures. All lengths are in cm.

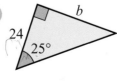

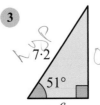

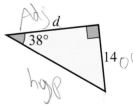

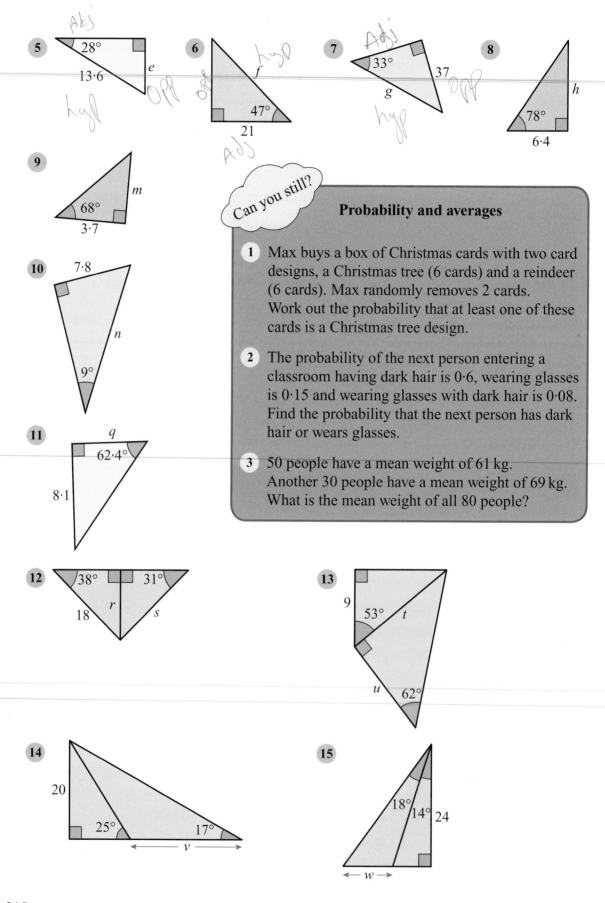

**5** 28° / 13·6 / e (Adj, Opp, Hyp)

**6** 47° / 21 / f (Opp, Hyp, Adj)

**7** 33° / 37 / g (Adj, Opp, hyp)

**8** 78° / 6·4 / h

**9** 68° / 3·7 / m

**10** 7·8 / 9° / n

**11** q / 62·4° / 8·1

Can you still?

**Probability and averages**

**1** Max buys a box of Christmas cards with two card designs, a Christmas tree (6 cards) and a reindeer (6 cards). Max randomly removes 2 cards.
Work out the probability that at least one of these cards is a Christmas tree design.

**2** The probability of the next person entering a classroom having dark hair is 0·6, wearing glasses is 0·15 and wearing glasses with dark hair is 0·08. Find the probability that the next person has dark hair or wears glasses.

**3** 50 people have a mean weight of 61 kg.
Another 30 people have a mean weight of 69 kg.
What is the mean weight of all 80 people?

**12** 38° / 31° / r / s / 18

**13** 9 / 53° / t / u / 62°

**14** 20 / 25° / 17° / v

**15** 18° / 14° / 24 / w

318

# Key Facts

## Finding an angle in a right-angled triangle

Follow the same method as for finding a side until you have sin $\theta$, cos $\theta$ or tan $\theta$ equal to a number.

For example,

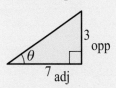 

$\tan \theta = \dfrac{\text{Opp}}{\text{Adj}}$    so    $\tan \theta = \dfrac{3}{7}$

Since $\tan \theta = \dfrac{3}{7}$, we need to go backwards on the calculator to find out what angle gives a tangent equal to $\dfrac{3}{7}$.

We do this by pressing the 'inverse' button [INV] before the tan button.

[INV] [tan] [(] [3] [÷] [7] [)] [=] 23·2° (to 1 decimal place).

On some calculators the 'inverse' button is [SHIFT] or [2ⁿᵈF].

---

### M11.10

For each triangle below, find the angles marked, correct to one decimal place.
All lengths are in cm.

**1**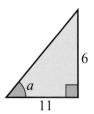

**2 3**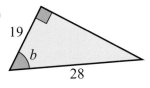

**4**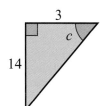

**5 6**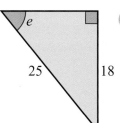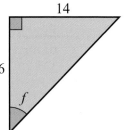

**7 8**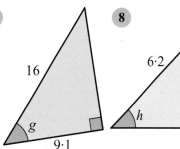

319

**9**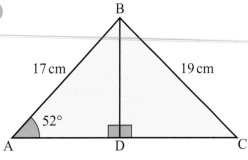

17 cm    19 cm

52°

A    D    C

   (i) Find BD    (ii) Find BĈD

**10**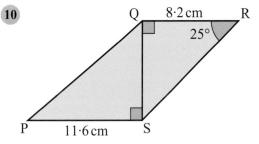

Q    8·2 cm    R

25°

P    11·6 cm    S

   (i) Find QS    (ii) Find QP̂S

**11** Triangle PQR has a right-angle at Q.
PQ = 14 cm and PR = 21 cm.
Calculate the angle PRQ.

**12**

L

16°

19 cm

K    N    M

NM is twice as long as KN.

Find KL̂M.

**13**

B

9 cm

A

39·6°

C

12 cm

48·2°

D

Find the value
of angle ADB.

# Key Facts

You are required to memorise the sine, cosine and tangent values for 30°, 45° and 60°.
The two triangles below will help you to remember them.

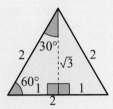

$$\sin 45° = \frac{1}{\sqrt{2}} \left(\text{or } \frac{\sqrt{2}}{2}\right) \qquad \sin 30° = \frac{1}{2} \qquad \sin 60° = \frac{\sqrt{3}}{2}$$

$$\cos 45° = \frac{1}{\sqrt{2}} \left(\text{or } \frac{\sqrt{2}}{2}\right) \qquad \cos 30° = \frac{\sqrt{3}}{2} \qquad \cos 60° = \frac{1}{2}$$

$$\tan 45° = 1 \qquad \tan 30° = \frac{1}{\sqrt{3}} \left(\text{or } \frac{\sqrt{3}}{3}\right) \qquad \tan 60° = \sqrt{3}$$

Knowing these will make you faster at working out trig values.
You will no longer always need a calculator.

> You should also learn:
>
> $\sin 0° = 0$ $\qquad \cos 0° = 1$ $\qquad \tan 0° = 0$
>
> $\sin 90° = 1$ $\qquad \cos 90° = 0$

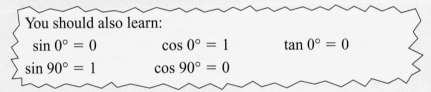

Find the exact value of $x$.

$$x = \sin 60° \times 6 = \frac{\sqrt{3}}{2} \times 6 = \frac{\sqrt{3}}{2} \times \frac{6}{1} = 3\sqrt{3} \text{ cm}$$

## E11.3

For each triangle below, find the 'exact' value of $x$. All lengths are in cm.

 **1**

**2**

**3**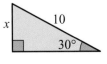

**4**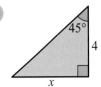

**5**

**6**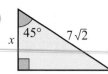

**7**

**8**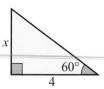

**9**

**10**

**11** Find the 'exact' area of the triangle below.

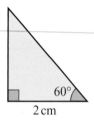

Can you still?

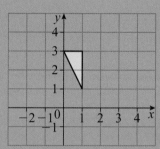

**Mixed geometry**

**1** If $\mathbf{a} = \begin{pmatrix} 3 \\ -1 \end{pmatrix}$ and $\mathbf{b} = \begin{pmatrix} 5 \\ 2 \end{pmatrix}$, find the column vector for $3\mathbf{a} - 2\mathbf{b}$.

**2**

Copy the grid and triangle above. Enlarge the triangle by a scale factor 2 about $(-1, 3)$. Write down the co-ordinates of each vertex of the new triangle.

**3** ABCD is a square and BE = FD. Prove that triangles ABE and ADF are congruent.

**4** Draw the vector $\begin{pmatrix} 5 \\ 12 \end{pmatrix}$. Calculate its length.

---

### M11.11

**Mixed problems involving trigonometry**

**1**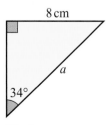

Find $a$.

**2**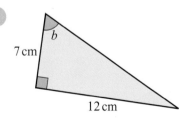

Find $b$.

**3**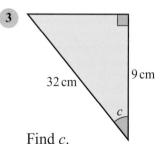

Find $c$.

4   A ladder leans against a vertical wall so that it makes an angle of 31° with the wall. The base of the ladder is 1·8 m from the wall. How high does the top of the ladder reach up the wall?

5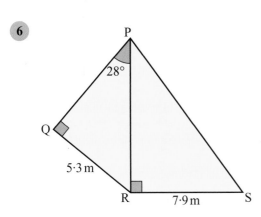
    What angle does a diagonal make with the horizontal?

6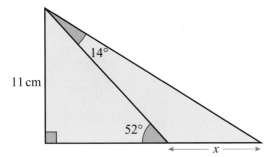
    (a) Find PR.
    (b) Find PS.

7   A ladder leans against a vertical wall so that its base is 1·15 m from the wall and the top of the ladder is 3·6 m up the wall. What angle does the ladder make with the vertical wall?

8   Find the length x.

9   Find the length x.
    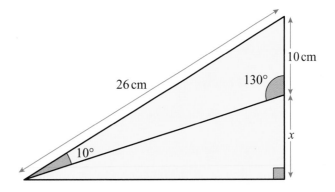

323

**1** Find the value of the lettered angle in each triangle below:

(a)

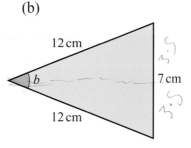

(b)

(c)

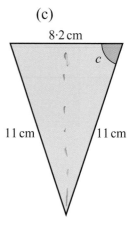

**2** Find PR.

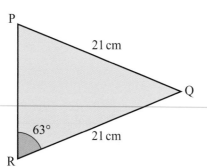

**3** Find the area of triangle ABC.

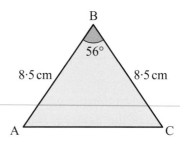

**4** A port is due South of a lighthouse.
A ship sails from the port on a bearing of 070° until it is 18 km due East of the lighthouse. Calculate how far the ship is now from the port.

**5** *Do not use a calculator* in this question.

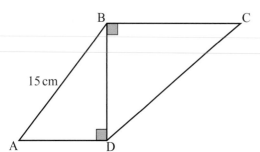

$\cos A\hat{B}D = \dfrac{3}{5}$

$\sin A\hat{B}D = \dfrac{4}{5}$

$\tan B\hat{C}D = \dfrac{2}{3}$

(a) Work out BD.

(b) Work out BC.

**6** Alma walks 6 km due North from her camp. She then walks on a bearing of 235° until she is due West of her camp. She then walks directly back to her camp. Calculate the total distance she has walked.

**7**

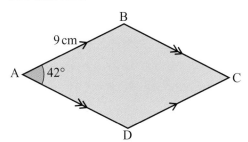

A regular octagon is inscribed in a circle of radius 5 cm.

(a) Find angle $x$.

(b) Find the length of a side of the octagon.

**8** ABCD is a rhombus. Find the lengths of the diagonals AC and BD.

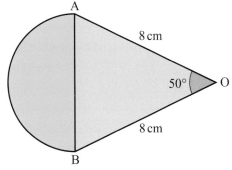

**9** The diagram below shows a sector of a circle centre O.

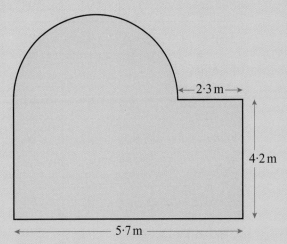

Calculate
(a) the length AB
(b) the orange segment area

## USE YOUR MATHS! – Spruce it up

Jenny has been given some money to get a new carpet for her bedroom and to buy a new sofa.

Jenny can only buy carpet which has a 4 m width. Each piece of carpet must be laid in the same direction.

When working out how much carpet is needed, an extra 5 cm must be added to the length and width to allow for cutting errors.

This is a plan of Jenny's bedroom.

The shape is a semi-circle connected to a rectangle.

**Task A**

1. What is the least area of carpet that Jenny will need to buy to cover her bedroom entirely, following the guidelines given on the previous page.

2. If the carpet is cut perfectly, what percentage of the carpet will be wasted when dealing with Jenny's bedroom?

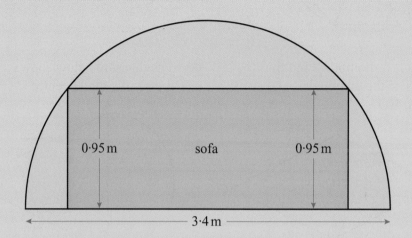

Jenny wants to buy a sofa which will fit into the semi-circular part of her bedroom.

The sofa is 0.95 m deep and the sofa must fit perfectly as shown.

| Sofas | | | | |
|---|---|---|---|---|
| Name | Height (cm) | Width (cm) | Depth (cm) | Price |
| Colston | 91 | 293 | 95 | £617 |
| Mowbray | 91 | 281 | 95 | £789 |
| Edwins | 91 | 280 | 105 | £756 |
| Parkhead | 97 | 291 | 95 | £938 |
| Canston Leather | 93 | 286 | 95 | £785 |
| Bintons Luxury | 101 | 284 | 95 | £1060 |
| Harrows Deluxe | 91 | 281 | 95 | £1130 |
| Tindwells Deluxe | 91 | 279 | 105 | £795 |

**Task B**

Jenny has been given £2000 to spend on the carpet and sofa. She is not allowed to spend more than 40% of the money on a sofa.

Calculate the length of sofa needed then select the sofa from the list opposite which fits all the requirements.

*Explain clearly your reasons for this choice.*

| Carpet | |
|---|---|
| Name | Price per m² |
| Howton Twist | £25·40 |
| Palton Weave | £22·65 |
| Cotswold Twist | £19·85 |
| Mendip Supreme | £31·35 |
| Classic Weave | £24·90 |
| Winchester Pile | £28·30 |
| Dalby Tuff Weave | £14·70 |
| Cheasley Deluxe Twist | £37·40 |
| Canton High Pile | £16·15 |
| Paris Classic Twist | £38·25 |

## Task C

If Jenny buys the sofa you chose in Task B, which is the most expensive carpet she can afford from the table opposite in order to carpet her bedroom entirely?

*Explain clearly your reasons for the choice.*

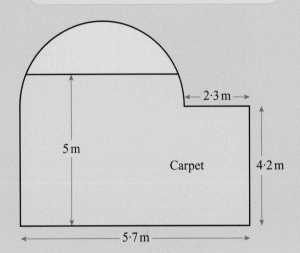

## Task D

Jenny finds a carpet which is sold with a 5 m width. She decides to buy one piece of this carpet and to leave one part of the semi-circle with no carpet as shown. Calculate what percentage of her room will now *not* be carpeted.

## TEST YOURSELF ON UNIT 11

| **1.** Consolidating previous geometry work |
|---|

(a) A map has a scale of 1 : 4 000 000. What is the distance between 2 cities on the map if the real distance between them is 66 km?

(b)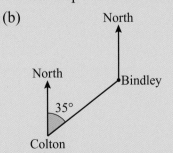

Write down the bearing of:
  (i) Bindley from Colton
  (ii) Colton from Bindley

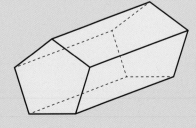

(c) Write down the total number of vertices, faces and edges for the prism shown opposite.

## 2. Constructing with compasses

(a) Draw a vertical line PQ of length 8 cm.
Construct the perpendicular bisector of PQ.

(b) Draw an angle of 70°. Construct the bisector of the angle.

(c) Construct this triangle.

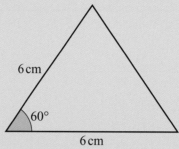

6 cm

60°

6 cm

(d) •

_____

Draw any line and point as shown opposite. Construct the perpendicular from the point to the line.

## 3. Drawing loci

(b) Draw the locus of all points which are 3·5 cm from the line PQ.

P ————————— Q

7 cm

(b) The diagram shows a rectangular room ABCD.
Draw *three* diagrams using a scale of 1 cm
for every 1 m. Use a separate diagram to show
each locus below:

B ——————————— C

4 m

A —————— D

5 m

   (i) Points in the room less than or equal to
3 m from B.

  (ii) Points in the room which are an equal
distance from both B and C.
('*equidistant*' from B and C).

 (iii) Points in the room which are greater than or equal to 2 m from D.

## 4. Using plans and elevations

(a) Draw this object using the plan
and elevations opposite.

(b) If each square is 1 cm², work out
the volume of the solid.

front elevation

plan view

side elevation

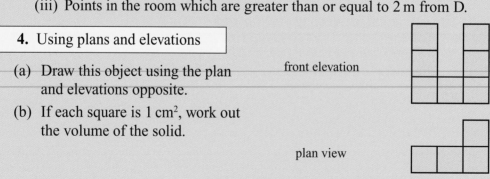

328

(c) Draw and label the plan and a side elevation for this solid (called a frustum)

(d)

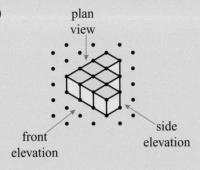

Draw the plan view, the front view and the side view of this object.

---

**5.** Using Pythagoras' theorem

(*Give your answers correct to one decimal place*)

(a)

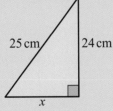

find *x*

(b)

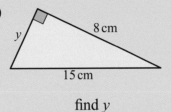

find *y*

(c)

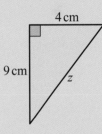

find *z*

(d) Calculate the length of the line joining (3, 1) to (7, 6).

(e)

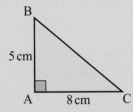

*Do not use a calculator for this question.*
Work out the 'exact' value of BC, leaving the answer in the form $\sqrt{n}$.

---

**6.** Using trigonometry

(*Give your answers correct to one decimal place*)

(a)

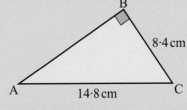

Find $A\hat{C}B$.

(b)

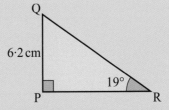

Find RQ.

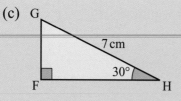

(c) Without using a calculator,
find the 'exact' value of FG.

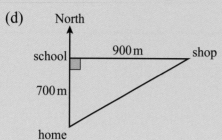

(d) Use the diagram opposite to calculate the
bearing of Tia's home from the shop.

## Mixed examination questions

**1**

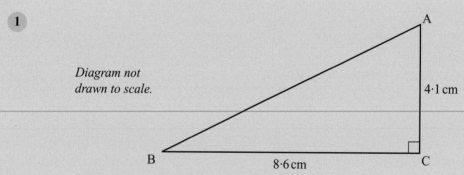

*Diagram not drawn to scale.*

(a) Calculate the area of the triangle *ABC*.

(b) Calculate the perimeter of the triangle *ABC*, giving your answer correct
to 2 significant figures. (WJEC)

**2** The front elevation and the side elevation of a cuboid are drawn on the grid.
Copy the diagram onto grid paper and draw the plan of the cuboid.

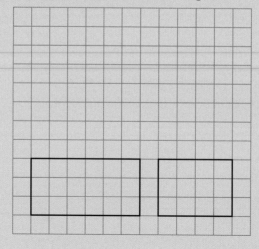

(EDEXCEL)

**3** (a) Copy the angle below. Using a ruler and compasses, bisect the angle.

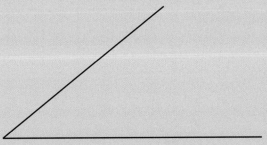

(b) Copy the line below. Using a ruler and a pair of compasses, construct a perpendicular to the line AB at X.

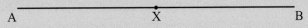

A        X        B

(WJEC)

**4** The diagram shows a quadrilateral ABCD.

AB = 16 cm.

AD = 12 cm.

Angle BCD = 40°.

Angle ADB = angle CBD = 90°.

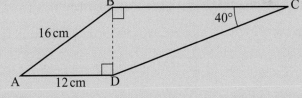

Calculate the length of CD.
Give your answer correct to 3 significant figures.      (EDEXCEL)

**5** The diagram shows a scale drawing of a corn field using a scale of 1 cm to 100 m.

A scarecrow is positioned in the field 325 m from corner A and 200 m from corner B.

Copy the diagram opposite.

Using a ruler and compasses, find and mark the position of the scarecrow.

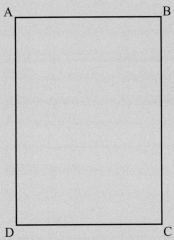

**Leave all construction lines.**      (CEA)

**6** Alec has 6 one-centimetre cubes.

Alec makes a solid with the six cubes.

Its front view and side view are shown opposite.

On a grid, draw the plan view of the solid.          (OCR)

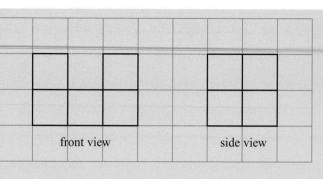

front view          side view

**7** The sketch shows a field which is in the shape of a right-angled triangle. The side PQ = 10 m and the side QR = 26 m.

Calculate the length of the side PR.          (CEA)

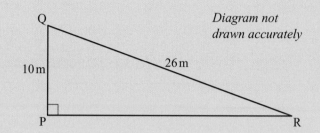

*Diagram not drawn accurately*

**8** The diagram shows the plan of a room.

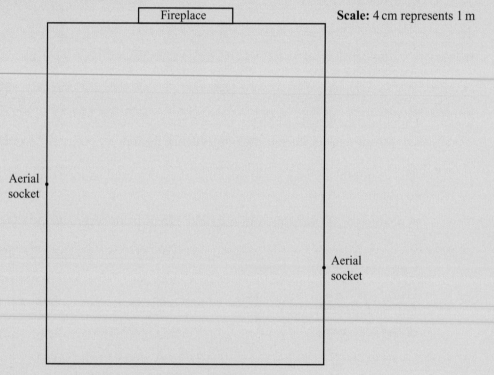

Fireplace

**Scale:** 4 cm represents 1 m

Aerial socket

Aerial socket

A new socket is to be fitted to one of the walls.

It must be    equidistant from the two aerial sockets
            at least half a metre from the fireplace.

Copy the above diagram.

Use a ruler and compasses to show where the socket should be fitted.
Mark the position of the new socket with the letter S.          (AQA)

**9**  ABCD is a trapezium.
AD = 10 cm
AB = 9 cm
DC = 3 cm
Angle ABC = angle BCD = 90°

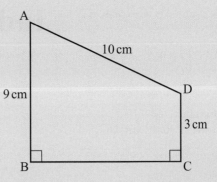

Calculate the length of AC.
Give your answer correct to 3 significant figures.          (EDEXCEL)

**10**  Use a ruler and a pair of compasses only to construct an accurate drawing of
the rhombus described below.

Rhombus
● All sides are of length 6 cm
● The acute angles are 60°

You must show all your construction lines.          (WJEC)

**11**  The diagram shows a solid prism.

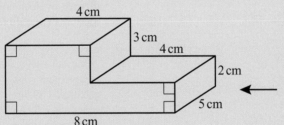

Diagram **NOT**
accurately drawn

Copy a centimetre square grid and draw the side elevation of
the solid prism from the direction shown by the arrow.          (EDEXCEL)

**12**  The diagram shows the net of a
square-based pyramid.

The area of the square base is 36 cm².

Work out the area of one triangular face.

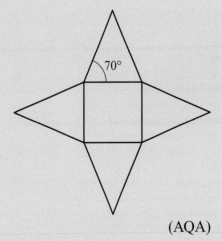

(AQA)

333

# Index

# Can you still? sections page numbers